DESIGNERS' GUIDES TO THE EUROCODES

DESIGNERS' GUIDE TO EN 1990
EUROCODE: BASIS OF STRUCTURAL DESIGN

DESIGNERS' GUIDES TO THE EUROCODES

DESIGNERS' GUIDE TO EN 1990
EUROCODE: BASIS OF STRUCTURAL DESIGN

H. GULVANESSIAN, J.-A. CALGARO and M. HOLICKÝ

Published by Thomas Telford Publishing, Thomas Telford Limited, 40 Marsh Wall, London E14 9TP
URL: http://www.thomastelford.com

Distributors for Thomas Telford books are
USA: ASCE Press, 1801 Alexander Bell Drive, Reston, VA 20191-4400
Japan: Maruzen Co. Ltd, Book Department, 3–10 Nihonbashi 2-chome, Chuo-ku, Tokyo 103
Australia: DA Books and Journals, 648 Whitehorse Road, Mitcham 3132, Victoria

First published 2002

Reprinted 2008, 2009

A catalogue record for this book is available from the British Library

ISBN: 0 7277 3011 8

Typeset by Helius, Brighton and Rochester
Printed and bound in Great Britain by CPI Antony Rowe, Chippenham, Wiltshire

Preface

EN 1990, *Eurocode: Basis of Structural Design*, is the head document of the Eurocode suite and describes the principles and requirements for safety, serviceability and durability of structures, and is intended to be used for direct application with *Eurocode 1: Actions on Structures* and the design Eurocodes 2 to 9. As such, it is the key Eurocode document.

Aims and objectives of this guide

The principal aim of this book is to provide the user with guidance on the interpretation and use of EN 1990, *Eurocode: Basis of Structural Design*. The guide also provides information on the implementation of the Eurocodes and their use with regard to National Annexes. In producing this guide the authors have endeavoured to provide explanations and commentary to the clauses in EN 1990 for all the categories of users identified in the foreword of the Eurocode. Although the design Eurocodes are primarily intended for the design of buildings and civil engineering works, EN 1990 is intended for the consideration of more categories of users who include:

- designers and contractors (as for the other Eurocodes), plus
- code-drafting committees
- clients
- public authorities and other bodies who produce regulations.

Layout of this guide

EN 1990, *Eurocode: Basis of Structural Design*, has a foreword and six sections together with four annexes. This guide has an introduction which corresponds to the foreword of EN 1990, and Chapters 1 to 6 of the guide correspond to Sections 1 to 6 of the Eurocode. Chapters 7 to 10 correspond to Annexes A, B, C and D of the Eurocode, respectively. The numbering of sections in this guide also corresponds to those in EN 1990; for example, Section 7.2 of the guide corresponds to clause A.2 of EN 1990, and Section 6.4 is a commentary to clause 6.4 of the Eurocode. All cross-references in this guide to sections, clauses, sub-clauses, annexes, figures and tables of EN 1990 are in *italic type*. The numbers for the expressions correspond unless prefixed by D (D for *Designers' Guide*). Expressions prefixed by D do not appear in EN 1990. Where text from a clause of EN 1990 has been directly reproduced, this is shown in italics.

This handbook has two types of appendix. Particular chapters may have their own appendices which provide further explanation to particular clauses; there, appendices may be of interest only to a particular category of user. Where background is given, this is in a box. These are referred to, for example, as Appendix 1 to Chapter 4. There are also four main appendices A to D provided as separate chapters which provide background and useful advice relating to the whole guide and should be of interest to all categories of users.

Acknowledgements

This book would not have been possible without the successful completion of EN 1990, *Eurocode: Basis of Structural Design*. Those involved in the process included:

- The Project Team, consisting of Professor H. Gulvanessian (convenor), Professor G. Augusti, Professor J.-A. Calgaro; Dr B. Jensen, Dr P. Lüchinger and Mr P. Spehl; and the two permanently invited experts to the Project Team, Mr T. Hagberg and Professor G. Sedlacek.
- Before the Project Team was formed, the foundations of the conversion were laid by the CEN/TC250 Basis of Design Ad-hoc Group, which consisted of Professor H. Gulvanessian (convenor), Professor J.-A. Calgaro, Professor J. Grünberg, Mr T. Hagberg, Dr P. Lüchinger and Mr P. Spehl.
- Particular members of the *Eurocode 7: Geotechnical Design* committees for contributing to the clauses in EN 1990 relating to soil–structure interaction, in particular Professor R. Frank, the Chairman of CEN/TC 250/SC 7.
- Those who advised on the translation of EN 1990 into French or German, and those who advised on the final editing, in particular Mr H. Mathieu, Professor Ziebke, Mr B. Haseltine, Professor J. Mills and Mr C. Taylor.
- National delegations to CEN/TC 250, and the national technical contacts, for their valuable and constructive comments.
- The two former chairmen of CEN/TC 250 Dr G. Breitschaft and Mr D. Lazenby, and the present chairman, Professor H. Bossenmeyer, whose advice was essential during the production of EN 1990.
- Professor L. Ostlund, Professor A. Vrouwenvelder and Mr R. Lovegrove for their advice and help to the project team.
- Professor H. Gulvanessian's personal assistant, Mrs C. Hadden, who gave considerable secretarial support of outstanding quality, both in the preparation of EN 1990 and for this guide.

This book is dedicated to all those mentioned above, and to:

- The authors' wives, Vera Gulvanessian, Elizabeth Calgaro and Nadia Holicka, for their support and patience.
- The authors' employers BRE Garston, Watford; SETRA, Paris; and the Klockner Institute, Czech Technical University, Prague.

H. Gulvanessian
J.-A. Calgaro
M. Holický

Contents

Introduction

The material in this introduction is covered in the foreword to EN 1990, *Eurocode: Basis of Structural Design*, in clauses on:

- the background to the Eurocode programme
- the status and field of application of the Eurocodes
- National standards implementing Eurocodes
- links between Eurocodes and harmonized technical specifications (ENs and ETAs) for products
- additional information specific to EN 1990
- National Annexes to EN 1990.

This introduction is also concerned with the implementation and use of the structural Eurocodes in the EU member states. An essential background paper to this is the CEC's *Guidance Paper L* (*Concerning the Construction Products Directive – 99/106/EEC*). *Application and Use of Eurocodes*.[1] Reference to this paper is made in this introduction. In addition, Appendix A of this guide 'The Construction Products Directive', gives detailed information on the Directive.

The following abbreviations are used in this chapter:

CEC	Commission of the European Communities
CEN	Comité Européen de Normalisation (European Committee for Standardization)
CPD	Construction Products Directive
EFTA	European Free Trade Association
EN	EuroNorm (European Standard)
ENV	EuroNorm Vornorm (European Pre-standard)
EOTA	European Organization for Technical Approval
ER	Essential Requirement
ETA	European Technical Approval
ETAG	European Technical Approval Guidelines
EU	European Union
hEN	Harmonized European Standard for a construction product (to enable CE marking)
ID	Interpretative Document
NDP	Nationally Determined Parameter
NSB	national standard body
PT	Project Team
SC	Subcommittee
TC	Technical Committee

The following definitions will aid the understanding of this introduction and Appendix A of this guide:

Approval body. Body authorized to issue ETAs (Article 10 of the CPD); member of the EOTA.

Construction works. Building and civil engineering works.

European Technical Approval (ETA). Favourable technical assessment of the fitness for use of a product for an intended use, based on the fulfilment of the ERs for building works for which the product is used (Articles 8, 9 and 4.2 of the CPD). ETA can be issued on the basis of guidelines (Article 9.1 of the CPD) or delivered without guidelines (Article 9.2 of the CPD).

European Technical Approval Guidelines (ETAGs). Document used as the basis of preparing ETAs which contain specific requirements for the products within the meaning of the ERs, the test procedures, the methods of assessing and judging the results of the tests, and the inspection and conformity procedures, written on the basis of the mandate received by the EOTA from the Commission (Article 11 of the CPD).

National Annex (to an EN Eurocode part). Annex to an EN Eurocode part containing the NDPs to be used for the structural design of buildings and civil engineering works in an EU member state. The National Annex is governed by the CEN rules.

National provisions. National laws, regulations and administrative provisions, imposed by all levels of public authorities, or private bodies acting as a public undertaking or as a public body on the basis of a monopoly position.

Nationally Determined Parameter (NDP). A national choice left open in an EN Eurocode about values (where symbols are given in the EN Eurocodes), a set of classes or alternative procedures permitted within the EN Eurocodes.

Technical specifications. hENs and ETAs for construction products (Article 4.1 of the CPD).

Structure. Load-bearing construction, i.e. an organized assembly of connected parts designed to provide mechanical resistance and stability to the works (ID 1, clause 2.1.1 (see Appendix A for comments on ID 1)).

Structural material. Material or constituent product with properties which enter into structural calculations or otherwise relate to the mechanical resistance and stability of works and parts thereof, and/or to their fire resistance, including aspects of durability and serviceability.

Structural component. Components to be used as load-bearing part of works designed to provide mechanical resistance and stability to the works and/or fire resistance, including aspects of durability and serviceability (ID 1, clause 2.1.1 (see Appendix A)).

Structural kit. Kit consisting of structural components to be assembled and installed on site. The assembled system made from the structural kit is a 'structure'.

Background to the Eurocode programme

The objectives of the Eurocodes and their status

In 1975, the CEC decided on an action programme in the field of construction based on Article 95 of the Treaty of Rome. The objective of the programme was the elimination of technical obstacles to trade and the harmonization of technical specifications.

Within this action programme the European Commission took the initiative to establish a set of harmonized technical rules for the structural design of construction works, with the following objective:

> The Eurocodes to establish a set of common technical rules for the design of buildings and civil engineering works which will ultimately replace the differing rules in the various Member States.

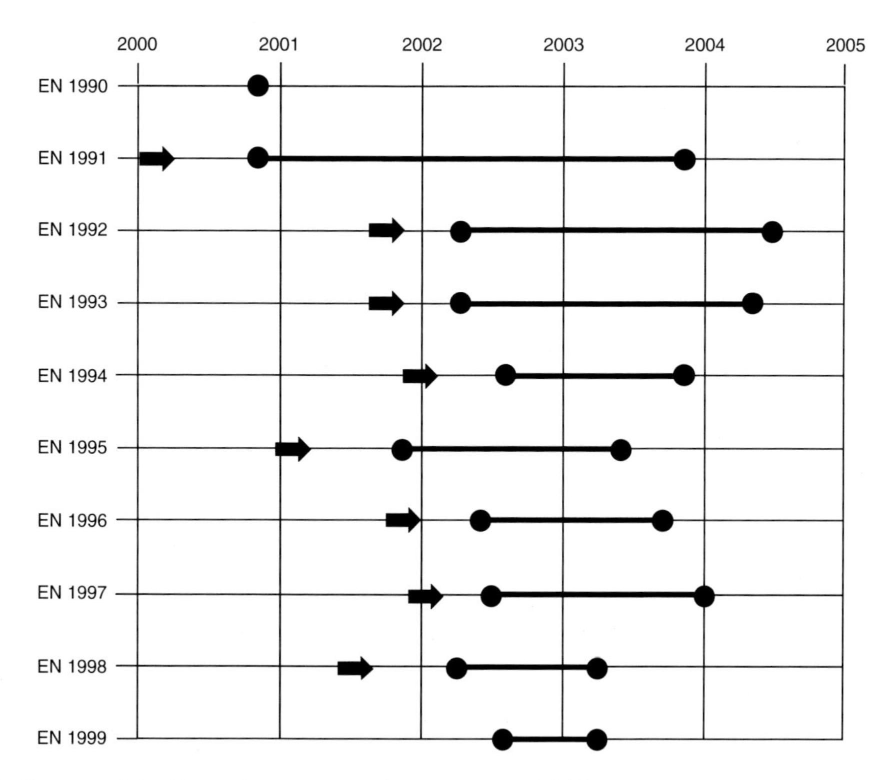

Fig. 1. *Progress of the Eurocode programme (status: January 2002)*

For 15 years, the Commission, with the help of a steering committee containing representatives of EU member states, oversaw the development of the Eurocodes programme, which led to the publication of a first-generation set of European codes in the 1980s.

In 1989 the special agreement between the CEN and the European Commission transferred the preparation and publication of the Eurocodes to the CEN, thus providing the Eurocodes with a future status of European EN standards.

This links, *de facto*, the Eurocodes with the provisions of all the Council's Directives and/ or the Commission's decisions dealing with European EN standards, e.g.

- The Construction Products Directive (see Appendix A of this guide for a brief description of this Directive)
- Public Procurement Directives, on public works and services for execution, design, etc., of civil engineering works.

See also the status of the Eurocodes in this introduction.

Figure 1 shows the progress of the Eurocode programme.

The Eurocode programme

EN 1990 lists the following structural Eurocodes, each generally consisting of a number of parts which are in different stages of development at present:

EN 1990	*Eurocode: Basis of Structural Design*
EN 1991	*Eurocode 1: Actions on Structures*
EN 1992	*Eurocode 2: Design of Concrete Structures*
EN 1993	*Eurocode 3: Design of Steel Structures*
EN 1994	*Eurocode 4: Design of Composite Steel and Concrete Structures*
EN 1995	*Eurocode 5: Design of Timber Structures*
EN 1996	*Eurocode 6: Design of Masonry Structures*
EN 1997	*Eurocode 7: Geotechnical Design*

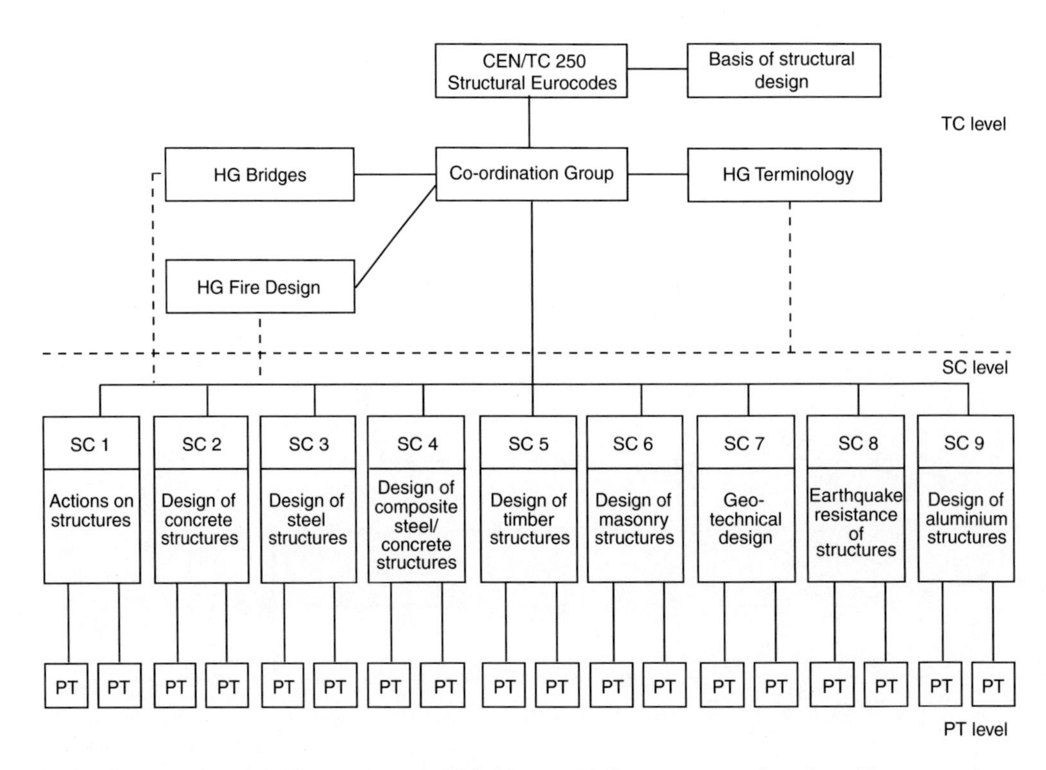

Fig. 2. *Organization of the Eurocode work (HG, Horizontal Group; see text for other abbreviations)*

EN 1998 *Eurocode 8: Design of Structures for Earthquake Resistance*
EN 1999 *Eurocode 9: Design of Aluminium Structures*

Each of the structural Eurocodes is produced by separate sub-committees under the guidance and co-ordination of a technical committee (CEN/TC 250). The organizational structure of the Eurocode work is shown in Fig. 2.

Drafts for the structural Eurocodes and their parts are elaborated by project teams which are selected by the appropriate sub-committee. A project team consists of about six experts, who represent their sub-committee. Delegates of the 19 CEN members are represented in CEN/TC 250 and its sub-committees. Voting is in accordance with the rules of the CEN.

Appendix B of this guide lists the 58 parts that make the Eurocode suite, together with their intended dates of publication.

Potential benefits of the use of the Eurocodes

The intended benefits of the Eurocodes include the following:

(1) to provide a common understanding regarding the design of structure between owners, operators and users, designers, contractors and manufacturers of construction products
(2) to provide common design criteria and methods to fulfil the specified requirements for mechanical resistance, stability and resistance to fire, including aspects of durability and economy
(3) to facilitate the marketing and use of structural components and kits in EU member states
(4) to facilitate the marketing and use of materials and constituent products the properties of which enter into design calculations, in EU member states
(5) to be a common basis for research and development, as the Eurocodes offer the opportunity for pan-European research for their future editions, leading to substantial savings in the cost of research
(6) to allow the preparation of common design aids and software
(7) to benefit European civil engineering firms, contractors, designers and product manufacturers in their world-wide activities, and to increase their competitiveness.

Responsibilities of EU member states

The layout of EN 1990, and indeed the complete Eurocode suite, takes account of the responsibilities of the EU member states, in the implementation of the structural Eurocodes where levels of safety of buildings and civil engineering works and parts thereof, including aspects of durability and economy, remain within the competence of each member state, even after the implementation of the EN Eurocodes.

Status and field of application of the Eurocodes

Status of the Eurocodes

The special agreement between the CEN and the European Commission (BC/CEN/03/89) specified that the Eurocodes are intended to serve as reference documents to be recognized by authorities of the EU member states for the following purposes:

(1) As a means of compliance of building and civil engineering works with the Essential Requirements (ERs) as set out in Council Directive 89/106/EEC (the CPD), particularly ER 1 (Mechanical Resistance and Stability) and ER 2 (Safety in Case of Fire). The use of EN Eurocodes in technical specifications for products is described in the Commission's guidance paper *Application and Use of Eurocodes*.[1]
(2) As a basis for specifying contracts for the execution of construction works and related engineering services in the area of public works. This relates to the following Council Procurement Directives:
   - Works Directive 93/37/EEC, which covers procurement by public authorities of civil engineering and building works, with a threshold in 2001 of about 5 million euros
   - Services Directive 92/50/EEC, which covers procurement of services by public authorities, with thresholds in 2001 for government departments of 130 000 euros and for others, including local authorities, of 200 000 euros.
(3) As a framework for drawing up harmonized technical specifications for construction products.

Relationship with the Interpretative Documents

The Eurocodes have a direct relationship with the Interpretative Documents (IDs) referred to in Article 12 of the CPD, although they are of a different nature from harmonized product standards (see Appendix A of this guide).

According to Article 3.3 of the CPD, the ERs shall be given concrete form in IDs for the creation of the necessary links between the essential requirements and the mandates for hENs and ETAs.

According to Article 12 of the CPD the IDs shall:

(1) give concrete form to the essential requirements by harmonizing the terminology and the technical bases and indicating classes or levels for each requirement where necessary
(2) indicate methods of correlating these classes or levels of requirement with the technical specifications, e.g. methods of calculation and of proof, and technical rules for project design
(3) serve as a reference for the establishment of harmonized standards and guidelines for European technical approval.

The Eurocodes, *de facto*, play a similar role of the field of the ER 1 (Mechanical Resistance and Stability) and a part of ER 2 (Safety in Case of Fire).

Therefore, technical aspects arising from the Eurocodes have to be taken into account by CEN technical committees, EOTA working groups and EOTA bodies working on product specifications, with a view to achieve full compatibility between the product specifications and the EN Eurocodes. For a full explanation see the paper *Application and Use of Eurocodes*.[1]

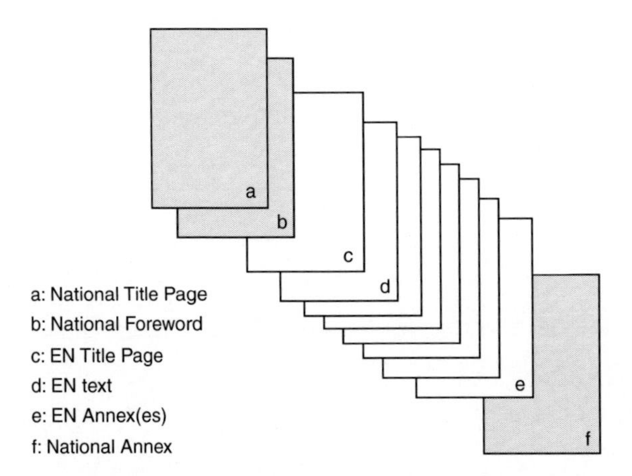

Fig. 3. *National standard implementing a Eurocode*

Field of application of the Eurocodes

The structural Eurocodes provide Principles and Rules of Application for the design of:

- whole structures and
- component products

of both traditional and innovative nature.

However, unusual forms of construction (e.g. use of certain materials) or design conditions (extreme hazards, e.g. large external explosions) are not fully covered, and additional expert guidance will be required in such situations.

National standards implementing Eurocodes

It is the responsibility of each NSB (e.g. the British Standards Institute (BSI) in the UK, the Association Française de Normalisation (AFNOR) in France, the Deutsche Institut für Normung (DIN) in Germany, and the Ente Nazionale Italiano di Unificazione (UNI) in Italy) to implement EN 1990 as a national standard.

The national standard implementing EN 1990 (and the national standards implementing each Eurocode part) will comprise, without any alterations, the full text of the Eurocode and its annexes as published by the CEN. This may be preceded by a National Title Page, and by a National Foreword, and may be followed by a National Annex (see Fig. 3).

National Annexes

As already stated in this introduction, EN 1990 recognizes the responsibility of regulatory authorities (e.g. the building regulations division of the department for Transport, Local Government and the Regions (DTLR) in the UK) or National Competent Authorities (e.g. the Highways Agency in the UK) in each EU member state, and it has safeguarded their right to determine values related to safety matters at national level where these continue from state to state, through a National Annex.

Possible differences in geographical or climatic conditions (e.g. wind or snow maps) or in ways of life, as well as different levels of protection that may prevail at national, regional or local level, will be taken into account, by choices left open about values, classes, or alternative methods, identified in the EN Eurocodes to be determined nationally.

These values, classes or methods to be chosen or determined at national level, called Nationally Determined Parameters (NDPs), will allow the EU member states to choose the level of safety, including aspects of durability and economy applicable to works in their territory.

The NSBs should publish a National Annex, on behalf of and with the agreement of the National Competent Authorities. A National Annex is not required if the EN Eurocode part is not relevant for the member state (e.g. seismic design for some countries).

The National Annex may only contain, directly or by reference to specific provisions, information on those parameters which are left open in the Eurocodes for national choice, the NDPs, to be used for the design of buildings and civil engineering works to be constructed in the country concerned, i.e.

- values and/or classes where alternatives are given in the Eurocode
- values to be used where only a symbol is given in the Eurocode
- country-specific data (geographical, climatic, etc.), e.g. snow maps
- procedures to be used where alternative procedures are given in the Eurocode.

The National Annex may also contain the following:

- decisions on the application of informative annexes
- references to non-contradictory complementary information to assist the user in applying the Eurocode.

A National Annex cannot change or modify the content of the EN Eurocode text in any way other than where it indicates that national choices may be made by means of NDPs.

In EN 1990, for example, all safety factors are given as symbols, with recommended values for the symbols given in notes (see Chapter 7 of this guide). The National Annex may either adopt the recommended values or give alternative values.

In addition, EN 1990 gives alternative procedures for the load combination expressions, and different approaches for treating soil–structure interaction (see Chapters 6 and 7). Here, the National Annex needs to make a choice as to the approach to be used nationally.

Each EU member state will have a different National Annex – the National Annex used must be the one applicable to where the building or civil engineering work is being constructed. For example, a UK designer will have to use EN 1990 with the UK National Annex when designing a building in the UK. The same designer, designing a building in Italy, will have to use EN 1990 with the Italian National Annex.

Links between Eurocodes and harmonized technical specifications (ENs and ETAs) for products

There is a need for consistency between the technical specifications for construction products (hENs and ETAs) and the technical rules for works.

For construction products, which contribute to the mechanical resistance and stability of works, two types of properties are distinguished, according to the validation method:

(1) properties determined by testing (generally in the case of structural materials and products, such as concrete, reinforcing steel for concrete, structural steel, etc.), and
(2) properties determined by calculation following methods given by the Eurocodes, which are also used for the structural design of works (generally in the case of prefabricated structural components and kits, such as prefabricated concrete components, prefabricated stairs, timber frame buildings kits, etc.).

For both types of product properties the resulting values are 'declared' in the information accompanying the CE marking of the product and used in the structural design of works or parts thereof.

As a consequence, for the consideration or use of EN Eurocodes in harmonized product specifications and ETAGs distinction is made in the following between:

- materials and constituent products with properties determined by testing, and
- structural components or kits with properties calculated according to EN Eurocode methods.

Additional information specific to EN 1990

Technical objectives of EN 1990

EN 1990 describes the principles and requirements for safety, serviceability and durability of structures and is intended to be used for direct application with *Eurocode 1: Actions on Structures* and the design Eurocodes (Eurocodes 2 to 9).

Figure 4 shows the structure of the European standards system for building and civil engineering works, using *Eurocode 2: Design of Concrete Structures*, as an example.

In addition, EN 1990 provides guidelines for the aspects of structural reliability relating to safety, serviceability and durability for design cases not covered by the Eurocodes (e.g. other actions, other materials and types of structures not treated), and to serve as a reference document for other CEN committees concerned with structural engineering aspects.

Layout and organization of EN 1990

The layout of EN 1990, to aid usability, is as follows:

- *Sections 1* to *6* of EN 1990 are applicable to all types of construction works within the fields of application of the structural Eurocodes defining requirements and criteria.
- Separate normative annexes (e.g. *Annex A1*, 'Application for buildings') which are derivations from the general sections specific for each structural type (e.g. buildings, bridges, towers and masts).
- Informative specialist annexes applicable to all structures.

Intended users of EN 1990

EN 1990 is intended for the consideration of more categories of users than are the other Eurocodes. It lists the intended users as:

- standard drafting committees for both structural design and related products, testing and execution standards
- clients, for the specific requirements on reliability levels and durability
- designers
- contractors
- relevant authorities.

Each of these users will have a different perspective on the provisions of EN 1990.

Intended uses of EN 1990

EN 1990 is intended for the design of structures within the scope of the Eurocodes (see Chapter 1). Additionally, it can be used as a guidance document in the design of structures outside the scope of the Eurocodes for

- assessing other actions and their combinations
- modelling material and structural behaviour
- assessing numerical values of the reliability format.

When EN 1990 is used as a reference document by other CEN committees the numerical values provided in the document for safety factors should be used.

National Annex for EN 1990

EN 1990 allows national choice through a number of clauses in *Annex A1* of EN 1990, 'Application for Buildings'. The choice relates mainly to selecting partial factor and combination coefficients where symbols (together with recommended values) are given, and where alternative procedures are given.

A national standard implementing EN 1990 should have a National Annex containing all NDPs to be used for the design of construction works in the relevant country.

The clauses of EN 1990 where national choice is allowed is listed in the foreword of EN 1990.

Appendix D of this guide gives the names and addresses of the appropriate national standard organizations to whom enquiries may be made with regard to the availability of National Annexes for a particular country.

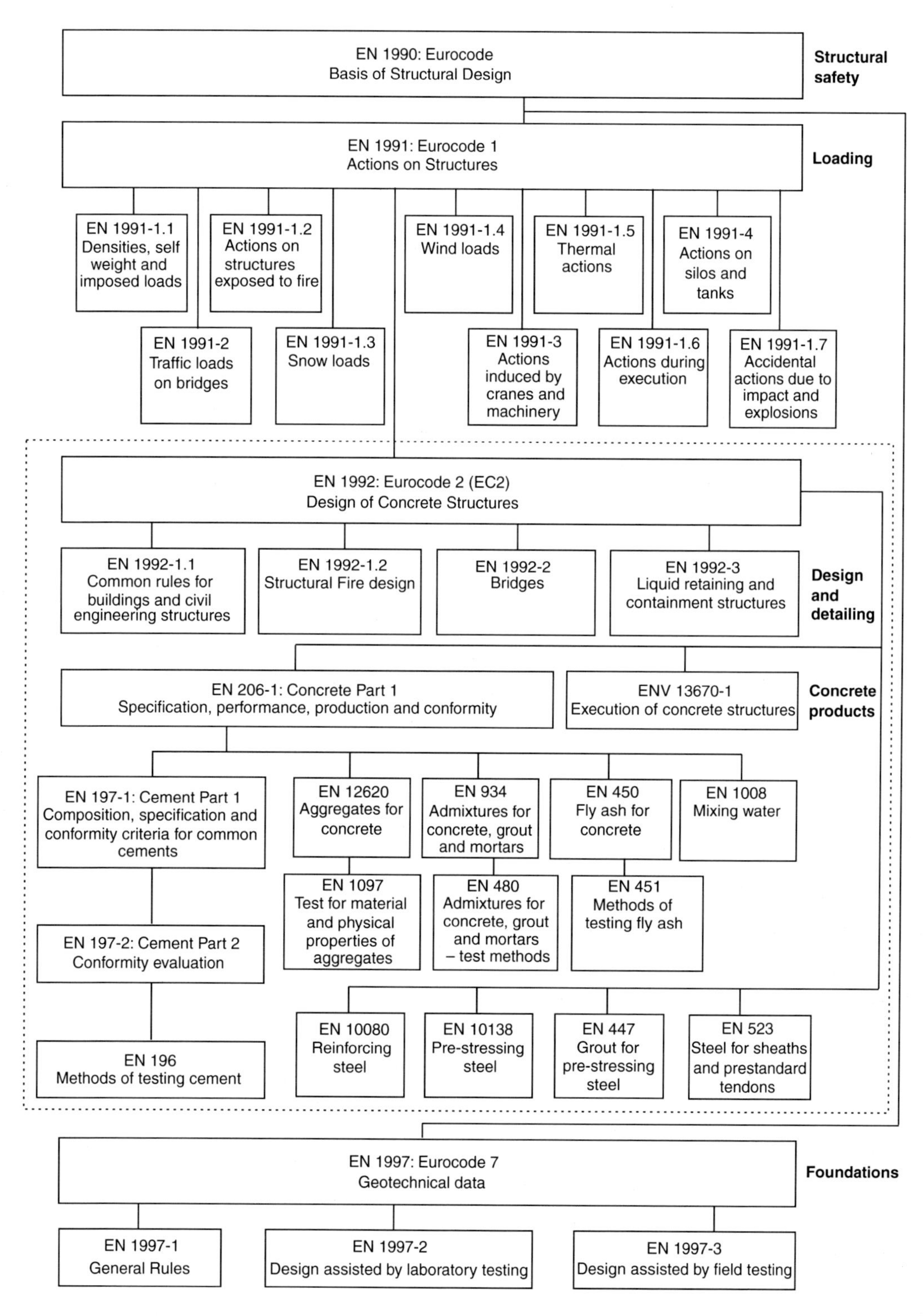

Fig. 4. *Structure of the European EN standard system for building and civil engineering works using Eurocode 2 as an example*

CHAPTER 1

General

This chapter is concerned with the general aspects of EN 1990, *Eurocode: Basis of Structural Design*. The material described in this chapter is covered in *Section 1*, in the following clauses:

- Scope — *Clause 1.1*
- Normative references — *Clause 1.2*
- Assumptions — *Clause 1.3*
- Distinction between Principles and Application Rules — *Clause 1.4*
- Terms and definitions — *Clause 1.5*
- Symbols — *Clause 1.6*

1.1. Scope

1.1.1. Primary scope

Clause 1.1(1)

EN 1990, *Eurocode: Basis of Structural Design*, is the head document in the Eurocode suite, and it establishes for all the structural Eurocodes the principles and requirements for safety, serviceability and durability of structures; it further describes the basis of design and verification and provides guidelines for related aspects of structural reliability.

Clause 1.1(2)

Most importantly, in addition to establishing the principles and requirements it provides the basis and general principles for the structural design of buildings and civil engineering works (including geotechnical aspects, structural fire design and situations involving earthquakes, execution and temporary structures) and is intended to be used in conjunction with EN 1991 to EN 1999.

EN 1990, alone within the Eurocode suite, gives all the operative material independent rules (e.g. partial factors for actions, load combination expressions for ultimate and serviceability limit states), and therefore EN 1992 to EN 1999, which do not provide material independent guidance, cannot be used without EN 1990.

Figure 1.1 shows the structure and links of the Eurocodes.

1.1.2. Scope in relation to design cases not covered by the Eurocodes

Clause 1.1(2)

Some of the principles of EN 1990 may be used for the design of special construction works (e.g. nuclear installations, dams) but provisions other than those provided by the Eurocodes will probably be necessary, in particular for determining specific actions, and for specific additional requirements.

Clause 1.1(3)

As already covered in the introduction in the section 'Additional information specific to EN 1990', EN 1990 can be used for the aspects of structural reliability relating to safety, serviceability and durability for design cases outside the scope of the Eurocodes, e.g.

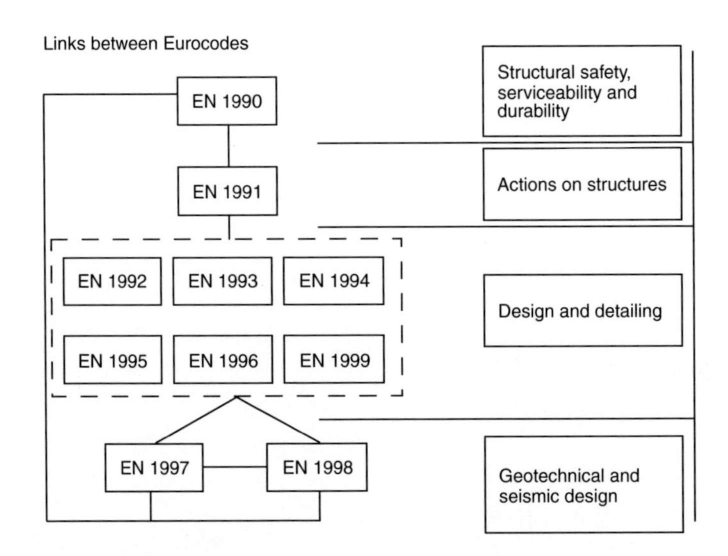

Fig. 1.1. *Links between the Eurocodes*

- assessing actions not covered by EN 1991 and their combinations
- modelling materials not covered by the Eurocodes (e.g. new and innovative materials, glass), and their structural behaviour
- assessing numerical values of reliability elements (e.g. partial factors and combination factors, not covered by EN 1990 to EN 1999).

1.1.3. Scope in relation to structural design for execution stage and temporary structures

Clause 1.1(2)

EN 1990 is also applicable to the structural design for the execution stage and to temporary (or auxiliary) structures. Further information can be found for the execution stage in EN 1991-1-6 (Actions during Execution), and in *Annexes A* and *B* of EN 1990 and Chapters 7 and 8 of this guide for temporary structures.

1.1.4. Scope in relation to assessment of existing construction

Clause 1.1(4)

EN 1990 is applicable for the structural appraisal of existing construction, for the design of repairs and alterations or for assessing changes of use. However, *clause 1.1(4)* does recognize that additional or amended rules and provisions might be necessary where appropriate. For example, the material properties used in the assessment should be estimated using measured (actual) material properties of the existing structure, which may include statistical techniques, and additional guidance will be required for this.

There are no current CEN codes or standards that directly apply for the appraisal of existing structures. There is, however, an ISO standard, ISO 13822, *Basis of Design of Structures – Assessment of Existing Structures*,[2] which gives additional and amended provisions that may be used with EN 1990.

Currently in the UK, the Building Regulations suggest that guidance can be obtained from the Institution of Structural Engineers' publication *Appraisal of Existing Structures*,[3] and *BRE Digest 366*.[4] Guidance is also available in several countries, e.g. Switzerland[5] and the Czech Republic.[6]

1.2. Normative references

Clause 1.2

No comment is necessary.

1.3. Assumptions

'*A design which employs the Principles and Application Rules is deemed to meet the requirements of EN 1990, provided the following assumptions are satisfied.*' *Clause 1.3(1)*

The assumptions that need to be satisfied (*clause 1.3(2)*) are: *Clause 1.3(2)*

(1) '*The choice of the structural system and the design of a structure is made by appropriately qualified and experienced personnel.*'

(2) '*Execution is carried out by personnel having the appropriate skill and experience.*'

Annex B of EN 1990 (see Chapter 8 of this guide) provides additional guidance with regard to 'appropriately qualified and experienced personnel', mentioned in assumptions 1 and 2.

(3) '*Adequate supervision and quality control is provided during execution of the work, i.e. in design offices, factories, plants, and on site.*'

Annex B of EN 1990 also gives guidance on 'adequate supervision and quality control', mentioned in assumption 3, which is based upon the assumed consequences of failure and exposure of the construction works to hazards.

(4) '*The construction materials and products are used as specified in EN 1990, and ENs 1991 to 1999 or in the relevant supporting material or product specifications.*'

With regard to assumption 4 it is the intention for the material Eurocodes together with EN 1990 and EN 1991, and their supporting standards, to be grouped into appropriate packages and used together when the package is available. In the case of new and innovative materials, the principles of EN 1990 are assumed to be used.

(5) '*The structure will be adequately maintained.*'

(6) '*The structure will be used in accordance with the design assumptions.*'

Assumptions 5 and 6 relate to the responsibilities of the owner/user, who must be aware of his or her responsibilities regarding a maintenance regime for the structure, and ensuring no overloading takes place. The designer of the structure should recommend a maintenance regime, and state the assumptions made on loading (e.g. maximum loads, removal of snow, etc.) for the design, to the owner.

Depending upon the complexity of the construction works to be designed and executed, assumptions 1 to 6 may need to be supplemented.

1.4. Distinction between Principles and Application Rules

The clauses in EN 1990 are set out as either Principles or Application Rules: *Clause 1.4(1)*

- '*Principles comprise general statements for which there is no alternative and requirements and analytical models for which no alternative is permitted unless specifically stated.*' *Clause 1.4(2)*
- '*Principles are distinguished by the prefix 'P' following the paragraph number*'. The verb 'shall' is always used in the Principle clauses. *Clause 1.4(3)*
- '*Application rules are generally acceptable methods, which follow the principles and satisfy their requirements.*' *Clause 1.4(4)*
- '*Alternative rules to those given in EN 1990 are permissible provided that it can be demonstrated that they comply with the principles and are at least equivalent with regard to the structural safety, serviceability and durability which would be expected when using the Eurocode clause.*' *Clause 1.4(5)*

Clause 1.4(5) EN 1990 through a note to *clause 1.4(5)* states:

If an alternative rule is substituted for an application rule, the resulting design cannot be claimed to be wholly in accordance with EN 1990 although the design will remain in accordance with the Principles of EN 1990. When EN 1990 is used in respect of a property listed in an Annex Z of a product standard or an ETAG (European Technical Approval Guidelines), the use of an alternative design rule may not be acceptable for CE marking.

With regard to the note to *clause 1.4(5)*, the European Commission guidance paper *Application and Use of the Eurocodes*[1] states:

National Provisions should avoid replacing any EN Eurocode provisions, e.g. Application Rules, by national rules (codes, standards, regulatory provisions, etc).

When, however, National Provisions do provide that the designer may – even after the end of the co-existence period – deviate from or not apply the EN Eurocodes or certain provisions thereof (e.g. Application Rules), then the design will not be called 'a design according to EN Eurocodes'.

The Principles and Rules of Application format was originally chosen for the Eurocodes to encourage innovation, where an engineer could consider using different individual application rules (e.g. based on new research, testing) where he felt innovation was being stifled by the Eurocodes. Although this is workable for an individual design for a construction works, it could cause problems when the Eurocode is being used to design a product so that it may be granted CE marking.

Clause 1.4(6) '*Application rules are identified by a number in brackets only*.' The verb 'should' is normally used for application rules. The verb 'may' is also used for example as an alternative application rule. The verbs 'is' and 'can' are used for a definitive statement or as an 'assumption'.

1.5. Terms and definitions

Clause 1.5 Most of the definitions given in EN 1990 derive from ISO 8930.[7] EN 1990 provides a list of terms and definitions which are applicable to EN 1990 to EN 1999, thus ensuring a common basis for the Eurocode suite.

Clause 1.5 With regard to the definitions in *clause 1.5* there are significant differences from usages in current national codes and standards (e.g. definitions in British codes), to improve precision of meaning and to facilitate translation into other European languages.

For the Eurocode suite, attention is drawn to the following key definitions which may be different from current national practices:

- *Clause 1.5.3.1* '*Action*' means a load, or an imposed deformation (e.g. temperature effects or settlement)
- *Clause 1.5.2.16* '*Strength*' is a mechanical property of a material, in units of stress
- *Clause 1.5.2.15* '*Resistance*' is a mechanical property of a component or a cross-section of a member, or a member or structure
- *Clause 1.5.3.2* '*Effects of Actions*' are internal moments and forces, bending moments, shear forces and deformations caused by actions.

The definitions given in EN 1990 are subdivided into the following clauses:

clause 1.5.1	Common terms used in the structural Eurocodes
clause 1.5.2	Special terms relating to design in general
clause 1.5.3	Terms relating to actions
clause 1.5.4	Terms relating to material properties
clause 1.5.5	Terms relating to geometric data
clause 1.5.6	Terms relating to structural analysis.

The definitions contained in *clause 1.5.6* on structural analysis may not necessarily relate to terms in EN 1990, but have been included in the head Eurocode to ensure a harmonization of terms relating to structural analysis for EN 1991 to EN 1999.

Clause 1.5.6

However, the definitions are difficult to locate even in the subparagraphs as they are not listed alphabetically. To help the reader, an alphabetical list referencing the clauses for a particular definition is provided in an appendix to this chapter.

The following comments are made to help the understanding of particular definitions. Most comments are made taking into account the definitions provided in ISO 2394, *General Principles on Reliability for Structures*.[8] Where no alternative is provided, the definition in EN 1990 accords with or is very similar to that in ISO 2394.

- *Clause 1.5.2.4*: 'persistent design situation'. This definition generally refers to conditions of normal use. Normal use includes wind, snow and imposed loads likely to occur during the working life, which may be taken as equal to 50 years for common buildings. *Clause 1.5.2.4*
- *Clause 1.5.2.9*: 'hazard'. Another example is: gross human errors during design and execution are frequently occurring hazards. *Clause 1.5.2.9*
- *Clause 1.5.2.12*: 'limit states'. The note for the definition from ISO 2394, 'A specified set of states which separate desired states from undesired states', complements the definition provided in EN 1990. *Clause 1.5.2.12*
- *Clause 1.5.2.14*: 'serviceability limit state'. The definition from ISO 2394, 'A limit state concerning the criteria governing function related to normal use', complements the definition provided in EN 1990. *Clause 1.5.2.14*
- *Clause 1.5.2.20*: 'maintenance'. With regard to the definition, 'working life' is the actual physical period of the structure during which it is used for an intended purpose with anticipated maintenance while the 'design working life' (*clause 1.5.2.8*) is an assumed period. *Clause 1.5.2.20* *Clause 1.5.2.8*
- *Clause 1.5.3.18*: 'quasi-permanent value of a variable action'. The part of the EN 1990 definition 'for which will be exceeded is a large fraction of the reference period', is given in the latest draft of ISO 2394 as 'during which it is exceeded is of the magnitude half the period'. The ISO definition is only applicable to buildings. *Clause 1.5.3.18*
- *Clause 1.5.4.1*: the ISO 2394 definition complements the EN 1990 definition. 'Characteristic value of a material property': an *a priori* specified fractile of the statistical distribution of the material property in the supply produced within the scope of the relevant material standard. *Clause 1.5.4.1*

1.6. Symbols

The notation in *clause 1.6* is based on ISO 3898.[9]

Clause 1.6

With regard to the notation for actions it has already been stated that actions refer not only to forces directly applied to the structure but also to imposed deformations. Actions are further subdivided as permanent (G) (self-weight), variable Q (imposed loads, snow loads, etc.) and accidental actions (A) and seismic actions (A_E).

Characteristic values of any parameter are distinguished by the subscript 'k'. Design values have the subscript 'd'. The subscript 'inf' refers to lower value of a characteristic or design value of an action or a material property, while the subscript 'sup' refers to the upper value.

Appendix: alphabetical index of definitions

The clause in which a term is defined is given in parentheses.

Clause 1.5

Accidental action, A	*Clause 1.5.3.5*
Accidental design situation	*Clause 1.5.2.5*

Accompanying value of a variable action, ψQ_k	*Clause 1.5.3.19*
Action, F	*Clause 1.5.3.1*
Basic variable	*Clause 1.5.2.19*
Characteristic value of an action, F_k	*Clause 1.5.3.14*
Characteristic value of a geometrical property, a_k	*Clause 1.5.5.1*
Characteristic value, X_k or R_k	*Clause 1.5.4.1*
Combination of actions	*Clause 1.5.3.22*
Combination value of a variable action, $\psi_0 Q_k$	*Clause 1.5.3.16*
Construction material	*Clause 1.5.1.5*
Construction works	*Clause 1.5.1.1*
Design criteria	*Clause 1.5.2.1*
Design situations	*Clause 1.5.2.2*
Design value of an action, F_d	*Clause 1.5.3.21*
Design value of a geometrical property, a_d	*Clause 1.5.5.2*
Design value of a material or product property, X_d or R_d	*Clause 1.5.4.2*
Design working life	*Clause 1.5.2.8*
Dynamic action	*Clause 1.5.3.12*
Effect of action, E	*Clause 1.5.3.2*
Elasto-plastic analysis (first or second order)	*Clause 1.5.6.10*
Execution	*Clause 1.5.1.11*
Fire design	*Clause 1.5.2.6*
First-order elastic–perfectly plastic analysis	*Clause 1.5.6.8*
First-order linear–elastic analysis without redistribution	*Clause 1.5.6.3*
First-order linear–elastic analysis with redistribution	*Clause 1.5.6.4*
First-order non-linear analysis	*Clause 1.5.6.6*
Fixed action	*Clause 1.5.3.8*
Form of structure	*Clause 1.5.1.8*
Free action	*Clause 1.5.3.9*
Frequent value of a variable action $\psi_1 Q_k$	*Clause 1.5.3.17*
Geotechnical action	*Clause 1.5.3.7*
Global analysis	*Clause 1.5.6.2*
Hazard	*Clause 1.5.2.9*
Irreversible serviceability limit states	*Clause 1.5.2.14.1*
Limit states	*Clause 1.5.2.12*
Load arrangement	*Clause 1.5.2.10*
Load case	*Clause 1.5.2.11*
Maintenance	*Clause 1.5.2.20*
Method of construction	*Clause 1.5.1.4*
Nominal value of a material or product property, X_{nom} or R_{nom}	*Clause 1.5.4.3*
Nominal value	*Clause 1.5.2.22*
Permanent action, G	*Clause 1.5.3.3*
Persistent design situation	*Clause 1.5.2.4*
Quasi-permanent value of a variable action, $\psi_2 Q_k$	*Clause 1.5.3.18*
Quasi-static action	*Clause 1.5.3.13*
Reference period	*Clause 1.5.3.15*
Reliability	*Clause 1.5.2.17*
Reliability differentiation	*Clause 1.5.2.18*
Repair	*Clause 1.5.2.21*
Representative value of an action, F_{rep}	*Clause 1.5.3.20*
Resistance	*Clause 1.5.2.15*
Reversible serviceability limit states	*Clause 1.5.2.14.2*
Rigid plastic analysis	*Clause 1.5.6.11*
Second-order elastic–perfectly plastic analysis	*Clause 1.5.6.9*
Second-order linear–elastic analysis	*Clause 1.5.6.5*

Second non-linear analysis	*Clause 1.5.6.7*
Seismic action, A_E	*Clause 1.5.3.6*
Seismic design situation	*Clause 1.5.2.7*
Serviceability criterion	*Clause 1.5.2.14.3*
Serviceability limit states	*Clause 1.5.2.14*
Single action	*Clause 1.5.3.10*
Static action	*Clause 1.5.3.11*
Strength	*Clause 1.5.2.16*
Structural analysis	*Clause 1.5.6.1*
Structural member	*Clause 1.5.1.7*
Structural model	*Clause 1.5.1.10*
Structural system	*Clause 1.5.1.9*
Structure	*Clause 1.5.1.6*
Transient design situation	*Clause 1.5.2.3*
Type of building or civil engineering works	*Clause 1.5.1.2*
Type of construction	*Clause 1.5.1.3*
Ultimate limit states	*Clause 1.5.2.13*
Variable action, Q	*Clause 1.5.3.4*

CHAPTER 2

Requirements

This chapter is concerned with basic requirements of EN 1990, *Eurocode*: *Basis of Structural Design*. The material described in this chapter is covered in *Section 2*, in the following clauses:

- Basic requirements *Clause 2.1*
- Reliability management *Clause 2.2*
- Design working life *Clause 2.3*
- Durability *Clause 2.4*
- Quality management *Clause 2.5*

2.1. Basic requirements

2.1.1. Principal requirements

There are four principal fundamental requirements concerning the bearing capacity for any structure and structural members. These are covered by *clauses 2.1(1)P*, *2.1.(2)P*, *2.1(3)P* and *2.1(4)P*, and may be summarized as follows.

Clause 2.1(1)P
Clause 2.1(2)P
Clause 2.1(3)P
Clause 2.1(4)P

The structure and structural members should be designed, executed and maintained in such a way that during their intended life with appropriate degrees of reliability and in an economic way they will:

- withstand actions and influences occurring during their construction and anticipated use (relating to the ultimate limit state requirement) (*clause 2.1(1)P*) *Clause 2.1(1)P*
- remain fit for use under all expected actions (relating to the serviceability limit state requirement) (*clause 2.1(1)P*) *Clause 2.1(1)P*
- have adequate structural resistance, serviceability and durability (*clause 2.1 (2)P*) *Clause 2.1(2)P*
- have adequate structural resistance for the appropriate required period of time, in case of fire (*clause 2.1(3)P*) *Clause 2.1(3)P*
- not be damaged by events such as explosions, impact or consequences of human errors, to an extent disproportionate to the original cause (robustness requirement) (*clause 2.1(4))P*). *Clause 2.1(4)P*

The design should consider all of the above requirements since any may be decisive for appropriate structures or structural member. These requirements may be generally interrelated and partly overlapping.

Structural safety and resistance, serviceability, durability and robustness are the four components of the structural reliability concept. Figure 2.1 illustrates this concept, which will be developed in this chapter.

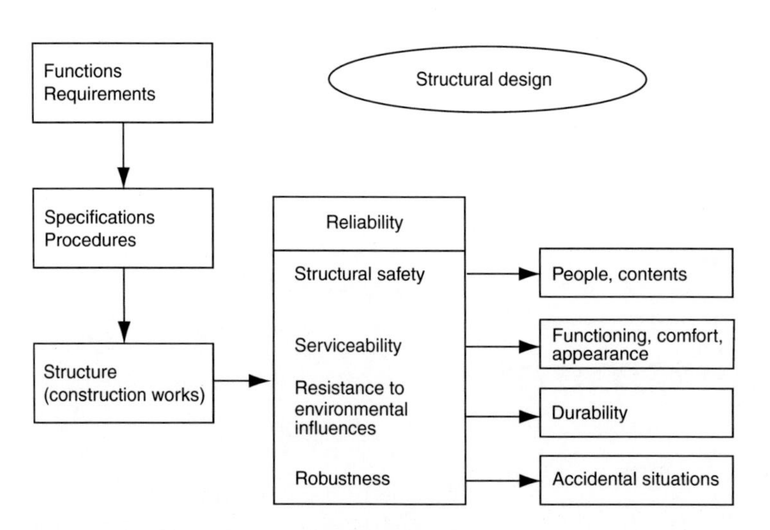

Fig. 2.1. *Representation of the structural reliability concept*

2.1.2. Serviceability and ultimate limit states requirements

Clause 2.1(1)P

The first two requirements (*clause 2.1(1)P*), concerning serviceability and ultimate strength requirements in general, are mutually dependent. In many common cases, a structure, which has sufficient resistance has also sufficient stiffness. However, the use of new and improved technologies, advanced analytical techniques, and higher strength materials, together with more emphasis being given to economy, are leading to more slender structures and structural member for which a stiffness design is becoming critical. For example, a large span structure may have sufficient strength but not have the required stiffness. Thus, due regard should be given to both safety and serviceability, including durability in both cases (*clause 2.1(2)*).

Clause 2.1(2)

2.1.3. Requirements in the case of fire

Clause 2.1(3)P

The requirement for the structure or structural member to have adequate structural resistance for the appropriate required period of time is specified in *clause 2.1(3)P*. During fire it is necessary to ensure the load-bearing capacity and, since large movements and constraint forces occur during fire, the structural integrity remain adequate for a defined period of time, in order to:

- permit evacuation of the occupants
- afford appropriate protection to fire-fighting services
- protect the building and adjoining property from fire spread.

'The required period of time' will normally be a matter for regulations made by a National Competent Authority (e.g. the Building Regulations in the UK). 'The required period of time', or the 'minimum period of fire resistance' is dependent on the use of a building, the height of the building concerned, and on the size of the building or compartment. In basements the provisions are generally more onerous than for ground or upper storeys in the same building in view of the greater difficulty in dealing with a basement fire.

The verification for fire resistance for a structure or a structural member may be carried out by:

- compliance with EN 1991-1-2 and the fire parts of EN 1992 to 1996
- standard fire tests on structural members
- calculation verified by experimental data.

2.1.4. Robustness requirements

The robustness (i.e. the ability of a structure (or part of it) to withstand events (e.g. explosion) or consequences of human errors without being damaged to an extent disproportionate to the original cause) requirement (*clause 2.1(4)P*) is additional to the serviceability and ultimate limit state requirements, and refers to limiting the damage of a structure by events such as explosion, impact or consequences of human error. The events to be taken into account may be those specified by the National Competent Authority, and the structural form, size and the consequences of failure of the individual project will also have a bearing on the events to consider. Further guidance is also given in EN 1991-1-7, *Accidental Actions*, which describes the possible safety strategies in case of general accidental situations, and covers accidental actions due to impact and internal explosions. At the present time the scope of EN 1991-1-7 excludes actions arising from external explosions, warfare and sabotage.

Clause 2.1(4)P

This book gives practical guidance for the design of buildings and bridges to withstand events, without disproportional damage.

To avoid damage or to ensure that damage is not disproportional to the original cause, EN 1990 in *clauses 2.1(5)P* and *2.1(6)* requires the appropriate choice of one or more of the following measures. The measures are reproduced from EN 1990, and given below with additional explanation in paragraphs 1 to 5:

Clause 2.1(6)
Clause 2.1(5)P

(1) *'Avoiding, eliminating or reducing the hazards which the structure can be subjected'.*

This first measure can be satisfied, for example, by:

- the provision of barriers or bollards to avoid impact from heavy vehicles on the columns of a building or a bridge
- the avoidance of piped gas systems within a building or within a box girder bridge deck that may cause an internal explosion
- reducing the consequences of human errors by quality management.

(2) *'Selecting a structural form which has low sensitivity to the hazards considered'.*

For this measure:

- the structure should safely resist the notional horizontal design loads as specified in EN 1992 to EN 1996
- the structure should have continuity, for example in the form of horizontal and vertical ties
- in particular for masonry construction it will be necessary to consider the layout of the structure in plan, returns to the ends of walls, interactions between intersecting walls and, in the case of masonry, the interaction between masonry walls and other parts of the structure
- each load-bearing structural member should be examined in turn to see whether after its removal, adequate means exist to transmit the loads to the foundations through alternative load paths.

(3) *'Selecting a structural form and design that survive adequately the accidental removal of an individual element or a limited part of the structure or the occurrence of acceptable localised damage'.*

For this measure:

- each load-bearing member of the structure is examined in turn to see whether its removal would allow collapse of more than the permitted amount
- where structural members are identified that if they failed would allow damage of more than the permitted amount, they are designed as a key element.

(4) *'Avoiding as far as possible a structural system that can collapse without warning'.*

For example, structural types which depend upon single structural members are considered highly vulnerable. It is important that a structure or structural member may have large (and visible) displacements, deformations or damage before attaining the conditions of a potential collapse.

(5) '*Tying the structural members together*'.

Practical guidance based on UK practice is summarized below.[10] The guidance provided relates to avoiding disproportionate damage for:
- multistorey buildings (e.g. greater than four storeys) and
- buildings which have a roof with a large (e.g. exceeding 9 m), clear span between supports.

2.1.5. Multistorey buildings

To reduce the sensitivity of the building to disproportionate collapse in the event of an accident the following approach is recommended:

(1) The provision of effective horizontal and vertical ties in accordance with the appropriate recommendations given in appropriate codes and standards.[10–14] If these measures are followed, then no further action is likely to be necessary, although this depends on regulations set by the National Competent Authority.
(2) If effective horizontal tying is provided and it is not feasible to provide effective vertical tying of any of the vertical load-bearing members, then each such untied member should be considered to be notionally removed, one at a time in each storey in turn, to check that its removal would allow the rest of the structure to bridge over the missing member, albeit in a substantially deformed condition. In considering this option, it should be recognized that certain areas of the structure (e.g. cantilevers or simply supported floor panels) will remain vulnerable to collapse. In these instances, the area of the structure at risk of collapse should be limited to that given in paragraph (3) below. If it is not possible to bridge over the missing member, that member should be designed as a protected member (see paragraph (4) below).
(3) If it is not feasible to provide effective horizontal and vertical tying of any of the load-bearing members, then the following accidental situation should be verified: each support member should be considered to be notionally removed, one at a time in each storey in turn, and it should be checked that, on its removal, the area at risk of collapse of the structure within the storey and the immediately adjacent storeys is limited to:

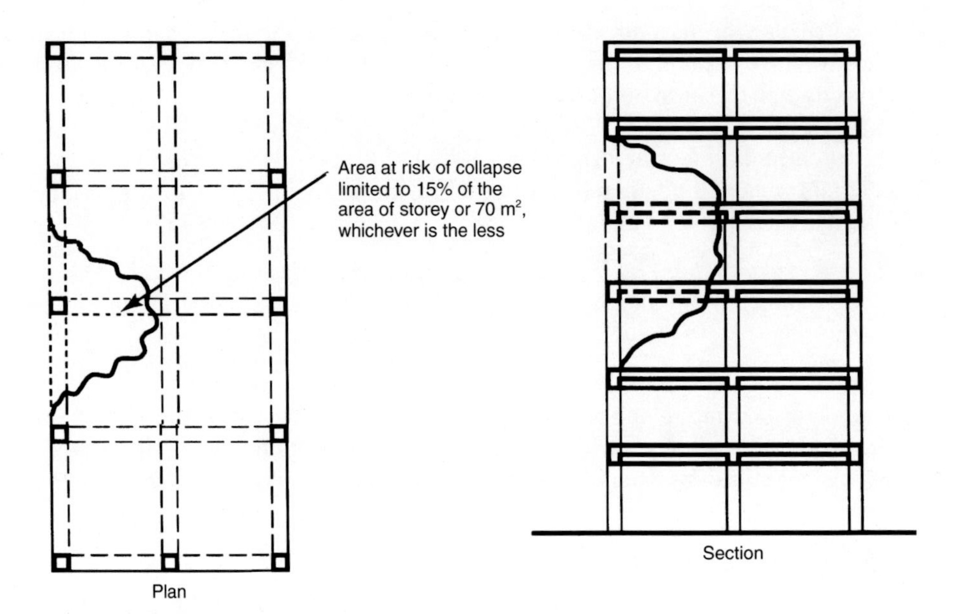

***Fig. 2.2.** Area of risk of collapse in the event of an accident*

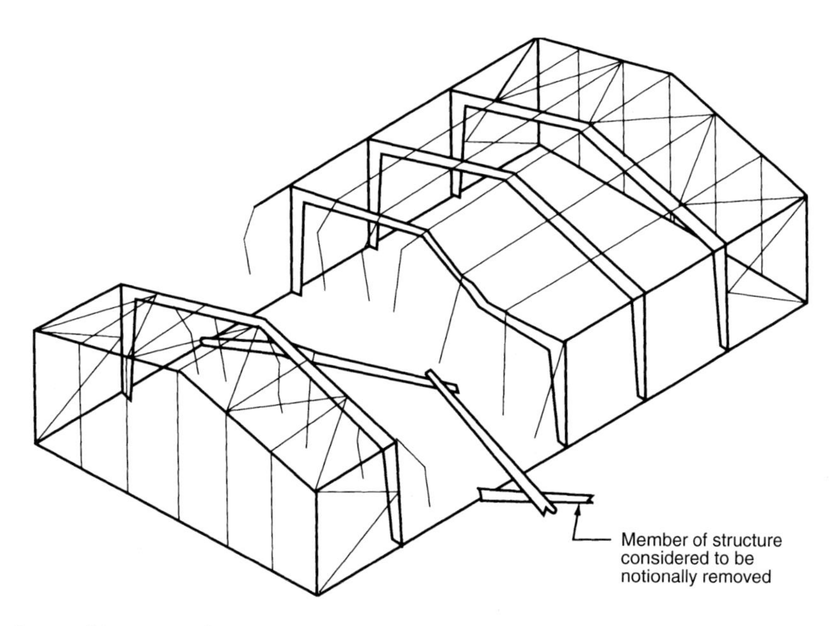

Fig. 2.3. *Acceptable extent of collapse in the event of a local failure in the roof structure it supports*

– 15% of the area of the storey, or
– 70 m^2

whichever is the less (see Fig. 2.2). It should be noted that the area at risk is the area of the floor at risk of collapse on the removal of the member and not necessarily the entire area supported by the member in conjunction with other members.

If, on removal of a member, it is not possible to limit the area put at risk of collapse as above, that member should be designed as a protected member (see paragraph (4)).

(4) The protected members (sometimes called 'key' elements) should be designed in accordance with the recommendations given in appropriate UK codes and standards.[10–14]

2.1.6. Buildings which have a roof with a large clear span between supports

To reduce the sensitivity of the building to disproportionate collapse in the event of a local failure in the roof structure or its supports the following approach is recommended.[10] Each member of the structure of the roof and its immediate supports should be considered to be notionally removed in turn one at a time, to check that its removal would not cause the building to collapse. In such circumstances it may be acceptable that:

(1) other members supported by the notionally removed member collapse (see Fig. 2.3) and/or
(2) the building deforms substantially.

Notwithstanding the foregoing approach, consideration should be given to reducing the risks of local failure of the roof structure and its supports by:

(1) protecting the structure from foreseeable physical damage
(2) protecting the structure from adverse environmental conditions
(3) making careful assessment and provision for movement and deformation of the structure
(4) providing access for inspection of main structural components and joints.

Clause 2.1(7)

EN 1990 in *clause 2.1(7)* stresses the importance that appropriately qualified people and organizations (see also Chapter 8) should interpret the fundamental requirements of *Section 2.*

Fig. 2.4. Example of accidental impact on a bridge deck

2.1.7. Bridges

In the case of bridges, most accidental situations entailing a collapse are due to gross errors during execution or impacts when in use. These types of risk may be avoided, or strongly limited, by appropriate design and execution measures (e.g. stabilizing devices) and by rigorous control of quality procedures. During its working life, the collapse of a bridge may be the consequence of:

- a possible accidental situation (e.g. exceptional scour around pile foundations)
- impact (e.g. due to lorry, ship or train collision on a bridge pier or deck, or even an impact due a natural phenomenon – see Fig. 2.4)
- development of hidden fatigue cracks in a structure with low redundancy (e.g. cracks in a welded joint in one of the two girders of a composite steel–concrete bridge deck); concerning this question, the design Eurocodes establish a distinction between damage-tolerant and non-tolerant structures
- brittle behaviour of some construction materials, e.g. brittle steel at low temperatures (this type of risk is very limited in the case of recent or new bridges, but it may be very real in the case of old bridges).

2.2. Reliability management

2.2.1. Basic concepts

Clause 2.2

Clause 2.2 in EN 1990, explains in conceptual form the ways of achieving different 'levels of reliability'. EN 1990 also contains *Annex B*, 'Management of structural reliability for construction works', which provides further and operative guidance (explained in Chapter 8 of this guide).

Clause 2.2(1)P

Clause 2.2(1)P makes the very important statement that *'the reliability required for the structures within the scope of EN 1990 shall be achieved by design in accordance with EN 1990 to EN 1999 and appropriate execution and quality management measures'*. The term 'reliability' with regard to a structure or a structural member should be considered as its ability to fulfil the specified requirements, including the design working life (see Section 2.3,

'Design working life') for which it has been designed. In a narrow sense, it is the probability that a structure will not exceed specified limit states (ultimate limit states and serviceability limit states) during a specified reference period.

EN 1990 (*clause 2.2(2)*) allows for different levels of reliability to be adopted for both structural resistance (further explained in Chapter 8) and serviceability.

Clause 2.2(2)

2.2.2. Choice of level of reliability

EN 1990 allows the level of reliability to be adjusted (*clause 2.2(3)*) in the design, but the guidance provided for this is more conceptual than specific. The degree of reliability should be adopted so as to take into account:

Clause 2.2(3)

- the cause and mode of failure – this implies that, for example, a structure or structural member which would be likely to collapse suddenly without warning (e.g. a member with low ductility) should be designed for a higher degree of reliability than one for which a collapse is preceded by some kind of warning in such a way that measures can be taken to limit the consequences
- the possible consequences of failure in terms of risk to life, injury, potential economic losses and the level of social inconvenience
- the public's aversion to a failure, and social and environmental conditions in a particular location
- the expense, level of effort and procedures necessary to reduce the risk of failure.

Further information is given in Chapter 8 of this guide.

2.2.3. Levels of reliability and classification

The differentiation of the required degrees of reliability (*clause 2.2(4)*) in relation to structural safety and serviceability may be obtained by classification of whole structures or by classification of structural components and members. Thus, as an example, degrees of reliability may be selected according to the consequences of failure as follows:

Clause 2.2(4)

- risk to life low, and economic, social and environmental consequences small or negligible
- risk to life medium, or economic, social or environmental consequences considerable
- risk to life high, or economic, social or environmental consequences very great.

As an example, Table 2.1 indicates a possible classification of buildings and civil engineering works which may be used to select appropriate degree of reliability according to consequences of failure.

Table 2.1. *Examples of reliability differentiation according to the risk to life, and economic losses and social inconveniences*

Degree of reliability	Risk to life, and economic and social losses	Examples of buildings and civil engineering works
Extremely high	High	Nuclear power reactors Major dams and barriers Strategic defence structures
Higher than normal	High	Significant bridges Grandstands Public buildings where consequences of failure are high
Normal (obtained by using EN 1990 *clause 2.2(1)* and *Table B2*)	Medium	Residential and office buildings Public buildings where consequences of failure are medium
Lower than normal	Low	Agricultural buildings where people do not normally enter Greenhouses Lightning poles

2.2.4. Recommended measures for reliability management

Clause 2.2(5)

Various possible measures by which the required level of reliability may be achieved include measures (*clause 2.2*(*5*)) relating to:

Clause 2.2(5)(a)
Clause 2.2(5)(d)
Clause 2.2(5)(b)
Clause 2.2(5)(e)
Clause 2.2(5)(f)

- preventative and protective measures (*clauses 2.2*(*5*)(*a*) and *2.2*(*5*)(*d*))
- design matters (e.g. the fundamental requirements and the degree of robustness; durability and the choice of design working life; soil investigations; accuracy of models used; detailing) (*clauses 2.2*(*5*)(*b*) and *2.2*(*5*)(*e*))
- efficient execution (*clause 2.2*(*5*)(*f*))
- quality management, which includes measures aimed to reduce errors in design and execution and gross human errors (*clause 2.2*(*5*)(*c*) and *2.2*(*5*)(*g*)).

Clause 2.2(5)(c)
Clause 2.2(5)(g)

Clause 2.2(6)

The differing levels of applying the above measures may be interchanged, in appropriate circumstances, to a limited extent provided that the required reliability levels are maintained (*clause 2.2*(*6*)). An example is during a refurbishment when it may be necessary with the approval of the controlling authority to compensate for a slightly lower partial factor by a high level of quality management.

There are attempts to check degrees of reliability across materials (e.g. structural steel and reinforced concrete) and different structures, including geotechnical aspects. At present, however, the reliability level is likely to be different in structures built of different materials.

2.3. Design working life

Clause 2.3
Clause 1.5.2.8
Clause 2.3(1)
Clause A1.1(1)

The design working life (*clause 2.3*) is the term used (*clause 1.5.2.8*) for which a structure or part of it is to be used for its intended purpose with anticipated maintenance but without major repair being necessary. *Table 2.1* of EN 1990 (*clause 2.3*(*1*)) (reproduced in Table 2.2) gives indicative categories together with the indicative design working life for a number of common types of construction work. The values may be adopted nationally either unaltered, or altered and/or extended as appropriate, depending upon national practice, through the National Annex (*clause A1.1*(*1*)). Clients and owners of construction works, who increasingly use whole-life costing in optimizing the balance between initial and running costs, will find the indicative figures a very useful guide.

Clause 2.1(1)P

The concept of design working life is connected to the basic requirements defined in *clause 2.1*(*1*)*P*. The design working life is considered in the design, for example where there may be problems of corrosion (e.g. sheet piles, steel piles in chemically aggressive water or ground, or reinforced earth) or of fatigue (e.g. in steel or composite steel–concrete bridges). But in the case of important construction works this concept of design working life is increasingly used, e.g. concerning durability, on the penetration speed of chlorides into concrete, or other analogous physicochemical phenomena.

It should also be noted that all parts of a construction works have not necessarily the same working life. For example, in the case of bridges, the structural bearings or the waterproofing layer may have to be regularly replaced (see Table 2.2); therefore, if a bridge is designed for an intended working life of 100 years, it should be clear that this working life applies to the bearing structure (deck, piers and foundations).

The present state of knowledge is insufficient to enable precise prediction of the life of a structure. The behaviour of materials and structures over extended periods of time can only be estimated. The likely period of maintenance of the structure or time of replacements of the various components of a structure can, however, be determined.

A minimum design working life of 10 years for temporary structures has been recommended by *Table 2.1* of EN 1990 (see Table 2.2 of this guide) for reasons of safety.

However, the notion of a design working life is useful for:

- the selection of design actions (e.g. design wind or earthquake) and the consideration of material property deterioration (e.g. fatigue or creep)

Table 2.2. *Indicative design working life (based on* Table 2.1 *of EN 1990)*

Design working life category	Notional design working life (years)	Examples
1	10	Temporary structures (e.g. scaffolding)
2	10–25	Replaceable structural parts, e.g. gantry girders, bearings (see appropriate standards)
3	15–30	Agricultural and similar structures (e.g. buildings for animals where people do not normally enter)
4	50	Building structures and other common structures (e.g. hospitals, schools)
5	100	Monumental building structures, bridges and other civil engineering structures (e.g. churches)

- comparison of different design solutions and choice of materials, each of which will give a different balance between the initial cost and cost over an agreed period – life cycle costing will need to be undertaken to evaluate the relative economics of the different solutions
- evolving management procedures and strategies for systematic maintenance and renovation of structures.

Structures designed to the Eurocodes should perform and remain fit for the appropriate time, provided the client develops a maintenance (including replacement) strategy. In developing such a strategy the following aspects should be considered:

- costs of design, construction of use
- costs arising from hindrance of use
- risks and consequences of failure of the works during its working life and costs of insurance covering these risks
- planned partial renewal
- costs of inspections, maintenance, care and repair
- costs of operation and administration
- disposal
- environmental aspects.

2.4 Durability

Clause 2.4(1)P

The durability of a structure is its ability to remain fit for use during the design working life given appropriate maintenance (*clause 2.4(1)P*). The structure should be designed in such a way that, or provided with protection so that, no significant deterioration is likely to occur within the period between successive inspections. The need for critical parts of the structure to be available for inspection, without complicated dismantling, should be a part of the design.

Figure 2.5 represents possible evolutions of a structure during its working life using a suitable 'performance indicator' that is assumed to be a monotonously decreasing function of time. It can be expressed in terms of various units: mechanical, financial, reliability, etc. This 'indicator' remains constant during a certain time, for example in the case of a steel structure correctly protected against corrosion. In other cases, the structural value may increase with time, for example in the case of concrete structures in which concrete resistance grows.

In all cases, after a certain period of time, the 'performance indicator' decreases, for example due to corrosion of steel, carbonation of concrete, repeated (irreversible) opening

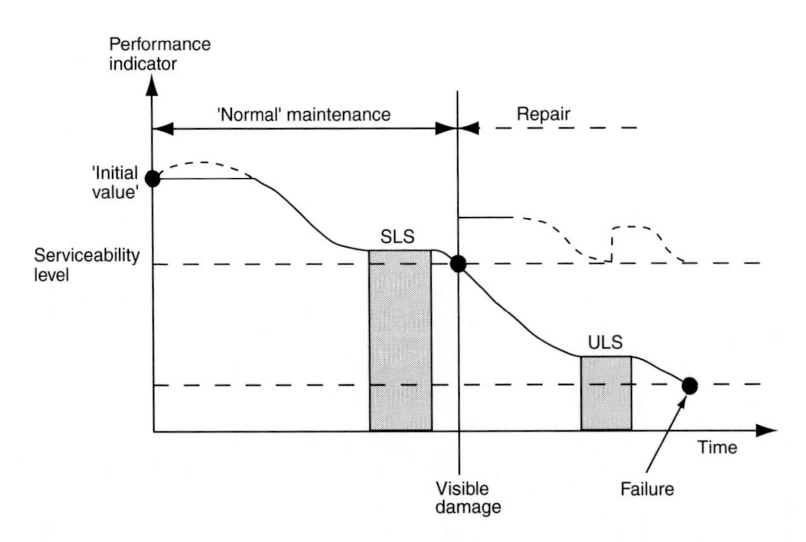

Fig. 2.5. Evolution with time of a structure. SLS, serviceability limit state; ULS, ultimate limit state

of cracks in concrete members, etc. A regular inspection being assumed, some types of damage may appear, such as destruction of concrete due to corrosion of reinforcement steel, wide cracks in concrete members which remain open, or fatigue cracks in steel members. This damage reveals that some irreversible serviceability limit states have been attained or exceeded.

Assuming no maintenance at this stage, damage to the structure increases and its condition worsens, progressing to a possible structural failure.

If the structure is repaired, a reliability level is ensured above what can be designated by the 'serviceability level'.

Clause 2.4(1)P

Clause 2.4(1)P of EN 1990 should be interpreted in the following way: at the end of its design working life, the reliability level of the structure should not be below the 'serviceability level', as shown in Fig. 2.5.

Clause 2.4(2)

Other interrelated factors that shall be considered to ensure an adequately durable structure are listed in principal *clause 2.4(2)*, and each is considered and explained below:

(1) '*The intended and future use of the structure*'. One example to consider is the abrasion on industrial floors due to machinery loads. The effects of the change of use on the durability of the structure should be considered when, for example, the micro-climate of a room may change (e.g. humidity in a laundry) or the exposure conditions alter.

Clause 2.3

(2) '*The required design criteria*'. The design life requirement given in *clause 2.3* of EN 1990 is the principal requirement to be considered in the overall strategy for achieving durability: in particular, decisions with regard to the life performance required from the structural members and whether individual members are to be replaceable, maintainable or should have a long-term design life.

(3) '*The expected environmental influences*'. The deterioration of concrete and timber, and the corrosion of steel, are affected by the environment, and adequate measures need to be examined when considering the strategy to achieve durability. In addition, the variability of environmental actions, e.g. wind, snow and thermal actions, and their effects on the durability of a structure is an important consideration. As an example, using 'design-out' techniques, such as cladding, can help protect vulnerable parts of the structure from the external environment, although durability will remain a key issue for the cladding itself.

(4) '*The composition, properties and performance of materials*'. The use of materials that provide increased durability should be considered in the overall strategy for durability, with the use of, for example, preservative-treated timber, epoxy-coated reinforcing

steels, stainless steel wall ties, or concrete with low permeability. For storage structures the choice of the material for the structure can be critical with regard to durability, e.g. for storing corrosive substances such as potash a glued laminated timber structural system is preferable to either reinforced concrete or structural steel.

(5) '*The choice of a structural system*'. The structural form selected at the design stage should be robust, and the provision of redundancy in the structural system should be considered when designing for the consequences of known hazards. The design should avoid structural systems which are inherently vulnerable and sensitive to predictable damage and deterioration, and have flexibility 'built in' to enable the structure to tolerate changes in environmental conditions, movements, etc. For example, good drainage can minimize the risk of reinforcement corrosion in structures such as multistorey car parks. As a further example, the elimination of movement joints in bridges removes a path by which de-icing salts can travel from the road surface and gain access to structural members, consequently reducing chloride-induced reinforcement corrosion.

(6) '*The shape of members and structural detailing*'. The shape of members together with their detailing will influence the durability of a structure, for example an angle or channel steel section may retain or not retain moisture depending upon the orientation of the section. For concrete, transverse reinforcement can restrict deleterious effects arising through processes such as reinforcement corrosion and the alkali–silica reaction.

(7) '*The quality of workmanship and level of control*'. The level of control of workmanship during execution can have an effect on the durability of a structure. For example, poor compaction can create honeycombs in reinforced concrete, and thus reduce durability. See also Section 2.5 of this chapter.

(8) '*The particular protective measures*'. To increase durability, structural members should be protected from detrimental environments. For example, timber may be preservative treated and/or given protective coatings, and steel members may be galvanized or clad with paints or concrete. Other measure such as cathodic protection of steel should also be considered.

(9) '*The maintenance during the intended life*'. Maintenance should be considered during the design, and a strategy developed which is compatible with the design concept. Provision should be made for inspection, maintenance and possible replacement if this is part of the performance profile. Whenever possible, a structure should be designed and detailed such that vulnerable, but important, members can be replaced without difficulty. An example is the provision for the replacement of post-tensioning tendons of prestressed concrete structures in corrosive environments.

The appropriate measures for various structural materials should be found in the material Eurocodes 2 to 9.

Clause 2.4(3)P

It is necessary (*clause 2.4(3)P*) to appraise the environmental conditions and their significance in relation to durability at the design stage.

Clause 2.4(4)

The rate of deterioration may be estimated (*clause 2.4(4)*). There are a large number of factors that can effect the rate of deterioration, and consequently the prediction of design working life (called service life in this chapter, in the context of durability) is a complex issue. There are, however, a number of approaches that can be used in predicting service working life. These include:

- the use of knowledge and experience acquired from laboratory and field trials to make semi-quantitative predictions
- estimates based on the performance of similar materials in a similar environment
- the use of accelerated testing
- modelling degradative processes
- combinations of these.

All of these approaches have advantages and disadvantages. The use of experience and knowledge acquired from laboratory and field testing, and from the performance of existing structures, may be adequate for structures with a short design working life in environments that are not too severe. However, the approach may be less suitable where long service lives are required in new and aggressive environments or where new materials have been used. Accelerated testing can, in principle, be used to predict service life under in-service conditions provided the degradation proceeds by the same mechanism in both cases and an acceleration factor can be established. However, the lack of long-term in-service data that can be used to calibrate the tests is a problem.

2.5. Quality management

2.5.1. General

Clause 2.5(1)

EN 1990 assumes (*clause 2.5(1)*) that an appropriate quality policy is implemented by parties involved in the management of all stages in the life cycle of the construction process so as to fulfil the fundamental requirements described in Section 2.1. The measures highlighted in EN 1990 comprise:

- definitions of the reliability requirements
- organizational measures
- controls at the stages of design, execution and maintenance.

Practical experience shows that a quality system including organization measures and control at the stages of design, execution, use and maintenance is the most significant tool to achieve an appropriate level of structural reliability. For additional explanation, see Chapter 8.

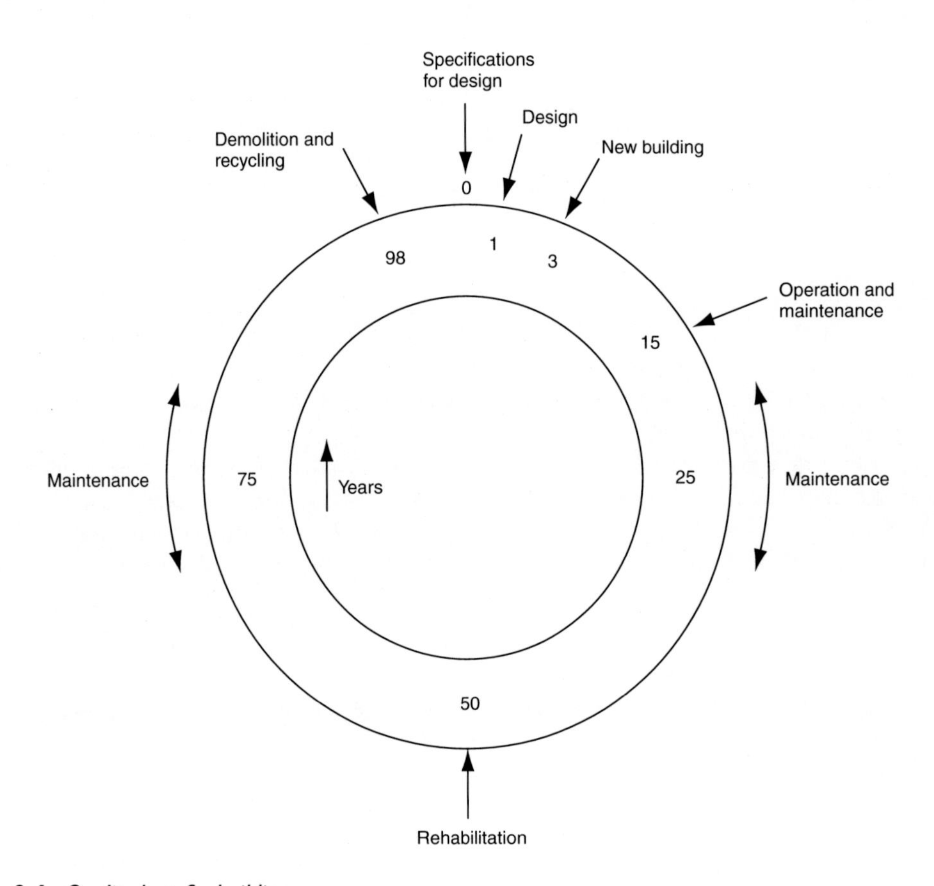

Fig. 2.6. *Quality loop for buildings*

Table 2.3. *Construction process and quality*

Stage in quality loop	Activities
Conception	Establishing appropriate levels of performance for construction works and components Specification for design Specification for suppliers Preliminary specifications for execution and maintenance Choice of intervening parties with appropriate qualifications for the personnel and organization
Design	Specification of performance criteria for materials, components and assemblies Confirming acceptability and achievability of performance Specification of test options (prototype, *in situ*, etc.) Specification for materials
Tendering	Reviewing design documents, including performance specifications Accept requirements (contractor) Accept tender(s) (client)
Execution	Reviewing of process and product Sampling and testing Correction of deficiencies Certification of work according to compliance tests specified in the design documentation
Completion of building and hand-over to client	Commissioning Verification of performance of completed building (e.g. by testing for anticipated operational loads)
Use and maintenance	Monitoring performance Inspection for deterioration or distress Investigation of problems Certification of work
Rehabilitation (or demolition)	Similar to above

The quality system of an organization is influenced by the objectives of the organization, by the product or services, and by the practices specified by the organization. Therefore, the quality system varies from one organization to another. The CEN series EN 29 000 and the series of international standards (ISO 9000 to 9004) embody a rationalization of the many and various national approaches in this sphere.

2.5.2. Specific aspects of quality policy in the field of construction works

A primary concern of a construction project is the quality of the construction works and, in particular, the reliability of the structure. In this aspect the construction works should:

- meet a well-defined need, use or purpose
- satisfy client expectations
- comply with applicable codes, standards and specifications
- comply with statutory (and other) requirements of society.

The objective of quality management is to meet these requirements.

2.5.3. Quality management through the construction works process life cycle

Quality management is an essential consideration in every stage in the design working life of any construction works. The various stages in a construction works life cycle, and the associated specific quality assurance activities are identified schematically in the quality loop diagram in Fig. 2.6 and in Table 2.3.

2.5.4. Quality policy

The quality management selected for implementing the quality policy should include consideration of:

- the type and use of the structure
- the consequences of quality deficiencies (e.g. structural failures)
- the management culture of the involved parties.

In the structural design of the construction works, reliability is the most important aspect to consider to achieve quality. Codes and standards for structural design should provide a framework to achieve structural reliability as follows:

- provide requirements for reliability
- specify the rules to verify the fulfilment of the requirements for reliability
- specify the rules for structural design and associated conditions.

The conditions to be fulfilled concern, for example, choice of the structural system, the use of information technology with regard to design through to execution, including supply chains with regard to materials being used, level of workmanship, and maintenance regime, and are normally detailed in the structural design standards. The conditions should also take into account the variability of material properties, the quality control and the criteria for material acceptance.

CHAPTER 3

Principles of limit states design

This chapter is concerned with the general concepts of design situations and limit states. The material described in this chapter is covered in *Section 3* of EN 1990, *Eurocode*: *Basis of Structural Design*, in the following clauses:

- General — *Clause 3.1*
- Design situations — *Clause 3.2*
- Ultimate limit states — *Clause 3.3*
- Serviceability limit states — *Clause 3.4*
- Limit state design — *Clause 3.5*

3.1. General

Traditionally, according to the fundamental concept of limit states, it is considered that the states of any structure may be classified as either satisfactory (safe, serviceable) or unsatisfactory (failed, unserviceable). Distinct conditions separating satisfactory and unsatisfactory states of a structure are called limit states (see also Chapter 2). In other words, limit states are an idealization of undesirable events or phenomena. Sometimes, certain states just preceding these undesirable events are considered, in the design, as limit states. In general, the limit states are those beyond which the structure no longer satisfies the design criteria (see the definition given in *clause 1.5.2.12*). Each limit state is therefore associated with a certain performance requirement imposed on a structure. Often, however, these requirements are not formulated sufficiently clearly so as to allow for precise (sharp) definition of appropriate limit states.

Clause 1.5.2.12

Generally, it may be difficult to express the performance requirements qualitatively and to define the limit states unambiguously (particularly the ultimate limit states of structures made of ductile materials, and also the serviceability limit states, typically those affecting user comfort or appearance of the structure). In these cases, only a suitable approximation is available (e.g. the conventional yield point of metals, or a limiting value for vertical deflection or for vibration frequency).The principles of this are indicated in Fig. 3.1, and provided here as a background to the uncertainties of the limit state concept. According to the traditional (sharp) concept of limit states described above, a given structure is assumed to be fully satisfactory up to a certain value of the load effect E_0 and beyond this value the structure is assumed to be fully unsatisfactory (Fig. 3.1(a)). However, it may be very difficult to define precisely such a distinct value E_0, separating the desired and undesired structural conditions, and the simplification in Fig. 3.1(a) may not be adequate. In these cases a transition region $\langle E_1, E_2 \rangle$, in which a structure is gradually losing its ability to perform satisfactorily, provides a more realistic (vague) concept (Fig. 3.1(b)). Uncertainties in the vague concept of limit states may be taken into account only in reliability analyses

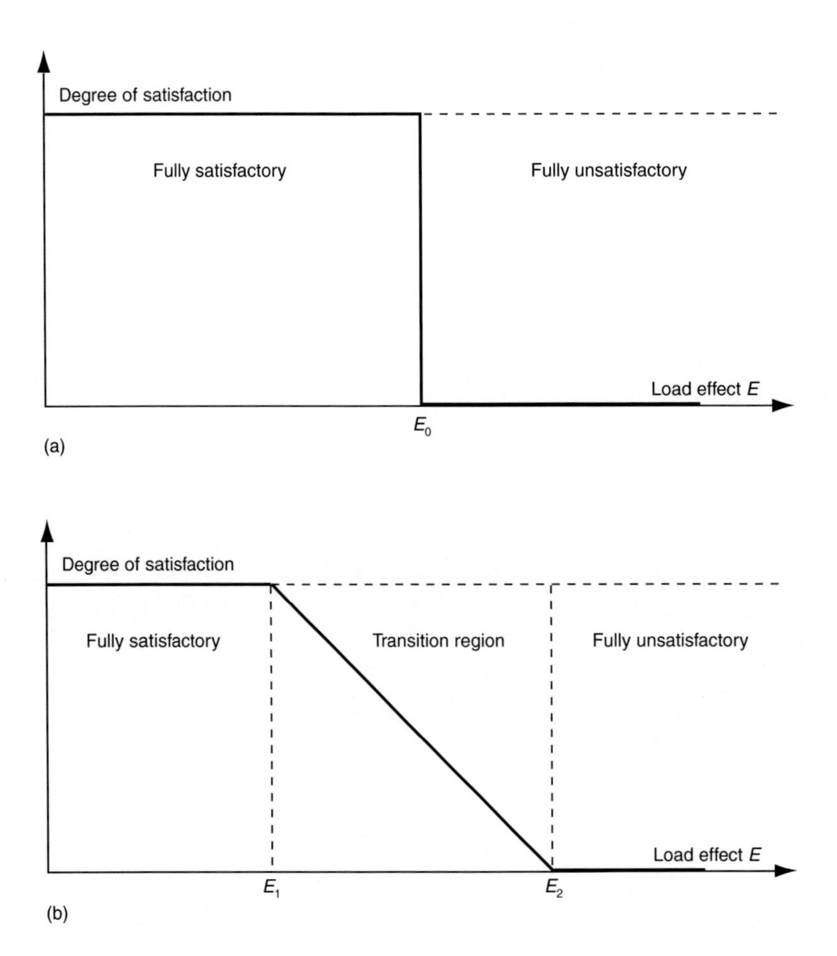

Fig. 3.1. *(a) Sharp and (b) vague definitions of a limit state*

using special mathematical techniques which are not covered in the present generation of Eurocodes.

In order to simplify the design procedure, two fundamentally different types of limit states are generally recognized (*clause 3.1(1)P*):

Clause 3.1(1)P

Clause 1.5.2.13
Clause 1.5.2.14

(1) ultimate limit states (see also the definition in *clause 1.5.2.13*).
(2) serviceability limit states (see also the definition in *clause 1.5.2.14*).

Ultimate limit states are associated with collapse or other similar forms of structural failure. Serviceability limit states correspond to conditions of normal use (deflections, vibration, cracks, etc.). In general the design should include both safety and serviceability, including durability in both cases (*clause 2.1(2)P*). The nature of ultimate limit states is essentially different from the nature of serviceability limit states. There are two main reasons for this distinction:

Clause 2.1(2)P

(1) While the infringement of ultimate limit states leads almost always to structural failure and to the removal or fundamental repair of the structure, infringement of the serviceability limit states does not usually lead to such fatal consequences for the structure, and the structure may normally be used after the removal of those actions which caused the infringement. Nevertheless, a distinction is made between reversible and irreversible serviceability limit states (see Section 3.4).
(2) While the criteria of ultimate limit states involve parameters of the structure and appropriate actions only, the criteria of serviceability limit states are also dependent on the requirements of the client and users (sometimes very subjective), and on the characteristics of the installed equipment or non-structural elements.

The differences between the ultimate limit states and serviceability limit states result in a separate formulation of reliability conditions, and in dissimilar reliability levels assumed in the verification of both types of limit states. However, verification of one of the two limit states may be omitted if sufficient information is available to ensure that the requirements of one limit state are met by the other limit state (*clause 3.1(2)*). For example, in the case of reinforced concrete beams satisfying the ultimate limit state conditions, the verification of deflection can be omitted provided that the span/effective depth ratio is less than 18 for highly stressed concrete or less than 25 for lightly stressed concrete.

Clause 3.1(2)

It should be noted that not all undesirable events or phenomena can be easily classified into ultimate or serviceability limit states. For example, in the case of a railway bridge some serviceability limit states of the deck can be considered as ultimate limit states for the supported track: significant deformation of the track may cause the derailment of a train with loss of human life. Another example is the vibration of a building floor or footbridge: this may be very uncomfortable, or even dangerous to human health, without being structurally damaging. The design of construction works intended to protect against accidental phenomena such as avalanches also needs to be reflected in the limit states to be taken into account according to the acceptable degree of damage.

The variations in actions, environmental influences and structural properties which will occur throughout the life of a structure should be considered in the design by selecting distinct situations (persistent, transient, accidental and seismic) representing a certain time interval with associated hazards (*clauses 3.1(3)P* and *3.1(4)*). In fact, the concept of design situation complements the concept of limit state. For example, a design situation for a bridge crossing a river may correspond to a given scour depth around its piers. The ultimate and serviceability limit states should be considered in all these design situations (*clauses 3.2(1)P*, *3.2(2)P* and *3.2(3)P*), and should be selected so as to encompass all conditions which are reasonably foreseeable or will occur during the execution and use of the structure. If two or more independent loads act simultaneously, their combination should be considered in accordance with Chapter 6 (see also *Section 6* of EN 1990). Within each load case, a number of realistic arrangements should be assumed, to establish the envelope of action effects which should be considered in the design.

Clause 3.1(3)P
Clause 3.1(4)
Clause 3.2(1)P
Clause 3.2(2)P
Clause 3.2(3)P

If the limit states considered in design are dependent on time-variant effects (described by action and/or resistance variables), the verification of a structure should be related to the design working life (*clause 3.1(5)*, see also the definition in *clause 1.5.2.8* and Chapter 2 of this guide). It should be mentioned that most time-dependent effects (e.g. fatigue) have a cumulative character that needs to be taken into account.

Clause 3.1(5)
Clause 1.5.2.8

3.2. Design situations

In design the variations in actions, environmental influences and structural properties which will occur throughout the design working life of a structure should be considered by selecting distinct situations representing a certain time interval with associated hazards or conditions (*clause 3.2(1)P*).

Clause 3.2(1)P

Four design situations are classified as follows (*clause 3.2(2)P*):

Clause 3.2(2)P

(1) Persistent situations. These refer to conditions of normal use. These are generally related to the design working life of the structure. Normal use can include possible extreme loading conditions from wind, snow, imposed loads, etc.
(2) Transient situations. These refer to temporary conditions of the structure, in terms of its use or its exposure, e.g. during construction or repair. For example, for the maintenance of a bridge, a lane of the carriageway may be temporarily closed for normal traffic, entailing a modification of the conditions of use of the bridge. This implies reference to a time period much shorter than the design working life. Appropriate representative values of actions need to be defined (see Chapter 4 of this guide). For actions during execution, rules are given in EN 1991-1-6.

(3) Accidental situations. These refer to exceptional conditions of the structure or of its exposure, e.g. due to fire, explosion, impact or local failure. This implies the use of a relatively short period, but not for those situations where a local failure may remain undetected. Examples of accidental situations may be foreseen easily in common cases. However, in some specific cases the classification of an action as accidental may not be so obvious; for example, the effect of a snow or rock avalanche may not be considered an accidental action when a protective structure is considered.
(4) Seismic situations. These refer to exceptional conditions applicable to the structure when subjected to seismic events.

Clause 3.2(3)P

These design situations should be selected so as to encompass all conditions which are reasonably foreseeable or will occur during the execution and use of the structure (*clause 3.2(3)P*). For example, a structure after an accidental design situation due to an action such as fire or impact may need a repair (over a short time period of about 1 year) for which the transient design situation should be considered. In general, a lower reliability level and lower partial factors than those used for the persistent design situation might be applicable for this period of time. However, it should be mentioned that the repair should be designed considering all the other foreseeable design situations.

One major question is the way to take the risk into account during these design situations. Of course, the basic principles are generally applicable, but, for their application, data are in most cases specific; in particular, it is often possible to prevent or to reduce the consequences of an initially unexpected event.

Let us compare acceptable failure probabilities for transient and persistent design situations. It is difficult to perform scientifically based calculations of failure probabilities as functions of time: failure probabilities during the individual years of a persistent design situation are not mutually independent (many data are the same – permanent actions and material properties; and, in the usual case of an existing structure some distributions of basic variables can be progressively truncated); in addition, failure probabilities during transient situations are not fully independent of failure probabilities during persistent design situations in spite of the involvement of some specific basic variables. However, in common cases, the mutual dependency has very significant consequences on the reliability level only when permanent actions G are dominant (in influence) by comparison with variable actions Q. Therefore, it is generally agreed that equal failure probabilities should be accepted for transient and persistent design situations. This question of assessment of characteristic values during transient design situations is discussed in Chapter 4 of this guide.

3.3. Ultimate limit states

Clause 1.5.2.13
Clause 3.2(1)P
Clause 3.3.1(P)
Clause 3.3(2)

The ultimate limit states are associated with collapse and other similar forms of structural failure (see the definition in *clause 1.5.2.13* and *clause 3.2(1)P*). As already indicated in Section 3.1, the ultimate limit states concern the safety of people and/or the safety of the structure (*clause 3.3.1(P)*). However, in some cases the ultimate limit states may also concern the protection of the contents (*clause 3.3(2)*), for example certain chemicals or nuclear or other waste materials, or even masterpieces in a museum.

Clause 3.3(3)

In almost all cases which concern the ultimate limit states the first occurrence of the limit state is equivalent to failure. In some cases, e.g. when excessive deformations are decisive, states prior to structural collapse can, for simplicity, be considered in place of the collapse itself and treated as ultimate limit states (*clause 3.3(3)*). These important circumstances should be taken into account when specifying the reliability parameters of structural design and quality assurance. For example, in the case of foundations for rotating machinery, excessive deformation is decisive and entirely govern the design.

Clause 3.3(4)

The list provided in *clause 3.3(4)*, which cites the ultimate limit states that may require consideration in the design, can be extended as follows:

(1) loss of equilibrium of the structure or any part of it, considered as a rigid body
(2) failure of the structure or part of it due to rupture, fatigue or excessive deformation*
(3) instability of the structure or one of its parts
(4) transformation of the structure or part of it into a mechanism
(5) sudden change of the structural system to a new system (e.g. snap through).

The ultimate limit state of static equilibrium mainly refers to the bearing condition of a structure, and comprises the limit states of:

- overturning
- uplift, e.g. raised by buoyancy
- sliding with interface effects (as friction).

Often in this verification the structure may be considered as a rigid body. In some cases, however, e.g. in cases of sensitivity to deformations (second-order effect) or to vibrations (impact effects), the elastic properties of the structure may also be considered.

Often also the bearings may be considered as point bearings and thus rigid; in some cases, however, the stiffness properties of the bearings (e.g. when represented by the soil) have to be taken into account. This may lead to the effect that the ultimate limit state of equilibrium may also be used to determine the design action effects for bearings or stabilizing devices, and hence constitutes an ultimate limit state of strength.

The term 'ultimate limit state of strength' has been used to refer this ultimate limit state to failure induced by limited strength of a material as dealt with in the design Eurocodes EN 1992 to EN 1999. This ultimate limit state also comprises failures initiated by lack of stability, i.e. by limited stiffness because stability failures may be induced by second-order effects starting from imperfections and eventually lead to a strength problem (e.g. due to yielding).

There are also cases where the ultimate limit state of strength covers failure by large deflections (e.g. when a structure runs off the bearings due to deflections).

It is a common feature of all modes of ultimate limit states of strength that the verification is carried out with an extremely high, operational (i.e. without a real physical basis) design level of loads.

In structures loaded by fluctuating actions, fatigue failures may occur at load levels which are significantly lower than the load levels at which failure may normally be expected. When such a fatigue failure is due to crack growth phenomena, the complete mechanism comprises three stages:

(1) an initiation phase, in which cracks are formed
(2) a crack growth phase, in which stable crack growth takes place during every load cycle
(3) a failure phase, in which unstable crack growth occurs due to brittle fracture or ductile tearing, or in which the reduced cross-section fails due to general yielding.

When, during the crack growth phase, large alternating plastic zones are present, failure occurs after relatively few cycles, and the mechanism is referred to as low-cycle fatigue. When the plastic zones are small, the mechanism is called high-cycle fatigue. Two main methods of analysis can be distinguished:

- the S–N line approach, and
- the fracture mechanics approach.

Fatigue limit states are separated from ultimate limit states and serviceability limit states for various reasons:

---

*Defects due to excessive deformation are those which would lead to structural failure by mechanical instability.

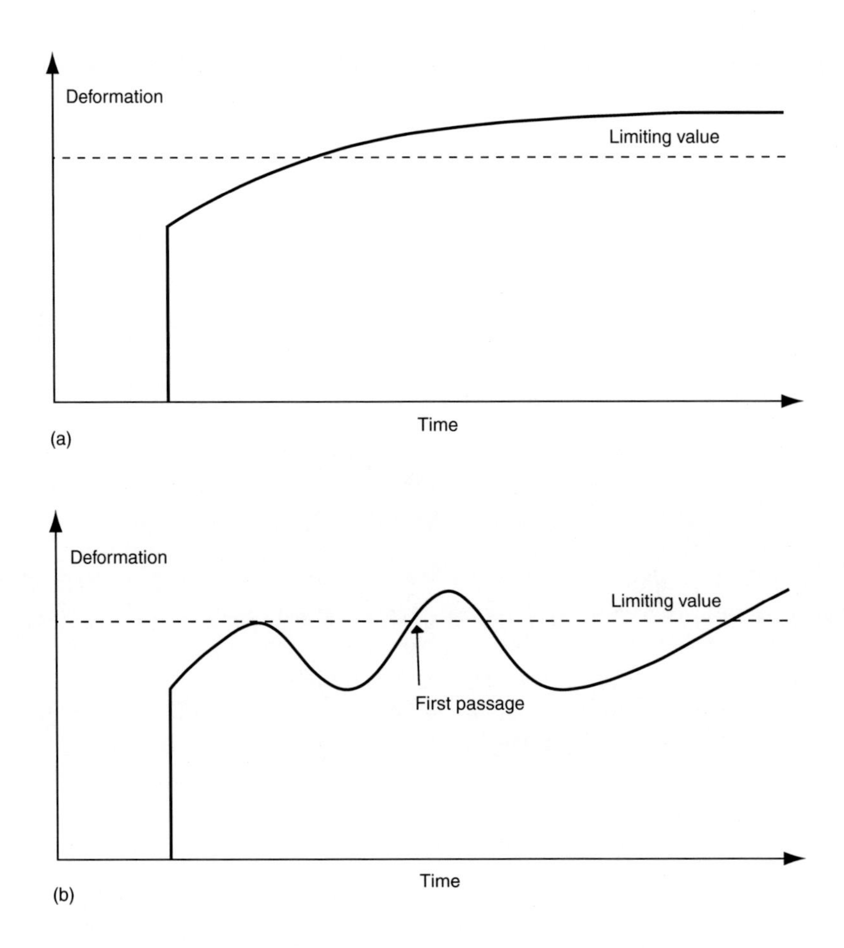

Fig. 3.2. *(a) Irreversible and (b) reversible limit states*

(1) Fatigue loading is different from other loadings as it is dependent on the magnitudes and ranges of actions under service conditions together with time effects (e.g. by the number of cycles).
(2) Fatigue effects are a local deterioration of material that may be benign when cracks lead to a reduction of restraints and will eventually stop, or destructive when cracks lead to more severe loading conditions that accelerate crack growth.
(3) When particular conditions are fulfilled (e.g. sufficient toughness of the material), crack growth may be detected by regular inspections before fatal effects from either insufficient strength or insufficient toughness occur.
(4) Taking account of this situation, a safety system has been introduced for fatigue limit states that takes into account the possibilities of prewarning and the consequences of failure.

In a general manner it is useful to distinguish two types of structure: damage-tolerant (i.e. robust) and damage-intolerant (sensitive to minor disturbance or construction imperfections). The effects of various deteriorating mechanisms on the ultimate limit states should then be taken into account according to the type of structure.

An adequate reliability level for damage-intolerant structures can also be assured by an appropriate quality control programme. In the case of damage-tolerant structures, fatigue damage may be regarded as a serviceability limit state. Note that different sets of partial factors may be associated with the various ultimate limit states, as indicated in Chapter 6 (*clause 6.4.1*), and in *Annex A1*, where appropriate sets of partial factors are provided.

Clause 6.4.1

3.4. Serviceability limit states

The serviceability limit states are associated with conditions of normal use (see the definition in *clause 1.5.2.14*). In particular, they concern the functioning of the structure or structural members, comfort of people and appearance of the construction works (*clause 3.4(1)P*).

Clause 1.5.2.14
Clause 3.4(1)P

Taking into account the time dependency of load effects, it is useful to distinguish two types of serviceability limit states, which are illustrated in Fig. 3.2 (*clause 3.4(2)P*):

Clause 3.4(2)P

(1) irreversible serviceability limit states (Fig. 3.2(a)), which are those limit states that remain permanently exceeded even when the actions which caused the infringement are removed (e.g. permanent local damage or permanent unacceptable deformations)
(2) reversible serviceability limit states (Fig. 3.2(b)), which are those limit states that will not be exceeded when the actions which caused the infringement are removed (e.g. cracks in prestressed components, temporary deflections, or excessive vibration).

For example, cracks due to bending may appear in a prestressed concrete beam: under a moderate loading these cracks close up after the loading has been removed; under a more severe loading, the cracks may not close up in the unloaded beam. In such a case, the cracking phenomenon is irreversible and may be associated with specific irreversible serviceability limit states. The exceedance of such limit states may necessitate limited repair of the structure.

For irreversible limit states the design criteria are similar to those of ultimate limit states. The first passage of the limit state is decisive (Fig. 3.2). This important aspect of irreversible limit states should be taken into account when determining the serviceability requirements in the contract or design documentation. For reversible limit states the first infringement (first passage) does not necessarily lead to failure and the loss of serviceability.

Various serviceability requirements can be formulated taking into account the acceptance of infringements, their frequency and their duration. Generally, three types of serviceability limit states are applicable:

(1) no infringement is accepted
(2) specified duration and frequency of infringements are accepted
(3) specified long-term infringement is accepted.

The correct serviceability criteria are then associated as appropriate with the characteristic, frequent and quasi-permanent values of variable actions (see Section 4.3 of EN 1990). The following combinations of actions corresponding to the above three types of limit state are generally used in verification of serviceability limit states for different design situations (see Chapter 6):

(1) characteristic combination, if no infringement is accepted
(2) frequent combination, if the specified time period and frequency of infringements are accepted
(3) quasi-permanent combination, if the specified long-term infringement is accepted.

The list of serviceability limit states (*clause 3.3(3)*) affecting the appearance or effective use of the structure, which may require consideration in the design, may be summarized as follows:

Clause 3.3(3)

(1) excessive deformation, displacement, sag and inclination, which can affect, for example, the appearance of the structure, comfort of users and function of the structure, and can cause damage to finishes and non-structural members
(2) excessive vibration (acceleration, amplitude, frequency), which can, for example, cause discomfort to people and limit the function of the structure
(3) damage that is likely adversely to affect the appearance (local damage and cracking), durability or function of the structure.

Depending on the type of structure, additional requirements related to serviceability limit states may be found in the material-oriented standards EN 1992 to EN 1999. For example, in the case of concrete structures the ultimate limit states may be induced by structural deformation. EN 1992 provides additional guidance concerning design procedure for various concrete elements.

3.5. Limit state design

The design procedure using the limit state concept consists of setting up structural and load models for relevant ultimate and serviceability limit states which are considered in the various design situations and load cases (*clause 3.5(1)P*). The aim of the limit state design is to verify that no limit state is exceeded when relevant design values for actions (see the definition given in *clause 1.5.3.21*), for material or product properties (see the definition given in *clause 1.5.4.2*) and for geometrical properties (see the definition given in *clause 1.5.5.2*) are used in appropriate structural and load models (*clause 3.5(2)P*).

Clause 3.5(1)P
Clause 1.5.3.21
Clause 1.5.4.2
Clause 1.5.5.2
Clause 3.5(2)P
Clause 3.5(3)P

All relevant design situations and load cases must be considered (*clause 3.5(3)P*) using the combination rules described in Chapter 6. To determine the design values of various basic variables the characteristic or representative values are defined in Chapter 4 and *Section 4* (*clause 3.5(4)*) should be used. It should be mentioned that the direct determination of design values (*clause 3.4(3)*) should be used exceptionally when well-defined models and sufficient data are available (see also Chapter 5 and *Section 5*). In this case the design values should be chosen cautiously and should correspond to at least the same degree of reliability for various limit states as implied in the partial factors method.

Clause 3.5(4)
Clause 3.4(3)

The verification of structural reliability should be done using the method of partial factors (*clause 3.5(4)*) described in Chapter 6 or, alternatively, using probabilistic methods (*clause 3.5(5)*). Probabilistic methods can be applied to unusual structures while respecting the conditions specified by the relevant authority. The bases of probabilistic methods are described in Appendix 3 (see also *Annex C*). For example, probabilistic methods may be required for reliability verification of nuclear power construction works in order to provide the data required for comprehensive risk analysis.

Clause 3.5(4)
Clause 3.5(5)

For each design situation considered in verification the critical load cases should be identified (*clause 3.5(6)P*). This may be a complicated task, which may require a comparison of several relevant load cases. It should, however, be noted that the selected load cases should represent compatible load arrangements for all possible actions (*clause 3.5(7)*). Obviously, the requirement of compatibility of various variable actions may reduce the number of relevant load cases and may therefore simplify the identification of the critical load cases.

Clause 3.5(6)P
Clause 3.5(7)

CHAPTER 4

Basic variables

This chapter is concerned with the basic variables describing actions and environmental influences, material and product properties, and geometrical data of construction works. The material in this chapter is covered in *Section 4* of EN 1990, *Eurocode*: *Basis of Structural Design*, in the following clauses:

- Actions and environmental influences *Clause 4.1*
- Material and product properties *Clause 4.2*
- Geometrical data *Clause 4.3*

Clause 4.1, 'Actions and environmental influences', is further subdivided into *subclauses 4.1.1* to *4.1.7*.

4.1. Actions and environmental influences

4.1.1. Classification of actions

Classifications of actions introduced in EN 1990 (*clauses 4.1*) (primarily *clauses 4.1.1(1)P* and *4.1.1(4)P*) provide the basis for modelling of actions and controlling structural reliability. The aim of the classifications is to identify the similar or dissimilar characteristics of various actions and to enable the use of appropriate theoretical action models and reliability elements in structural design. A complete action model describes several properties of an action, such as its magnitude, position, direction and duration. In some cases, interactions between actions and the response of the structure should be taken into account (e.g. wind oscillations, soil pressures and imposed deformations).

Clause 4.1
Clause 4.1.1(1)P
Clause 4.1.1(4)P

The classifications introduced in *clauses 4.1.1(1)P* and *4.1.1(4)P* take into account the following aspects of actions and environmental influences:

Clause 4.1.1(1)P
Clause 4.1.1(4)P

(1) variation in time
(2) origin (direct or indirect)
(3) variation in space (fixed or free)
(4) nature and/or structural response (static and dynamic).

Classification depending on variation in time

Considering their variation in time, actions are classified as (*clause 4.1.1(1)P*):

Clause 4.1.1(1)P

(1) Permanent actions G (a permanent action is an '*action that is likely to act throughout a given reference period and for which the variation in magnitude with time is negligible, or for which the variation is always in the same direction (monotonic) until the action attains a certain limit value*' – definition given in *clause 1.5.3.3* of EN 1990), e.g. self-weight of structures or weight of fixed equipment and road surfacing, as well as indirect actions caused by shrinkage or uneven settlements.

Clause 1.5.3.3

Clause 1.5.3.4

(2) Variable actions Q (a variable action is an '*action for which the variation in magnitude with time is neither negligible nor monotonic*' – definition given in *clause 1.5.3.4*), e.g. imposed loads on building floors or on bridge decks, wind actions or snow loads.

Clause 1.5.3.5

(3) Accidental actions A (an accidental action is an '*action, usually of short duration but of significant magnitude, that is unlikely to occur on a given structure during the design working life*' – definition given in *clause 1.5.3.5*), e.g. fire, explosions or impact loads. Actions due to earthquakes are generally identified as accidental actions (see below), and are identified by the symbol A_E.

This classification is operational for the establishment of combinations of actions. However, other classifications are also important for the assessment of representative values of actions. In all cases, engineering judgement is necessary to identify the nature of some actions: for example, the self-weight of a fixed crane is a permanent action, but the load lifted by it is a variable action. This is very important when selecting the partial factors to be used in combinations of actions.

Classification depending on origin

Regarding the distinction between a direct and indirect action, it is clear that a direct action is 'directly' applied to the structure, and its model can usually be determined independently of the structural properties or the structural response. Concrete shrinkage is an example of indirect action: it has structural effects where it is constrained.*

Uneven settlements are also considered as an indirect action (generally an unintentional imposed deformation) for the reason that they give rise to action effects where the structure is statically undetermined: this means that action effects can be determined only by taking the structural response into account. In a general manner, it is clear that imposed deformations may be taken as permanent (e.g. uneven settlements of supports) or variable (e.g. temperature effects) actions. In general, moisture variation is considered for timber and masonry structures only (see EN 1995 and EN 1996).

Classification depending on variation in space

Concerning spatial variation, a free action is an action that can be applied to a structure anywhere within specified limits. For example, models of road traffic loads correspond to free actions: they are applied to the bridge deck in order to obtain the most adverse effects. By contrast, the self-weight of fixed equipment is a fixed action because it must be applied at the correct location.

In fact, for most free actions, spatial variability is limited, and this variability should be directly or indirectly taken into account, or even neglected, depending on its limitation and on the sensitivity of the structural response to this variability (e.g. static equilibria are very sensitive to the spatial variability of self-weight).

For a free action, the representation by one or more scalars must be supplemented by load arrangements which identify the position, magnitude and direction of the action.

Practical examples

Clause 4.1.1(2)

Clause 4.1.1(3)

Examples of classification for most common types of action are given in Table 4.1. However, this classification corresponds to typical conditions only, and may not apply in certain cases. Depending on site location and the actual conditions, certain actions, such as seismic actions and snow loads, may be considered as either accidental and/or variable actions (*clause 4.1.1(2)*). Similarly actions caused by water may be considered as permanent and/or variable actions, depending on their variation in time (*clause 4.1.1(3)*). The assignment of a specific action to the above-mentioned classes may also depend on a particular design situation.

---

*Note that concrete creep is not an action: its effects are the consequences of other actions.

Table 4.1. Classification of actions

Permanent action	Variable action	Accidental action
Self-weight of structures, fittings and fixed equipment	Imposed floor loads	Explosions
Prestressing force	Snow loads	Fire
Water and earth pressure	Wind loads	Impact from vehicles
Indirect action, e.g. settlement of supports	Indirect action, e.g. temperature effects	

In the case of seismic actions, in some countries or regions of Europe, earthquakes are not rare events and they can be mathematically treated as variable actions. For example, in the particular case of railway bridges, two levels of magnitude may be defined: a moderate level, corresponding to a rather short return period (e.g. 50 years – see the concept of the return period in Section 4.1.2), where the tracks supported by the bridge deck must not be damaged, and a higher level (e.g. corresponding to a 475 year return period – see later), where the tracks may be damaged but the bridge structure remains usable (with more or less repair needed). Another example can be found in EN 1991-1-3, *Snow Loads*. This Eurocode allows the treatment of snow loads as accidental actions in some cases. This applies in specific climatic regions where local drifting of snow on roofs is considered to form exceptional snow loads because of the rarity with which they occur, and are treated as accidental loads in accordance with EN 1990.

The prestressing force P is normally considered as a permanent action (see Section 4.1.2); more detailed information on this is provided in the material Eurocodes EN 1992, EN 1993 and EN 1994.

As mentioned above, the complete action model describes several properties of the action, such as its magnitude, position, direction and duration. In most cases the magnitude of an action is described by one quantity. For some actions a more complex representation of magnitudes may be necessary, e.g. for multidimensional actions, dynamic actions and variable actions causing fatigue of structural materials (*clause 4.1(7)*). For example, in the case of fatigue analysis, it is necessary to identify a complete history of stress fluctuations, often in statistical terms, or to describe a set of stress cycles and the corresponding number of cycles.

Clause 4.1(7)

Classification depending on the nature and/or the structural response

Considering the nature of actions and the structural response, all actions are classified as either (*clause 4.1.1(4)P*):

Clause 4.1.1(4)P

- static actions, which do not cause significant acceleration of the structure or structural member, or
- dynamic actions, which cause significant acceleration of the structure or structural member.

Often, the dynamic effects of actions are considered as quasi-static actions by increasing the magnitude of the static actions or by the introduction of an equivalent static action. Some variable actions, static or dynamic, may cause stress fluctuations which may lead to fatigue of structural materials.

In most cases an action is represented by a single scalar, which may have several representative values (*clause 4.1.1(5)*). An example is the self-weight of a material with great variability (critical value of the coefficient of variation within the range 0.05–0.1, depending on the type of structure, see the note to *clause 4.1.2(3)P*) that has both favourable and

Clause 4.1.1(5)

Clause 4.1.2(3)P

unfavourable load effects. Then, two characteristic values, lower and upper, may be needed in design calculation (see also *clause 4.1.2(2)P*).

Clause 4.1.2(2)P

In addition to the above classification of actions, EN 1990 considers the environmental influences of chemical, physical and biological characteristics as a separate group of actions (*clause 4.1.7*). These influences have many aspects in common with mechanical actions; in particular, they may be classified according to their variation in time as permanent (e.g. chemical impacts), variable (e.g. temperature and humidity influences) and accidental (e.g. spread of aggressive chemicals). Generally, environmental influences may cause time-dependent deterioration of material properties, and may therefore cause a gradual decrease in the reliability of structures.

Clause 4.1.7

4.1.2. Characteristic values of actions

General

All actions, including environmental influences, are introduced in design calculations as various representative values. The most important representative value of an action F (*clause 4.1.2(1)P*) is the characteristic value F_k. Depending on the available data and experience, the characteristic value should be specified in the relevant EN standard as a mean, an upper or lower value or a nominal value (which does not refer to any statistical distribution).* Exceptionally, the characteristic value of an action can also be specified in the design or by the relevant competent authority, provided that the general provisions specified in EN 1990 are observed (*clause 4.1.2(1)P*).

Clause 4.1.2(1)P

Clause 4.1.2(1)P

There is a considerable lack of relevant statistical data concerning various actions and environmental influences. Consequently, the determination of a representative value of an action may involve not only the evaluation and analysis of available observations and experimental data, but often, when there is a complete lack of sufficient statistical data, also a fairly subjective assessment, judgement (e.g. for particular accidental actions) or decision (e.g. for loads permitted on existing structures). For these cases, when the statistical distribution is not known, the characteristic value will be specified as a nominal value (*clause 4.1.2(1)P*). Nevertheless, all the characteristic values, regardless of the methods used for their original determination, are treated in EN 1990 in the same way.

Clause 4.1.2(1)P

Permanent actions

Clause 4.1.2(2)P

With regard to determining the permanent actions G (*clause 4.1.2(2)P*), particularly for the determination of self-weight for traditional structural materials, sufficient statistical data may be available. If the variability of a permanent action is small, a single characteristic value G_k may be used. Then G_k should be taken as the mean (*clause 4.1.2(2)P*).

Clause 4.1.2(2)P

When the variability of a permanent action is not small, two values have to be used: an upper value $G_{k,\,sup}$ and a lower value $G_{k,\,inf}$ (*clause 4.1.2(3)P*).

Clause 4.1.2(3)P

For example, in the case of bridges:

- the self-weight of the bridge deck (for the assessment of the bending moment, shear force, torsion moment, etc.) is taken into account using its mean value because its variability is small (the execution of a bridge is generally strictly controlled by competent personnel)
- the self-weight of items such as vehicle parapets, waterproofing, coatings, railway ballast, etc., is taken into account using an upper and a lower characteristic value because the variability (even in time) may not be small (see EN 1991-1-1).

*In all Eurocodes, the wording 'nominal value' designates a value which is given in a design code, or in a regulation, or even in the design specification for a particular project, because it has not been possible to assess a characteristic value from statistical data. This is often the case for actions occurring during accidental design situations.

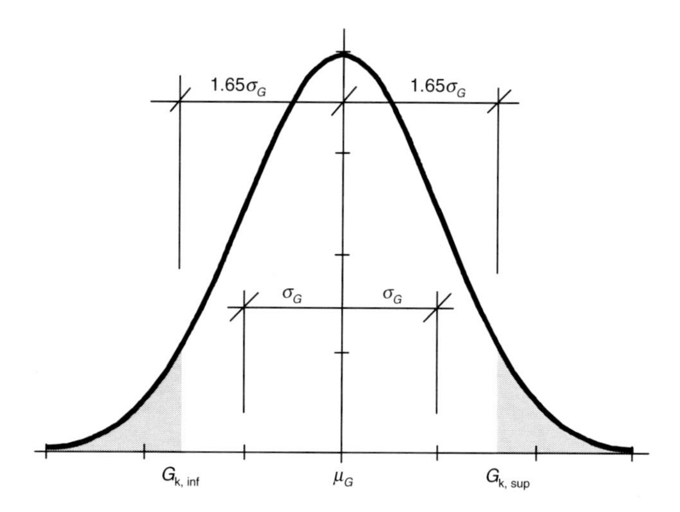

***Fig. 4.1.** Definition of lower ($G_{k, inf}$) and upper ($G_{k, sup}$) characteristic values of permanent actions based on a normal distribution*

The variability of permanent actions can usually be assumed to be small if the coefficient of variation during the design life is not greater than 0.05–0.1 (recommended value in *clause 4.1.2(3)*) depending on the type of structure. In fact, this range of values is intended to account for the effects of self-weight in common buildings. In the case of bridges, and in particular long-span bridges, the variability of the effects of self-weight may be in a smaller range, for example between 0.02 and 0.05.

Clause 4.1.2(3)

However, if the structure is very sensitive to variations in G (e.g. some types of prestressed concrete structures), two values have to be considered even if the coefficient of variation is small (*clause 4.1.2(6)*).

Clause 4.1.2(6)

In the case of self-weight, a single value may be used, and G_k can be assumed to be the mean value μ_G (Fig. 4.1; definitions of basic statistical parameters are given in Appendix 3 of this guide), calculated on the basis of nominal dimensions and mean unit mass (*clause 4.1.2(5)*), using values provided in EN 1991, Part 1.1, *Densities, Self Weight and Imposed Loads for Buildings*. In other cases, when two values are to be used (*clause 4.1.2(2)P* and *clause 4.1.2(4)*), a lower value $G_{k, inf}$ and an upper value $G_{k, sup}$, representing the 0.05 or 0.95 fractiles should be used respectively, as shown in Fig. 4.1. The normal (Gaussian) distribution may be generally assumed for self-weight.

Clause 4.1.2(5)
Clause 4.1.2(2)P
Clause 4.1.2(4)

In the latter case the following relationships (see Appendix 2 of this chapter for definitions of statistical terms and the basic statistical techniques involved) can be used to determine the lower value $G_{k, inf}$ and the upper value $G_{k, sup}$

$$G_{k, inf} = \mu_G - 1.64\sigma_G = \mu_G(1 - 1.64V_G) \quad \text{(D4.1)}$$

$$G_{k, sup} = \mu_G + 1.64\sigma_G = \mu_G(1 + 1.64V_G) \quad \text{(D4.2)}$$

where V_G denotes the coefficient of variation of G. It follows from the above equations (see also Fig. 4.1) that for a coefficient of variation of 0.10 (which is a hypothetical boundary between low and high variability of permanent actions), $G_{k, inf}$ and $G_{k, sup}$ will therefore be 16.4% less than or greater than the mean value μ_G.

There may be special cases of particular design situations (e.g. when considering overturning and strength of retaining walls) when both the lower value $G_{k, inf}$ and the upper value $G_{k, sup}$ should be used in the design (see also Chapter 6).

A special type of loading is represented by prestressing P, which should be, as indicated in Table 4.1, considered as a permanent action (*clause 4.1.2(6)*). The permanent action due to prestressing P may be caused either by controlled forces (e.g. prestressing by tendons)

Clause 4.1.2(6)

or controlled deformations (e.g. prestressing by an imposed deformation at a support). Physically, however, prestressing P is a time-dependent action (monotonous), and its characteristic values may, therefore, depend on time (see the note to *clause 4.1.2*(6)). It has to be noted that, in accordance with EN 1991-1-6, *Actions During Execution*, jack forces activated during the prestressing should be classified as variable actions for the anchor region.

Clause 4.1.2(6)

Variable actions

The volume of available statistical data for the most common variable actions allows an assessment of their characteristic value Q_k by a probabilistic approach. In some cases, as stated in *clause 4.1.1*(7)*P*, the characteristic value may be a nominal value.

Clause 4.1.1(7)P

For example, in most European countries, climatic data are available over more than the past 40 years and allow a scientific determination of actions due to wind, snow and temperature. For the calibration of traffic loads on road bridges (EN 1991-2), traffic records representing more than 200 000 heavy vehicles on a main European motorway were used. The situation regarding imposed loads on floor buildings or dynamic actions due to pedestrians on a footbridge is less satisfactory, but Eurocode 1 gives the right orders of magnitude.

When a statistical treatment is possible, the characteristic value Q_k corresponds either to an upper value with an intended probability of it not being exceeded (the most common case), or to a lower value with an intended probability of not falling below it, during an assumed reference period. Hence, two separate elements are used to define the characteristic value: the reference period during which the extreme (maximum or minimum) is observed, and the intended probability with which these extreme values should not exceed or should not fall below the characteristic value. In general, the characteristic value Q_k of climatic actions and imposed loads on building floors for persistent design situations is based on an intended probability of the value not being exceeded of 0.98, and a reference period of 1 year (see note 2 of *clause 4.1.2*(7)).

Clause 4.1.2(7)

The probability p of the characteristic value not being exceeded and the reference period τ are linked by the equation

$$T \cong -\frac{\tau}{\mathrm{Ln}(1-p)} \cong \frac{\tau}{p}$$

where T is the return period (expected period between two subsequent occurrences of the characteristic value being exceeded) of the value corresponding to probability p. Thus, for a probability $p = 0.02$ and a reference period of 1 year, the return period of the characteristic value is $T \cong 1/0.02 = 50$ years. According to note 2 of *clause 4.1.2*(7), depending on the character of the variable action, a different reference period may be more appropriate, and this will change the intended probability of the characteristic value not being exceeded and the return period.

Clause 4.1.2(7)

Note that some variable actions may not have a periodical character similar to climatic or traffic actions and the above concepts of reference period and return period may not be suitable. In this case the characteristic value of a variable action may be determined in a different way, taking into account its actual nature. For example, variable actions caused by water should generally be calculated by allowing for fluctuating water levels and for variation in appropriate geometric parameters, such as the profile of the structure or of components exposed to water.

Accidental actions

Less statistical information is available for accidental actions than for permanent and variable actions. The appropriate clauses (*clauses 4.1.2*(8) to *4.1.2*(9)) may be very simply summarized as follows. The design value A_d should be specified for individual projects, values for seismic actions are given in EN 1998, *Earthquake Resistant Design of Structures* (*clause 4.1.2*(9)). Note that:

Clause 4.1.2(8)
Clause 4.1.2(9))

Background

The concept of reference period is illustrated in Fig. 4.2, which shows variable action Q versus time t. The reference period τ is indicated as a certain time period (e.g. 1 year) on the abscissa axis. During each reference period τ the variable action Q reaches its maximum value Q_{max} (e.g. the annual extreme). In this way a sequence of values $Q_{1,max}$, $Q_{2,max}$, $Q_{3,max}$, ... can be obtained. The distribution of these values of Q_{max} (e.g. the distribution of annual extremes) is indicated in Fig. 4.2 by a probability density function $\varphi_{Q\max}(Q)$, where Q denotes a generic value of Q here. The characteristic value Q_k (Fig. 4.2) can then be defined by the requirement that it will be exceeded by Q_{max} (e.g. annual extremes) only with a limited probability p, say 0.02. Thus, the characteristic value Q_k is p-fractile of the extremes values Q_{max} ('fractile' is defined in Appendix 3 of this guide).

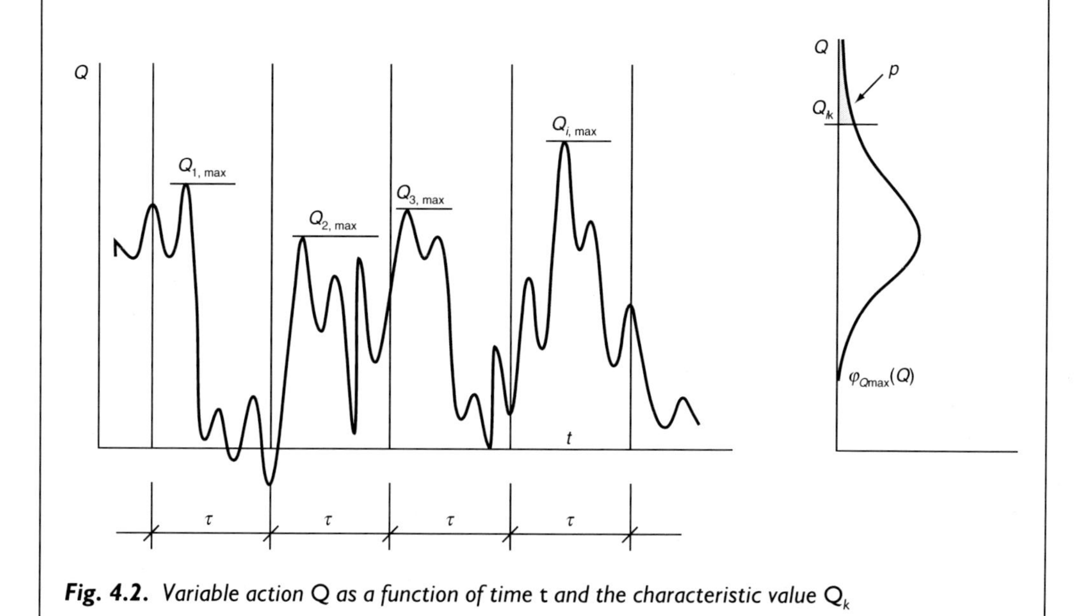

Fig. 4.2. *Variable action* Q *as a function of time* t *and the characteristic value* Q_k

- seismic action is defined in EN 1998, *Design of Structures for Earthquake Resistance*
- accidental loads due to fire are specified in EN 1991, Part 1.2, *Action on Structures Exposed to Fire*
- explosions and some impacts are defined in EN 1991, Part 1.7, *Accidental Actions due to Impact and Explosions* (see also Chapter 2 of this guide)
- actions during accidental design situations for bridges are defined in EN 1991, Part 2, *Traffic Loads on Bridges*.

For multicomponent actions and some types of verifications (e.g. verification of static equilibrium) the characteristic action should be represented by several values corresponding to each component (*clause 4.1.2(10)*).

Clause 4.1.2(10)

4.1.3. Other representative values of variable actions

In addition to the characteristic values of actions, other representative values are specified for variable actions in EN 1990. Three representative values are commonly used for variable actions: the combination value $\psi_0 Q_k$, the frequent value $\psi_1 Q_k$ and the quasi-permanent value $\psi_2 Q_k$ (*clause 4.1.3(1)P*). The factors ψ_0, ψ_1 and ψ_2 are reduction factors of the characteristic values of variable actions, but they have different meanings.

Clause 4.1.3(1)P

ψ_0, called the combination factor, is intended to take account of the reduced probability of the simultaneous occurrence of two (or more) independent variable actions.

For the persistent and transient design situations of ultimate limit states and for the characteristic combinations of serviceability limit states, only the non-leading variable actions may be reduced using the ψ coefficients. In other cases (for accidental design situation and combinations of serviceability limit states), the leading as well as non-leading actions may be reduced using the ψ coefficients (see Table 4.2 and Chapter 6). If it proves difficult to decide which action is leading (when considering the combination of actions) then a comparative study will be needed.

Clause A.1.2.2

Recommended values for all the three coefficients ψ_0, ψ_1 and ψ_2 for buildings are given in *Annex A* (*clause A.1.2.2*). Their application in the verification of ultimate limit states and serviceability limit states is indicated in Table 4.3 (see also Chapter 6 of this guide).

The combination value $\psi_0 Q_k$, the frequent value $\psi_1 Q_k$, and the quasi-permanent value $\psi_2 Q_k$ are represented schematically in Fig. 4.3.

Clause 4.1.3(1)P

The combination value $\psi_0 Q_k$ is associated with the combination of actions for ultimate and irreversible serviceability limit states in order to take account of the reduced probability of simultaneous occurrence of the most unfavourable values of several independent actions (*clause 4.1.3(1)P*). The statistical technique used to determine ψ_0 is presented in *Annex C* of EN 1990 (see also Chapter 9 of this guide). The coefficient ψ_0 for combination values of some imposed actions in buildings is typically equal to 0.7 (see *Annex A1* of EN 1990 and Chapter 7 of this guide); this value is approximately indicated in Fig. 4.3.

The frequent value $\psi_1 Q_k$ is primarily associated with the frequent combination in the serviceability limit states, and it is also assumed to be appropriate for verification of the accidental design situation of the ultimate limit states. In both cases the reduction factor ψ_1 is applied as a multiplier of the leading variable action. In accordance with EN 1990, the frequent value $\psi_1 Q_k$ of a variable action Q is determined so that the total time, within a chosen period of time, during which $Q > \psi_1 Q_k$ is only a specified (small) part of the period, or the frequency of the event $Q > \psi_1 Q_k$ is limited to a given value. The total time for which $\psi_1 Q_k$ is exceeded is equal to the sum of time periods Δt_1, Δt_2, ... shown in Fig. 4.3 by thick parts of the horizontal line indicating the frequent value $\psi_1 Q_k$.

Clause 4.1.3(1)P
Clause 4.1.3(1)P

According to note 1 of *clause 4.1.3(1)P*, the value of 0.01 for the reference period (50 years for buildings) is recommended. Specific conditions apply for traffic load on bridges (*clause 4.1.3(1)P*, notes 1 and 2. A detailed description is provided in EN 1991-2 for load traffic loads, in EN 1991-1-5 for thermal actions and in 1991-1-4 for wind; no further comment is made in this guide.

The coefficient ψ_1 for the frequent value of some imposed actions in buildings, and actions in car parks, is equal to 0.5 (see *Annex A1* of EN 1990 and Chapter 7 of this guide); this value is also indicated approximately in Fig. 4.3.

Table 4.2. *Application of coefficients ψ_0, ψ_1 and ψ_2 for leading and non-leading variable actions at ultimate and serviceability limit states*

Limit state	Design situation or combination	ψ_0	ψ_1	ψ_2
Ultimate	Persistent and transient	Non-leading	–	–
	Accidental	–	(Leading)	(Leading) and non-leading
	Seismic	–	–	All variable
Serviceability	Characteristic	Non-leading	–	–
	Frequent	–	Leading	Non-leading
	Quasi-permanent	–	–	All variable

–, not applied

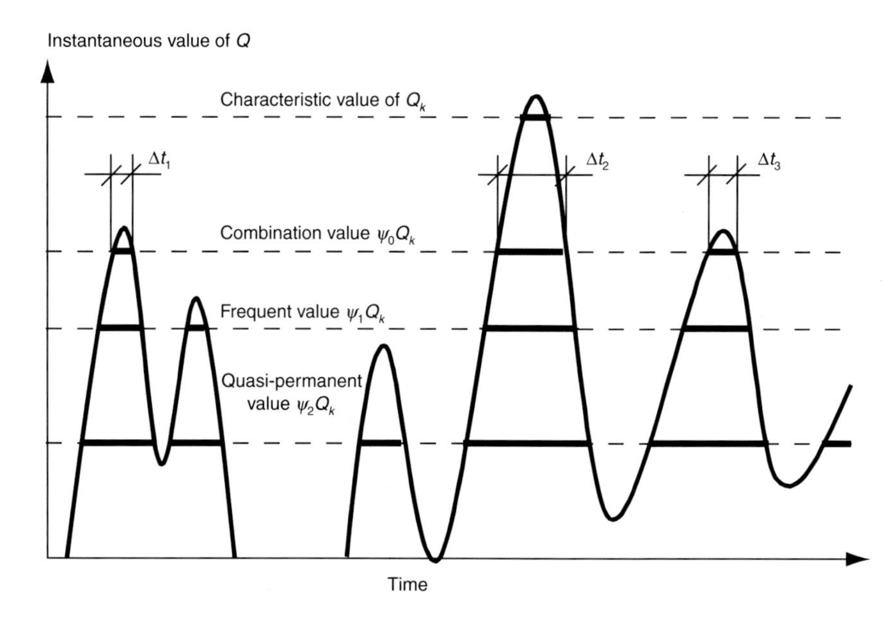

Fig. 4.3. *Representative values of variable actions*

Note that the recommended values may be altered depending on the type of construction works and design situations considered in the design. In some cases two (upper and lower) or more frequent values may be used.

The main use of quasi-permanent values $\psi_2 Q_k$ is the assessment of long-term effects, for example creep effects in continuous prestressed concrete bridges. However, they are also used for the representation of variable actions in accidental and seismic combinations of actions (ultimate limit states) and for verification of frequent and quasi-permanent combinations (long-term effects) of serviceability limit states (*clause 4.1.3(1)P*).

Clause 4.1.3(1)P

In accordance with EN 1990, the quasi-permanent value $\psi_2 Q_k$ is defined so that the total time, within a chosen period of time, during which it is exceeded, that is, when $Q > \psi_2 Q_k$, is a considerable part (0.5) of the chosen period of time (*clause 4.1.3(1)P*, note in point (c)). The value may also be determined as the value averaged over the chosen period of time. For some actions the coefficient ψ_2 may be very small. For example, in the case of traffic loads on road bridges, the quasi-permanent value is taken equal to 0 (except for heavily loaded bridges in urban areas, especially in seismic design situations).

Clause 4.1.3(1)P

The total time of $\psi_2 Q_k$ being exceeded is equal to the sum of periods, shown in Fig. 4.3 by thick parts of the horizontal line indicating the quasi-permanent value $\psi_2 Q_k$. In some cases the coefficient ψ_2 for the frequent value of imposed actions is equal to 0.3 (see *Annex A1* of EN 1990 and Chapter 7 of this guide); this value is indicated approximately in Fig. 4.3.

The representative values $\psi_0 Q_k$, $\psi_1 Q_k$ and $\psi_2 Q_k$ and the characteristic values are used to define the design values of the actions and the combinations of actions, as explained in Chapter 6. Their application in verification of the ultimate limit states and serviceability limit states is indicated in Table 4.2. Representative values other than those described above may be required for specific structures and special types of load, e.g. fatigue load (*clause 4.1.4*).

Clause 4.1.4

4.1.4. Representation of fatigue actions

It is well recognized that fluctuation of loads may cause fatigue. The models for fatigue actions should be taken from appropriate parts of EN 1991 relevant for the structure considered (*clause 4.1.4(1)*). When no information is available in EN 1991, then evaluation of measurements of the expected action spectra should be used (*clause 4.1.4(2)*). When evaluating the effects of fluctuating loads, the material Eurocodes EN 1992 to EN 1999

Clause 4.1.4(1)
Clause 4.1.4(2)

should be used to obtain the required information and, therefore, no further comment is offered in this guide.

4.1.5. Representation of dynamic actions

The effects of acceleration due to time-dependent actions are generally included in the characteristic fatigue models provided in EN 1991 either implicitly in the characteristic load or explicitly using the dynamic enhancement factors (*clause 4.1.5(1)*). However, time-dependent actions may cause significant effects, and then a dynamic analysis of the whole structural system should be used (*clause 4.1.5(2)*). General guidance concerning structural analysis is provided in *clause 5.1.3* of EN 1990 and in Chapter 5 of this guide.

Clause 4.1.5(1)
Clause 4.1.5(2)
Clause 5.1.3

4.1.6. Geotechnical actions

No specific information on geotechnical actions is provided in EN 1990. Guidance on geotechnical actions is found in EN 1997, however, and is thus outside the scope of this particular guide.

4.1.7. Environmental influences

Environmental influences (carbon dioxide, chlorides, humidity, fire, etc.) may affect the material properties markedly, and consequently affect the safety and serviceability of structures in an unfavourable way. These effects are strongly material-dependent, and therefore their characteristics have to be specified individually for each material in EN 1992 to EN 1999 (*clause 4.1.7(1)P*).

Clause 4.1.7(1)P

When environmental influences can be described by theoretical models and numerical values, then the degradation of the material can be estimated quantitatively by suitable calculation methods (*clause 4.1.7(2)*). In many cases, however, this may be difficult, and only an approximate assessment can be made. Often the combinations of various environmental influences may be decisive for the design of a particular structure under a given condition. The combination of various actions is considered further in *Section 6* of EN 1990 and in Chapter 6 of this guide. Other detailed rules concerning environmental influences for various structures using different materials are given in EN 1992 to EN 1999 (*clause 4.1.7(1)P*).

Clause 4.1.7(2)
Clause 4.1.7(1)P

4.2. Material and product properties

4.2.1. General

This section discusses various properties of construction materials and products used in the design of construction works. The topics described here are covered by 10 clauses in *Section 4.2* of EN 1990. The appendices to this chapter provide general information on the modelling of material properties (Appendix 1) and basic statistical techniques for the specification of the characteristic and design values of material and product properties (Appendix 2).

4.2.2. Characteristic values

The properties of materials and soils are an important group of basic variables for determining structural reliability. In design calculations the properties of materials (including soil and rock) or products are represented by characteristic values, which correspond to the prescribed probability not being infringed (*clause 4.2(1)* – the characteristic value is defined in *clause 1.5.4.1*). When a material property is a significant variable in a limit state verification, both upper and lower characteristic values of material properties should be taken into account (*clause 4.2(2)* – see also *clause 4.2(6)*) (Fig. 4.4).

Clause 4.2(1)
Clause 1.5.4.1
Clause 4.2(2)
Clause 4.2(6))

Usually the lower value of a material property or product is unfavourable, and the 5% (lower) fractile is then considered (*clause 4.2(3)*) as the characteristic value. There are, however, cases when an upper estimate of strength is required (e.g. for the tensile strength of concrete for the calculation of the effect of indirect actions). In these cases the use of the

Clause 4.2(3)

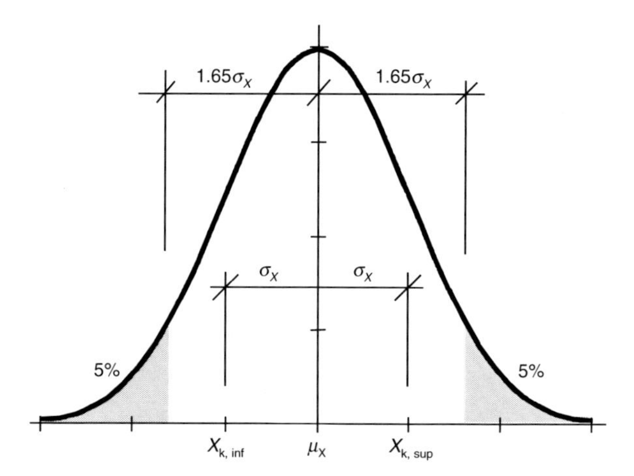

***Fig. 4.4.** Illustration of lower ($X_{k,\ inf}$) and upper ($X_{k,\ sup}$) characteristic values of a material or product property*

upper characteristic value of the strength should be considered. When the upper value is unfavourable, then the 95% (upper) fractile is considered (*clause 4.2(3)*) as the characteristic value. General information on the strength and stiffness parameters are given in Appendix 1 to this chapter.

Clause 4.2(3)

4.2.3. Determination of the characteristic values

A material property is normally determined from standardized tests performed under specified conditions (*clause 4.2(4)P*). It is sometimes necessary to apply a conversion factor to convert the test results into values which can be assumed to represent the behaviour of the structure or the ground. These factors and other details of standardized tests are given in EN 1992 to EN 1999. For traditional materials, e.g. steel and concrete, previous experience and extensive tests are available, and appropriate conversion factors are well established and presented in various design codes (see Chapters 6 and 10 of this guide). The properties of new materials should be obtained from an extensive testing programme, including tests on complete structures, revealing the relevant properties and appropriate conversion factors. New materials should be introduced only if comprehensive information on their properties (supported by experimental evidence) is available.

Clause 4.2(4)P

Assuming that the theoretical model for the random behaviour of a material property is known, or sufficient data are available to determine such a model, basic operational rules to obtain specified fractiles are described in Appendix 2 of this chapter. If only limited test data are available, then statistical uncertainty owing to limited data should be taken into account, and the above-mentioned operational rules should be substituted by more complicated statistical techniques (see *Annex D* of EN 1990 and also Chapter 10 and Appendix C to this guide).

According to *clause 4.2(5)*, whenever there is a lack of information on the statistical distribution of a property, a nominal value may be used in the design. In the case of insignificant sensitivity to the variability of a property, a mean value may be considered as the characteristic value. Relevant values for material properties and their definitions are available in EN 1992 to EN 1999 (*clause 4.2(7)P*).

Clause 4.2(5)

Clause 4.2(7)P

Note that stiffness parameters are normally defined as mean values (*clause 4.2(8)*). This can be explained in the following way. Very often, stiffness parameters are used in interaction models (e.g. ground–structure interaction) or in finite-element models associating several materials. The stiffness properties of materials cannot be altered by partial factors because the results of the calculation would be distorted. It is for this reason that it is recommended that stiffness parameters are not altered. Nevertheless, in some cases (e.g. for the calculation of piles subject to horizontal forces at the top), it may be necessary to

Clause 4.2(8)

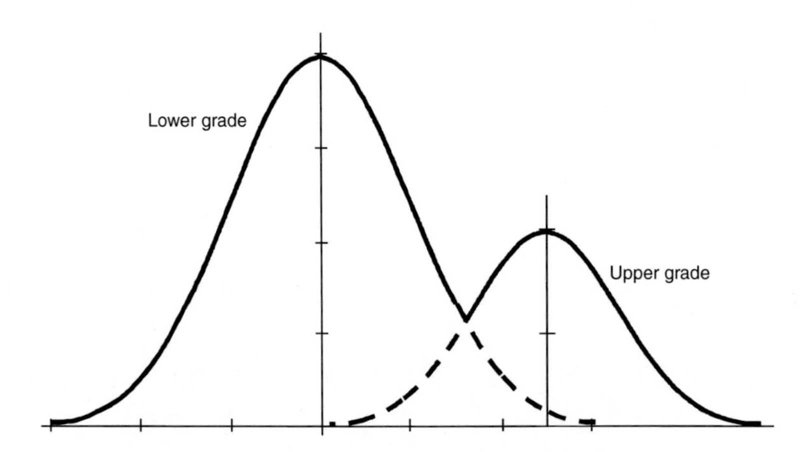

Fig. 4.5. *Distortion of a statistical distribution due to the combination of two material grades*

take into account a lower and an upper value of these parameters, generally assessed from engineering judgement.

In general, when the lower or upper characteristic value is derived from tests, the available data should be carefully examined for cases where a material (e.g. timber or steel) is classified using a grading system comprising a number of classes to account for the possibility that the manufacturer may have included specimens that fail in the upper grade in the lower grade, thus distorting the statistical characteristics (including the mean, standard deviation and fractiles) of the lower grade (Fig. 4.5). Obviously such a 'mixture' of two grades may significantly affect both the lower and upper characteristic values.

Clause 4.2(9)
Clause 4.2(10)

Specific values for material and product properties are given in the material-oriented EN 1992 to EN 1999 (*clause 4.2(9)*), where appropriate partial factors are also specified (*clause 4.2(10)*). Unless suitable statistical information exists, a conservative value of partial factors should be used (*clause 4.2(10)*).

4.3. Geometrical data

Clause 4.3(1)P
Clause 4.3(2)
Clause 4.3(3)
Clause 4.3(4)
Clause 4.3(5)P

This section is concerned with the geometrical data used in the design of building structures and civil engineering works. The material described here is covered in five clauses in EN 1990 (*clauses 4.3(1)P, 4.3(2), 4.3(3), 4.3(4)* and *4.3(5)P*. The appendices to this chapter provide information on the characteristics of geometrical quantities (Appendix 3) and tolerances for overall imperfections (Appendix 4).

Clause 4.3(1)P
Clause 4.3(2)
Clause 4.3(3)

Geometrical variables describe the shape, size and the overall arrangement of structures, structural members and cross-sections. In the design, account should be taken of the possible variation of their magnitudes, which depend on the level of workmanship in the manufacture and execution processes (setting out, execution, etc.) on the site. In design calculations the geometrical data should be represented by their characteristic values or, in the case of imperfections, directly by their design values (*clause 4.3(1)P*). According to *clause 4.3(2)* the characteristic values usually correspond to the dimensions specified in the design, which are the nominal values (see Fig. 4.5). However, where relevant, the values of geometrical quantities may correspond to some prescribed fractile of the available statistical distribution (*clause 4.3(3)*). This value may be determined using equation (D4.14) in Appendix 3 to this chapter.

Clause 4.3(3)

An important category of geometrical data that may have significant effect on structural reliability and should therefore be taken into account in the design consists of various types of imperfection (*clause 4.3(3)*). Depending on the material and type of structure, imperfections are specified in the material-oriented EN 1992 to EN 1999.

Clause 4.3(5)P

According to the important principle of *clause 4.3(5)P*, tolerances for connected parts should be mutually compatible. To verify the mutual compatibility of all the specified tolerances, a separate analysis taking into account the imperfections and the deviations provided in other standards (EN 1992 to EN 1999) may be necessary. Such an analysis is particularly important, for example, for the case when large-span precast components are used as structural elements or infill internal or external (cladding) components. Statistical methods described in BS 5606 give a detailed description of methods which may be applied to verify the mutual compatibility of all the considered tolerances.

Note that the permitted deviations for various geometric data describing concrete components are specified in ENV 13670-1, *Execution of Concrete Structures – Part 1: Common*.

Appendix 1: modelling of material properties

General notes

The material properties used in structural analysis and design should be described by measurable physical quantities corresponding to the properties considered in the calculation models. As a rule these physical quantities are time-dependent and may additionally be dependent upon temperature, humidity, load history and environmental influences. They also depend on specified conditions concerning the manufacturing, supply and acceptance criteria.

Material properties and their variation should generally be determined from tests using standardized test specimens. The tests should be based on random samples which are representative of the population under consideration. To determine the properties corresponding to the assumptions made in calculation models, the properties obtained from test specimens often require converting using appropriately defined conversion factors or functions. The uncertainties of the conversion factors should also be considered in calculation models. Conversion factors usually cover size effects, shape effects, time effects and the effects of temperature, humidity and other environmental influences.

For soils, as for existing structures, the materials are not produced but are found *in situ*. Therefore, the values of the properties have to be determined for each project using appropriate tests. A detailed investigation based on test results may then provide more precise and complete information than would pure statistical data, especially with respect to systematic trends or weak spots in the spatial distributions. However, fluctuations in homogeneous materials and the limited precision of the tests and their physical interpretations can be treated by statistical methods. For these materials the extent of investigation is an important element of their structural reliability, which is often difficult to quantify.

At the design stage, assumptions need to be made concerning the intended materials for the construction works. Therefore, corresponding statistical parameters have to be deduced from previous experience and existing populations which are considered appropriate to the construction works. The chosen parameters should be checked at the execution stage for quality using suitable (preferably statistical) methods of quality control. The identification of sufficiently homogeneous populations (e.g. appropriate divisions of the production in batches) and the size of samples are then other important aspects to specify appropriate elements of structural reliability.

Important material properties

The most important material properties introduced in design calculations describe the fundamental engineering aspects of building materials:

(1) strength f
(2) modulus of elasticity E
(3) yield stress (if applicable) σ_y
(4) limit of proportionality ε_y
(5) strain at rupture ε_f.

Figure 4.6 shows a typical example of a one-dimensional stress (σ)–strain (ε) diagram together with the above-mentioned fundamental quantities.

In design calculations, strength parameters are usually introduced by the lower 5% fractiles representing the characteristic values; stiffness parameters are introduced by their mean values (see Section 4.2). However, when stiffness affects the structural load-bearing capacity, an appropriate choice of the relevant partial factor should compensate for the mean value choice. As mentioned in Section 4.2, in some cases the upper characteristic value for the strength is of importance (e.g. for the tensile strength of concrete when the effect of indirect action is calculated). Some of the above-mentioned properties, e.g. strain at rupture, may be introduced in design calculations implicitly by appropriate conditions for the validity of theoretical models of cross-section or structural member behaviour.

In addition to the basic material properties in the one-dimensional stress (σ)–strain (ε) diagram above (see Fig. 4.6), other important aspects need to be considered:

(1) multi-axial stress condition (e.g. the Poisson ratio, yield surface, flow and hardening rules, crack creation and crack behaviour)
(2) temperature effects (e.g. coefficient of expansion, and effect on material properties including extreme conditions)
(3) time effect (e.g. effect of internal and external influences, creep, creep rupture, consolidation of soils, and fatigue deterioration)
(4) dynamic effects (e.g. mass density and material damping, and effect of loading rate)
(5) humidity effects (e.g. shrinkage, effect on strength, stiffness and ductility)
(6) effects of notches and flaws (e.g. unstable check growth, brittle fracture, stress intensity factor, effect of ductility and crack geometry, and toughness).

Fatigue behaviour

A very significant material property is the fatigue behaviour of structural members. This time-dependent effect of repeated loading of structural members is generally investigated by simplified tests, where the members are subjected to load variations of constant amplitude until excessive deformations or fracture due to cracks occur. The fatigue strength is then defined by characteristic $\Delta\sigma$–N curves that represent the 5% fractiles of failure. The test evaluation is carried out in accordance with *Annex D* of EN 1990 and the appropriate provisions of EN 1992 to EN 1999.

The characteristic $\Delta\sigma$–N curves are normally represented in a double logarithmic scale, as indicated in Fig. 4.7. The corresponding equation has the form

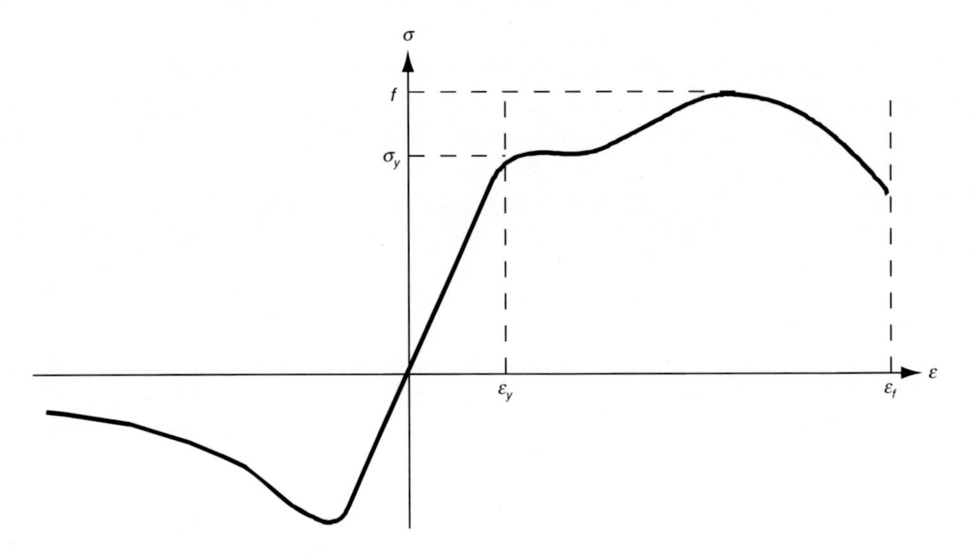

Fig.4.6. *One-dimensional σ–ε diagram*

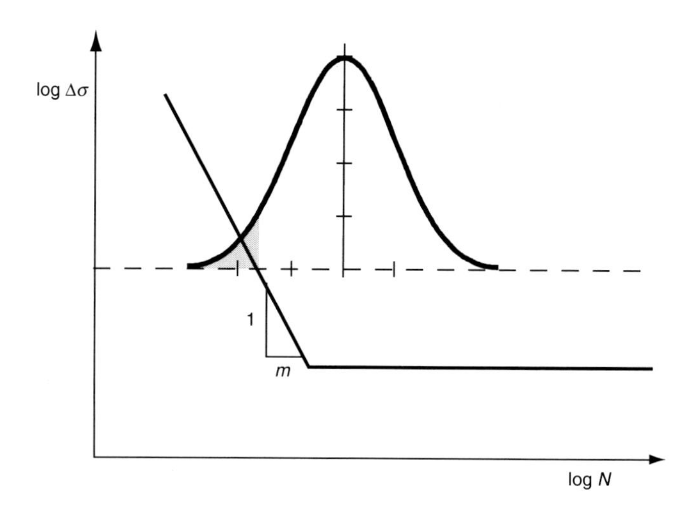

Fig.4.7. *The characteristic Δσ–N curve*

$$\Delta\sigma^m N = C = \text{constant} \tag{D4.3}$$

where $\Delta\sigma$ represents the stress range calculated from the load range using appropriate material and geometrical properties taking into account stress concentration factors, and N corresponds to the number of cycles. In some cases the stress concentration factors are introduced as an explicit coefficient of the nominal stress range.

Generally, the $\Delta\sigma$–N curves are dependent on geometric stress concentration and metallurgical aspects. Further details on the characteristic $\Delta\sigma$–N curves for different materials can be found in EN 1992 to EN 1999.

Appendix 2: basic statistical techniques for determination of the characteristic value

Normal and three-parameter log-normal distributions

As most material properties are random variables of considerable scatter, applied characteristic values should always be based on appropriate statistical parameters or fractiles. Commonly, for a given material property X the following statistical parameters are considered: the mean μ_X, standard deviation σ_X, coefficient of skewness (asymmetry) α_X or other statistical parameters, e.g. the lower or upper distribution limit. In the case of a symmetrical distribution (e.g. the normal distribution) the coefficient $\alpha_X = 0$, and only the mean μ_X and standard deviation σ_X are considered. This type of distribution is indicated in Fig. 4.8 by the solid curve.

The characteristic and design values of material properties are defined as specified fractiles of the appropriate distribution. Usually the lower 5% fractile is considered for the characteristic strength, and a smaller fractile probability (around 0.1%) is considered for the design value. If the normal distribution is assumed, the characteristic value X_k, defined as the 5% lower fractile, is derived from the statistical parameters μ_X and σ_X as

$$X_k = \mu_X - 1.64\sigma_X \tag{D4.4}$$

where the coefficient –1.64 corresponds to the fractile probability 5%. The statistical parameters μ_X, σ_X and the characteristic value X_k are shown in Fig. 4.8 together with the normal probability density function of the variable X (solid curve). The coefficient –3.09 should be used when the 0.1% lower fractile (design value) is considered.

Generally, however, the probability distribution of the material property X may have an asymmetrical distribution with positive or negative skewness α_X. The dashed curve in Fig. 4.8 shows the general three-parameter (one-sided) log-normal distribution having a positive coefficient of skewness $\alpha_X = 1$ and therefore the upper limit $X_0 = \mu_x = 3.10\sigma_x$.

In the case of an asymmetric distribution a fractile X_p corresponding to the probability P may then be calculated from the general relationship

$$X_p = \mu_X + k_{P,\alpha}\sigma_X \quad \text{(D4.5)}$$

where the coefficient $k_{P,\alpha}$ depends on the probability P and on the coefficient of skewness α_X. Assuming the three-parameter log-normal distribution, selected values of the coefficient $k_{P,\alpha}$ for determination of the lower 5% and 0.1% fractiles are given in Table 4.3.

It follows from Table 4.3 and equation (D4.5) that the lower 5% and 0.1% fractiles for the normal distribution (when $\alpha_X = 0$) may be considerably different from those corresponding to an asymmetrical log-normal distribution. When the coefficient of skewness is negative, $\alpha_X < 0$, the predicted lower fractiles for the log-normal distribution are less (unfavourable) than those obtained from the normal distribution with the same mean and standard deviation. When the coefficient of skewness is positive, $\alpha_X > 0$ (see Fig 4.8), the predicted lower fractiles for the log-normal distribution are greater (favourable) than those obtained from the normal distribution.

Log-normal distribution with the lower bound at zero

A popular log-normal distribution with the lower bound at zero, which is used frequently for various material properties, always has a positive skewness $\alpha_X > 0$ given as

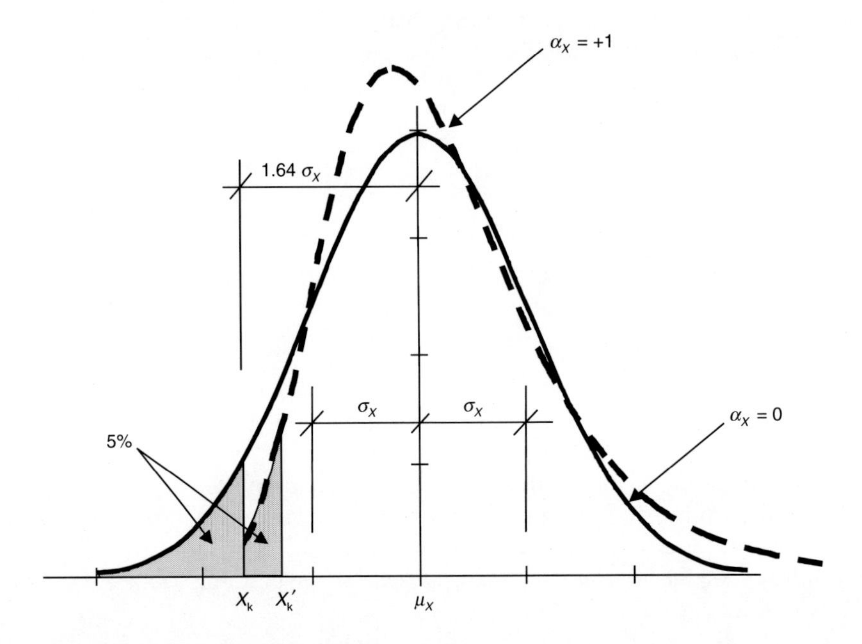

Fig. 4.8. Characteristics of a material property

Table 4.3. The coefficient $k_{P,\alpha}$ for determination of the lower 5% and 0.1% fractile assuming a three-parameter log-normal distribution

Coefficient of skewness α_X	Coefficient $k_{P,\alpha}$ for P = 5%	Coefficient $k_{P,\alpha}$ for P = 0.1%
–2.0	–1.89	–6.24
–1.0	–1.85	–4.70
–0.5	–1.77	–3.86
0.0	–1.64	–3.09
0.5	–1.49	–2.46
1.0	–1.34	–1.99
2.0	–1.10	–1.42

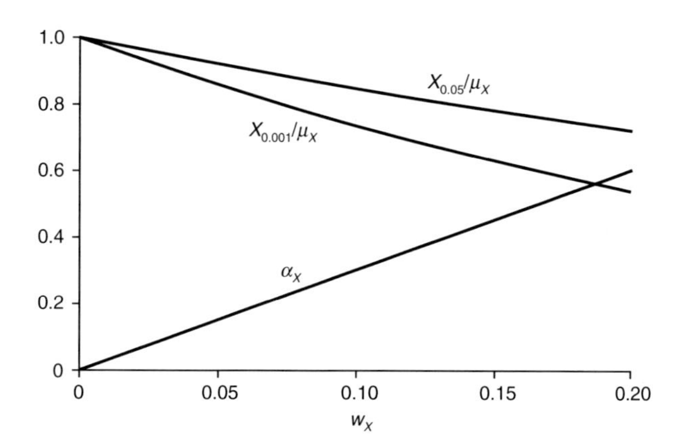

Fig. 4.9. *The skewness α_x and fractiles $X_{0.05}$ and $X_{0.001}$ (the characteristic and design values) as fractions of the mean μ_X for the log-normal distribution with the lower bound at zero versus the coefficient of variation w_X*

$$\alpha_X = 3w_X + w_X^3 \quad \text{(D4.6)}$$

where w_X denotes the coefficient of variation of X. When, for example, $w_X = 0.15$ (a typical value for *in situ* cast concrete) then $\alpha_X \cong 0.45$. For this special type of distribution the coefficients $k_{P,\alpha}$ can be obtained from Table 4.3, taking into account skewness α_X given by equation (D.4.6). Alternatively the fractile of the log-normal distribution with the lower bound at zero can be determined from the following equation:

$$X_P = \mu_X \exp[k_{P,0}\sqrt{\ln(1 + w_X^2)}]/\sqrt{(1 + w_X^2)} \quad \text{(D4.7)}$$

which is often simplified (for $w_X < 0.2$) as

$$X_P = \mu_X \exp(k_{P,0}w_X) \quad \text{(D4.8)}$$

Note that $k_{P,0}$ is the coefficient taken from Table 4.3 for the skewness $\alpha_x = 0$ (as for the normal distribution). Usually the probability $P = 0.05$ is assumed for the characteristic value $X_{0.05} = X_k$ and the probability $P = 0.001$ is approximately considered for the design value $X_{0.001} \cong X_d$. The relationship of these important fractiles determined from equation (D4.8) with the mean μ_X can be seen from the ratios $X_{0.05}/\mu_X$ and $X_{0.001}/\mu_X$ shown in Fig. 4.9 as functions of the coefficient of variation w_X. Figure 4.9 also shows the corresponding skewness α_X given by equation (D4.6).

The skewness α_X indicated in Fig. 4.9 should be used for verification of whether the assumed log-normal distribution with the lower bound at zero is a suitable theoretical model. If the actual skewness determined from available data for a given w_X is considerably different from that indicated in Fig. 4.9 (which is given by equation (D4.6)), then a more general three-parameter log-normal or other type of distribution should be used. In such a case, equation (D4.5) and coefficient $k_{P,\alpha}$ taken from Table 4.3 may provide a good approximation. If the actual skewness is small, say $|\alpha_X| < 0.1$, then the normal distribution may be used as a good approximation.

When the normal distribution is used and the actual distribution has a negative coefficient of skewness, $\alpha_X < 0$, the predicted lower fractiles will then have an unfavourable error (i.e. will be greater than the correct values). For the case when the correct distribution has a positive coefficient of skewness, $\alpha_X > 0$, the predicted lower fractiles will have a favourable error (i.e. will be less than the correct values). In the case of the 5% lower fractile value (commonly accepted for the characteristic value) with the coefficient of skewness within the interval $\langle -1, 1 \rangle$ the error created is about 6% for a coefficient of variation less than 0.2.

Considerably greater differences may occur for the 0.1% fractile value (which is approximate for design values) when the effect of asymmetry is significant. For example, in the case of a negative asymmetry with $\alpha_X = -0.5$ (indicated by statistical data for the strength of some grades of steel and concrete), and a coefficient of variation of 0.15 (suitable for concrete), the correct value of the 0.1% fractile value corresponds to 78% of the value predicted assuming the normal distribution. When the coefficient of variation is 0.2, then the correct value decreases to almost 50% of the value determined assuming the normal distribution.

However, when the material property has a distribution with a positive skewness, then the estimated lower fractile values obtained from the normal distribution may be considerably lower (and therefore conservative and uneconomical) than the theoretically correct value corresponding to the appropriate asymmetrical distribution. Generally, consideration of asymmetry to determine properties is recommended (see also Appendix B to this guide) whenever the coefficient of variation is greater than 0.1 or the coefficient of skewness is outside the interval ⟨–0.5, 0.5⟩. This is one of the reasons why the design value of a material property should preferably be determined as a product of the characteristic value, which is not very sensitive to asymmetry, and of the appropriate partial safety factor γ_m.

When the upper fractiles representing upper characteristic values are needed, equation (D4.5) may be used provided that all numerical values for the coefficient of skewness α_X and $k_{P,\alpha}$ given in Table 4.3 are taken with the opposite sign. However, in this case the experimental data should be carefully checked to avoid the possible effect of material not passing the quality test for the higher grade (see Section 4.2 and Figs. 4.3 and 4.4).

The above operational rules are applicable when the theoretical model for the probability distribution is known (e.g. from extensive experimental data or from previous experience). If, however, only limited experimental data are available, then a more complicated statistical technique should be used (see *Annex D*) to take account of statistical uncertainty due to limited information.

Example

Consider a concrete with mean $\mu_X = 30$ MPa and standard deviation $\sigma_X = 5$ MPa (coefficient of variation $w_X = 0.167$). Then the 5% fractile (the characteristic value) is:

- assuming a normal distribution (equation (D4.5)):

$$X_{0.05} = \mu_X - k_{P,0}\sigma_X = 30 - 1.64 \times 5 = 21.7 \text{ MPa} \qquad \text{(D4.9)}$$

- assuming a log-normal distribution with the lower bound at zero (equation (D4.8)):

$$X_{0.05} = \mu_X \exp(k_{P,0}w_X) = 30 \times \exp(-1.64 \times 0.167) = 22.8 \text{ MPa} \qquad \text{(D4.10)}$$

The 0.01% fractile (the design value) is

- assuming a normal distribution (equation (D4.5)):

$$X_{0.001} = \mu_X - k_{P,0}\sigma_X = 30 - 3.09 \times 5 = 14.6 \text{ MPa} \qquad \text{(D4.11)}$$

- assuming a log-normal distribution with the lower bound at zero (equation (D4.8)):

$$X_{0.001} = \mu_X \exp(k_{P,0}w_X) = 30 \times \exp(-3.09 \times 0.167) = 17.9 \text{ MPa} \qquad \text{(D4.12)}$$

Obviously the difference caused by the assumed type of distribution is much larger (23%) in the case of 0.001 fractile than in the case of the 0.05 fractile. Compared with the normal distribution the 0.05 fractile (the characteristic value) for the log-normal distribution is 5% larger, and the 0.001 fractile (the design value) 23% larger.

Note that in accordance with equation (D4.7) the log-normal distribution with the lower bound at zero has a positive skewness,

$$\alpha_X = 3w_X + w_X^3 = 3 \times 0.167 + 0.167^3 = 0.5 \qquad \text{(D4.13)}$$

which should be checked against actual data. As a rule, however, a credible skewness cannot be determined due to lack of available data (the minimum sample size to determine the skewness should be at least 30 units). It is then recommended that the log-normal distribution with the lower bound at zero is considered as a first approximation.

Appendix 3: characteristics of geometrical quantities

Geometrical data are generally random variables. In comparison with actions and material properties their variability can in most cases be considered small or negligible. Such quantities can be assumed to be non-random and as specified on the design drawings (e.g. effective span or effective flange widths). However, when the deviations of certain dimensions can have a significant effect on actions, action effects and resistance of a structure, the geometrical quantities should be considered either explicitly as random variables, or implicitly in the models for actions or structural properties (e.g. unintentional eccentricities, inclinations, and curvatures affecting columns and walls). Relevant values of some geometric quantities and their deviations are usually provided in Eurocodes 2 to 9. Selected values for geometric quantities describing the shape, size and overall arrangement of structures are given in Appendix 2 to this chapter.

The manufacturing and execution process (e.g. setting out and erection) together with physical and chemical causes will generally result in deviations in the geometry of a completed structure, compared with the design. Generally two types of deviations will occur:

(1) initial (time-independent) deviations due to loading, production, setting out and erection
(2) time-dependent deviations due to loading and various physical and chemical causes.

The deviations due to manufacturing, setting out and erection are also called induced deviations; the time-dependent deviations due to loading and various physical and chemical causes (e.g. creep, effect of temperature and shrinkage) are called inherent deviations (or deviations due to the inherent properties of structural materials).

For some building structures (particularly when large-span precast components are used) the induced and inherent deviations may be cumulative for particular components of the structure (e.g. joints and supporting lengths). In design, the effects of cumulative deviations with regard to the reliability of the structure including aesthetic and other functional requirements should be taken into account.

The initial deviations of a dimension may be described by a suitable random variable, and the time-dependent deviations may be described by the time-dependent systematic deviations of the dimension. To clarify these fundamental terms, Fig. 4.10 shows a probability distribution function of a structural dimension a, and its nominal (reference) size a_{nom}, systematic deviation $\delta a_{sys}(t)$, limit deviation Δa and tolerance width $2\,\Delta a$. The nominal (reference) size a_{nom} is the basic size which is used in design drawings and documentation, and to which all deviations are related. The systematic deviation $\delta a_{sys}(t)$ is a time-dependent quantity representing the time-dependent dimensional deviations. In Fig. 4.10 the limit deviation Δa is associated with the probability 0.05, which is the probability commonly used to specify the characteristic strength. In this case the limit deviation is given as $\Delta a = 1.64\sigma_a$. In special cases, however, other probabilities may be used and instead of the coefficient 1.64 other values should be chosen. Generally, a fractile a_p of a dimension a corresponding to the probability p may be expressed as

$$a_p = a_{nom} + \delta a_{sys}(t) + k_p \sigma_a \tag{D4.14}$$

where the coefficient k_p depends on the probability p and the assumed type of distribution (see also Appendix 4 of this chapter, and Appendix B).

Example

Consider the simple assembly shown in Fig. 4.11. A prefabricated horizontal component is erected on two vertical components. The relevant dimensions describing the setting out, erection and dimensions of the component are obvious from Fig. 4.11. The supporting length b (which is one of the lengths b_1 and b_2 indicated in Fig. 4.11) of the horizontal

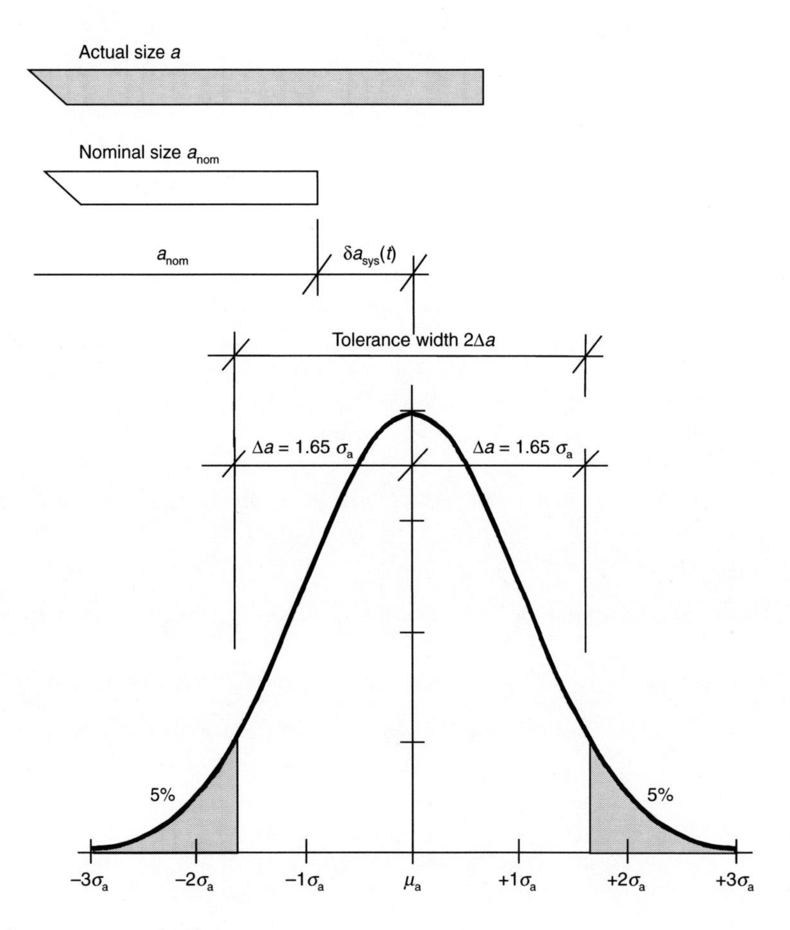

***Fig. 4.10.** Characteristics of a dimension* a

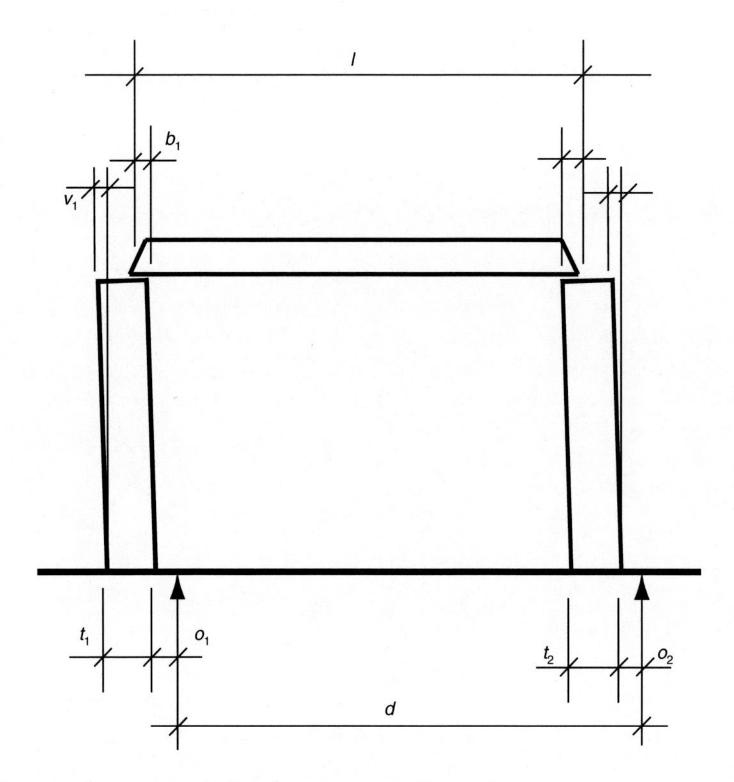

***Fig. 4.11.** A horizontal component erected on two vertical components*

component has a design nominal value $b_{nom} = 85$ mm. Taking into account deviations in the setting out, manufacture and erection, the supporting length was determined to have an approximate normal distribution with systematic deviation $\delta a_{sys}(t) = 0$ and standard deviation $\sigma_b = 12$ mm.

It follows from equation (D4.4) and the data given in Appendix B of this guide that the lower 5% fractile of the length is

$$b_{0.05} = 85 - 1.64 \times 12 = 65 \text{ mm} \qquad \text{(D4.15)}$$

and the upper 95% fractile is

$$b_{0.95} = 85 + 1.64 \times 12 = 105 \text{ mm} \qquad \text{(D4.16)}$$

Therefore, with a probability of 0.90 the supporting length will be within the interval 85 ± 20 mm and the corresponding eccentricity of the loading transmitted by the component to the supporting vertical member may differ by ±10 mm from an assumed value.

The initial and time-dependent deviations may lead to considerable variations in the shapes and sizes of structures and their parts as follows:

(1) in the shape and size of cross-sections, support areas, joints, etc.
(2) in the shape and size of components
(3) in the overall shape and size of the structural system.

For cases 1 and 2 where the variation of structural dimensions can affect the safety, serviceability and durability of the structures, specified permitted deviations or tolerances are given in relevant standards, EN 1992 to EN 1999. These tolerances are denoted as normal tolerances and should be taken into account if other smaller or larger tolerances are not specified in the design. When deviating from EN 1992 to EN 1999 with regard to tolerances, care should be taken to ensure that the design considers the implications of other deviations with regard to structural reliability. For case 3 some informative tolerances are given in Appendix 2 of this chapter.

Appendix 4: tolerances for the overall imperfections

Completed structures after erection should satisfy the criteria specified in Table 4.4 and Figs. 4.12–4.15. Each criterion should be considered as a separate requirement to be satisfied independently of any other tolerance criteria.

Table 4.4. *Normal tolerances after erection*

Criterion	Permitted deviation
Deviation of the distance between adjacent columns	±5 mm
Inclination of a column in a multistorey building in relation to storey height h (see Fig. 4.12)	$0.002h$
Horizontal deviation of column location in a multistorey building at a floor level $\sum h$ from the base, where $\sum h$ is the sum of n relevant storey heights, in relation to a vertical line to the intended column base location (see Fig. 4.13)	$0.0035\sum h/\sqrt{n}$
Inclination of a column of height h in a single-storey building other than a portal frame and not supporting a crane gantry (see Fig. 4.14)	$0.0035h$
Inclination of columns of height h in a portal frame not supporting a crane gantry (see Fig. 4.15)	Mean: $0.002h$ Individual: $0.001h$

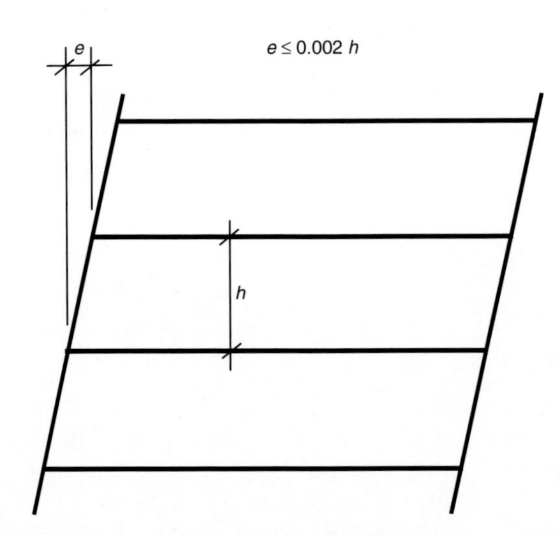

Fig. 4.12. Inclination of a column between adjacent floor levels

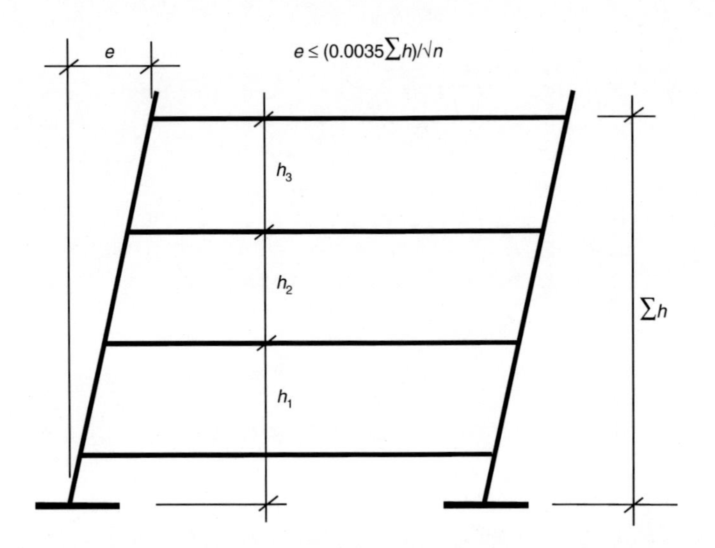

Fig. 4.13. Location of a column at any floor level

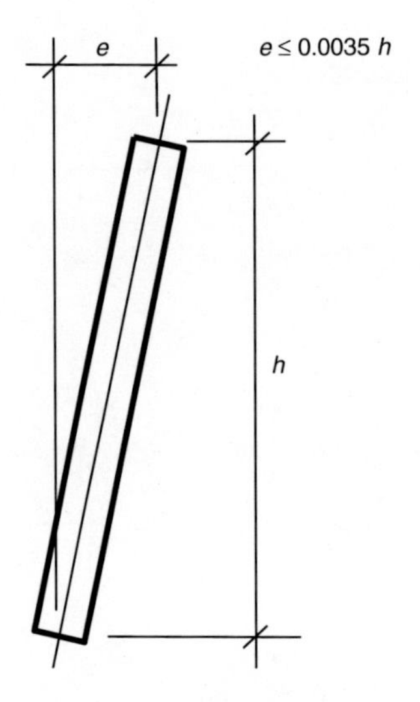

Fig. 4.14. Inclination of a column in a single-storey building

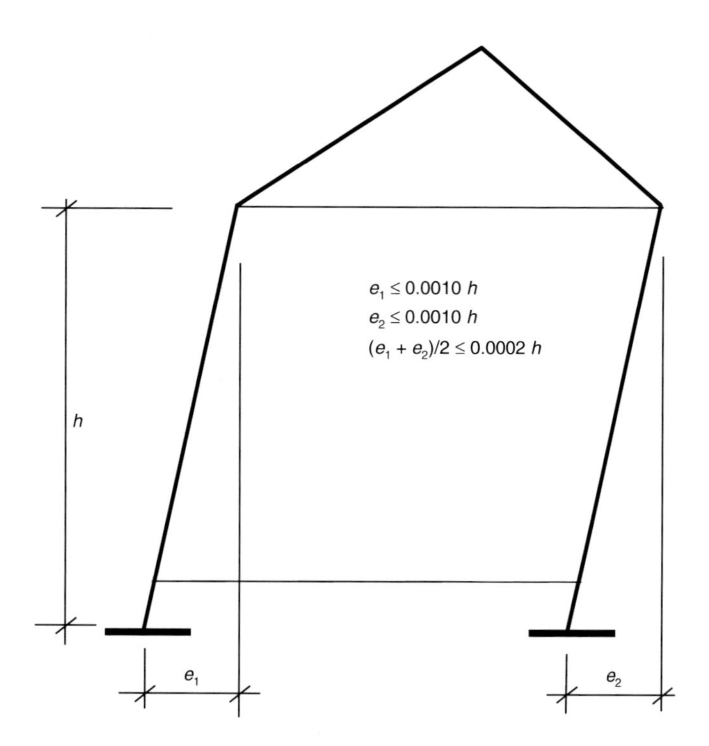

Fig. 4.15. *Inclination of the columns of a portal frame*

CHAPTER 5

Structural analysis and design assisted by testing

This chapter is concerned with the modelling of building and civil engineering structures for the purpose of determining action effects and resistances. The material described in this chapter is covered in *Section 5* of EN 1990, *Eurocode*: *Basis of Structural Design*, in the following clauses:

- Structural analysis *Clause 5.1*
- Design assisted by testing *Clause 5.2*

5.1. Structural analysis

5.1.1. Structural modelling

Clause 5.1.1

The Principles and Application Rules presented in *Section 5* of EN 1990 primarily deal with the modelling of structures. Action effects in cross-sections, joints or members determined through structural modelling and analysis can be used to verify the reliability of buildings and civil engineering works at their various limit states. In design calculations, the structural response to direct and indirect actions, in combination with the effects of environmental influences (e.g. interaction between fire and strength, stress and corrosion), should be generally considered.

The overall structural form of a building or civil engineering structure should be chosen with regard to the requirements of expected use, and for safety and serviceability under expected actions. It is assumed that the structural system is chosen by appropriately qualified and experienced personnel and satisfies all other requirements, e.g. concerning execution, quality control, construction materials, maintenance and use (*clause 1.3*).

Clause 1.3

Typically the structural system comprises three subsystems.

(1) the main structural system: the load-bearing elements of a building or civil engineering works and the way in which these elements function together
(2) secondary structural elements: e.g. beams and purlins that transfer the load to the main system
(3) other elements: e.g. cladding, roofing, partitions or facades that merely transfer loads to main and secondary elements.

While ultimate limit state failure of the main structural system can induce a global collapse with major consequences, an ultimate limit state failure of secondary or other elements would normally lead to local collapses with minor consequences. Hence, separate structural models and reliability levels may be needed for each of these subsystems or their combinations. For some structural systems, e.g. for frames with stiff infill elements such as cladding and partition walls, interaction between secondary or other elements and the main structural system should be considered.

Clause 5.1.1(1)P
Clause 5.1.1(2)
Clause 5.1.1(3)P

According to *clauses 5.1.1(1)P* and *5.1.1(2)* the appropriate design models should involve relevant variables, and should be appropriate for predicting the structural behaviour and the limit states considered with an acceptable level of accuracy. The models should be based on established engineering theory and practice, and verified experimentally if necessary (*clause 5.1.1(3)P*)). EN 1990 places very strong emphasis on *clause 5.1.1(3)P*.

Various assumptions will be necessary, such as those concerning the force–deformation or stress–strain relationships, distribution of strain in cross-sections, adequate boundary conditions, etc. Experimental verification may be needed, particularly for new structural systems and materials, or where new theories or numerical methods are being used to analyse the structure.

Generally, any structural model should be regarded as an idealization of the structural system. A simplified model should take account of significant factors and neglect the less important ones. The significant factors which may affect the choice of a structural model generally include the following:

(1) geometric properties (e.g. structural configuration, spans, cross-sectional dimensions, deviations, imperfections and expected deformations)
(2) materials properties (e.g. strength, constitutive relations, time and stress state dependence, plasticity, temperature and moisture dependence)
(3) actions (e.g. direct or indirect, variation in time, spatial variation, and static or dynamic).

The appropriate structural model should be chosen based on previous experience and knowledge of structural behaviour. The sophistication of the model should take into account the intended use of the results, and will normally involve consideration of the appropriate limit states, the type of results and the structural response expected. Often a simple global analysis with equivalent properties can be used to identify areas which need more complex and refined modelling.

Depending on the overall structural configuration, the structure may be considered as a three-dimensional system or as a system of planar frames and/or beams. For example, a structure with no significant torsional response may perhaps be considered as consisting of a set of planar frames. The investigation of torsional response is important for structures where centres of stiffness and mass do not coincide either by design, or unintentionally (e.g. imperfections); for example, continuous flat slabs supported directly by columns and structures asymmetric in stiffness and/or mass when the three-dimensional nature of the problem needs to be considered. In many cases the form of the anticipated structural deformations due to given actions can clearly indicate a suitable simplification of the structure and therefore an appropriate structural model.

When considering the stability of the structure, it is not only individual members which should be dealt with but also the whole structure: a structure properly designed with respect to individual members can still be susceptible to overall instability as a whole, e.g. torsional buckling of a uniform-lattice tower crane column.

5.1.2. Static actions

Clause 5.1.2(1)P

According to *clause 5.1.2(1)P* the modelling for static actions should be based (Principle) on an appropriate choice of the force–deformation relationships of the members and their connections, and between members and the ground. In almost all design calculations some assumptions concerning these relationships between forces and deformations are necessary. Generally, such assumptions are dependent on the chosen design situations, limit states and load cases being considered.

The theory of plasticity which assumes the development of plastic hinges in beams, and yield lines in slabs, should be used carefully for the following reasons:

(1) the deformation needed to ensure plastic behaviour of the structure may not be acceptable with regard to serviceability limit states, particularly for long-span frames and continuous beams
(2) these deformations should not, generally, be frequently repeated to avoid so-called low-cyclic fatigue
(3) special attention should be paid to structures in which load-carrying capacity is limited by brittle failure or instability.

Normally the action effects and the structural resistance are calculated separately using different design models. These models should, in principle, be mutually consistent. However, in many cases, this rule may be modified in order to simplify the analysis. For example, while the analysis of a frame or continuous beam for action effects usually assumes the theory of elasticity, structural resistance of cross-sections, joints or members may be determined taking into account various non-linear and inelastic properties of the materials.

Designers' attention is drawn to the fact that the boundary conditions applied to the model are as important as the structural model itself (*clause 5.1.2(2)P*). This is particularly true in the case of complex finite-element analyses, and the design boundary conditions should accurately represent the real boundary conditions in the structure after execution.

Clause 5.1.2(2)P

According to EN 1990, the effects of displacements and deformations, i.e. second-order effects in the analysis of structures, should be taken into account in the context of ultimate limit state verifications (including static equilibrium) if they result in a significant increase in the effects of actions (*clause 5.1.2(3)P*).

Clause 5.1.2(3)P

Background
In the previous version of the Eurocode (ENV 1991-1) an increase of more than 10% in the effects of actions was proposed but it is now recognized that such a value depends on the particular construction and/or its structural material.

The second-order effects may be taken into account by assuming equivalent initial imperfections and by performing a proper geometrical non-linear analysis. Alternatively, a set of additional non-linear forces, resulting from the deformations that correspond to collapse conditions, can be introduced into a first-order analysis.

Generally, two types of second-order effects may be recognized:

(1) overall second-order effects (effects of structural sway)
(2) member second-order effects.

A structure may be classified as non-sway, and the overall second-order effects neglected:

(1) if the increase of the relevant bending moments or sway shear due to second-order deformations is less than 10% of the first-order bending moment, or the storey shear, respectively
(2) if the axial forces within the structure do not exceed 10% of the theoretical buckling load.

In the case of regular steel or concrete frames the overall analysis may be based on a first-order method, and then the member analysis can take account of both overall and member second-order effects. This procedure should not be used in asymmetric or unusual cases.

Design models used to verify serviceability limit states and fatigue are usually based on the linear elastic behaviour of the structural material, while those used to verify the ultimate limit states often take account of non-linear properties and post-critical behaviour of structures. However, EN 1990 states that indirect actions should be taken into account in linear elastic analysis, directly or as equivalent forces, or in non-linear analysis, directly as imposed deformations (*clause 5.1.2(4)P*)). In particular, when phenomena such as

Clause 5.1.2(4)P)

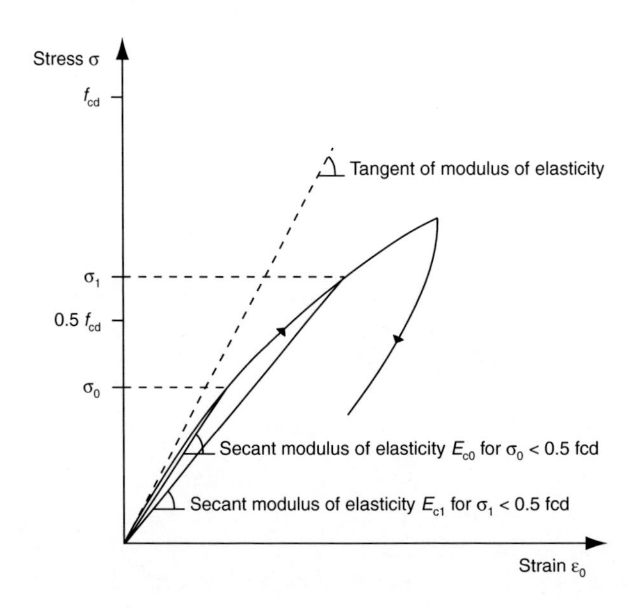

Fig. 5.1. *Typical curve $\sigma = f(\varepsilon)$ for concrete under compression, and definition of the secant modulus of elasticity*

differential settlement and whole-structure stability may affect the structural design under static conditions, the modelling of a structure should also include the consideration of the foundation, and this includes the soil. Soil–structure interaction can be addressed through either a simultaneous analysis of the soil–structure system or a separate analysis of each system.

5.1.3. Dynamic actions

Clause 1.5.3.12 In general, dynamic actions, i.e. those actions that '*cause significant acceleration of the structure or structural members*' (see *clause 1.5.3.12*) interact with the relevant structure or structural members which need, consequently, to be correctly modelled. The modelling should take into account – in addition to masses, strengths, stiffness, damping characteristics and properties of non-structural members (*clause 5.1.3(1)P*) – accurate and realistic boundary conditions (*clause 5.1.3(2)P*) as for static actions. For example, if the dynamic actions are caused by the motion of masses which are themselves being supported by the structure (e.g. people, machinery or vehicles), these masses should be considered in the analysis as they may affect the dynamic properties of light-weight systems.

Clause 5.1.3(1)P
Clause 5.1.3(2)P

Most of the actions as specified in EN 1990 are transformed into equivalent static actions. These equivalent forces are defined such that their effects are the same as, or similar to, the effects of the actual dynamic actions. When dynamic actions are simulated by quasi-static actions, the dynamic parts are considered either by including them in the static values, or by applying equivalent dynamic amplification factors to the static actions (*clause 5.1.3(3)*). For some equivalent dynamic amplification factors, the natural frequencies have to be determined.

Clause 5.1.3(3)

In the case of dynamic effects caused by significant soil–structure interaction (e.g. the transmission of traffic vibrations to buildings) the contribution of the soil may be modelled, for example, by appropriate equivalent springs and dampers. The soil may also be approximated with a discrete model (*clause 5.1.3(4)*).

Clause 5.1.3(4)

In some cases (e.g. for wind-induced vibrations, seismic actions or actions of pedestrians on footbridges) the actions are significantly controlled by the structural response, and can therefore be defined, as well as their effects, only when the dynamic behaviour of the structure has been estimated by using a modal analysis. A linear material and a linear geometric behaviour are usually acceptable (*clause 5.1.3(5)*) for such a modal analysis. Non-

Clause 5.1.3(5)

linear material properties can be approximated using iterative methods together with the secant stiffness (Fig. 5.1) as related to the response level.

For structures where only the fundamental mode is relevant, an explicit modal analysis may be replaced by an analysis with equivalent static actions, depending on mode shape, natural frequency and damping. Structural response to dynamic actions may be determined in terms of time histories or in the frequency domain (*clause 5.1.3(6)*).

Clause 5.1.3(6)

Particular attention should be given to those dynamic actions which may cause vibration that may infringe serviceability requirements, including comfort criteria. Guidance for assessing these limit states is given in *Annex A* of EN 1990 and in the design Eurocodes (*clause 5.1.3(7)*).

Clause 5.1.3(7)

5.1.4. Fire design

Clause 5.1.4

Clause 5.1.4 of EN 1990 provides only basic principles and application rules for the modelling of thermal actions on structures exposed to fire. A more detailed description of thermal actions due to fire and modelling for the structural design of buildings and civil engineering works is provided in Part 1.2 of Eurocode 1 (EN 1991) and relevant parts of the design Eurocodes 2 to 9. As stated in *clause 3.2(2)P*, the thermal actions on structures from fire are classified as accidental actions and considered in the accidental design situation (see also EN 1990, *Section 6*; EN 1991, Part 1.2; and Chapter 6 of this guide).

Clause 3.2(2)P

According to *clause 5.1.4(1)P*, appropriate models for the fire situation, which should be used to perform the structural fire design analysis, involve three fundamental aspects characterizing the appropriate accidental design situation:

Clause 5.1.4(1)P

(1) design fire scenario
(2) temperature evolution
(3) structural behaviour at elevated temperatures.

Clause 5.1.4(2) needs no further explanation.

Clause 5.1.4(2)

Thermal and mechanical actions to be considered in the fire situations are specified in EN 1991, Part 1.2, where two procedures are distinguished (*clause 5.1.4(3)*):

Clause 5.1.4(3)

(1) nominal fire exposure
(2) modelled fire exposure.

In most cases thermal actions on structures exposed to fire are given in terms of nominal temperature–time curves. These curves are applied for the specified period for which the structure is designed, using prescriptive rules or calculation models. Appropriate data for these actions are given in the main text of EN 1991, Part 1.2.

Parametric temperature–time curves are calculated on the basis of physical parameters for which structures are designed using calculation models. Some data and models for physically based thermal actions are given in the informative annexes of EN 1991, Part 1.2.

If they are likely to act in the fire situation, direct and indirect actions should be considered as for normal temperature design. Section 4 of EN 1991, Part 1.2, provides guidance regarding the simultaneity of actions and combination rules applicable to structures exposed to fire. This guidance concerns permanent actions, variable actions and additional actions due to the collapse of structural elements and heavy machinery. For the special cases, where indirect actions need not be considered, simplified rules for combining of actions are also indicated in EN 1991, Part 1.2.

Thermal and structural models for various construction materials, given in the design Eurocodes 2 to 9, should be used to analyse the structural behaviour at elevated temperatures (*clause 5.1.4(4)*).

Clause 5.1.4(4)

Clause 5.1.4(5) gives some simplified rules and assumptions concerning the thermal models and structural models in fire exposure, which may be used when relevant to the specific material and the method of assessment. Further, *clause 5.1.4(6)* allows consideration of the behaviour of materials or sections at elevated temperatures.

Clause 5.1.4(5)
Clause 5.1.4(6)

5.2. Design assisted by testing

Clause 5.2(1)

The Eurocode system permits a design based on a combination of tests and calculations for building and civil engineering structures (*clause 5.2(1)*). This clause is an introduction to *Annex D* to EN 1990 (see Chapter 10 of this guide), which gives guidance on the planning and evaluation of tests to be carried out in connection with structural design, where the number of tests is sufficient for a meaningful statistical interpretation of their results. Basic statistical techniques for estimating fractiles is briefly described in Appendix C of this guide. Some of the procedures described in Chapter 10 may also be useful for the assessment of existing structures.

Design assisted by testing is a procedure using physical testing (e.g. models, prototypes or *in situ*) for establishing design values. Such procedures can be used in particular for those cases where the calculation rules or material properties given in the design Eurocodes are considered insufficient, or where a more economical design may result.

Clause 5.2(2)P

An essential requirement for using design assisted by testing is given in *clause 5.2(2)P*. Tests should be set up and evaluated in such a way that the structure has the same level of reliability, with respect to all possible limit states and design situations, as would be achieved by design using the design Eurocodes. Hence, all uncertainties, such as those due to the conversion of experimental results and those arising from the statistical uncertainty associated with design assisted by testing (e.g. the application of experimental results, and any statistical uncertainties due to the sample size) should be taken into account. Furthermore, the conditions during testing should so far as possible be representative of those which can be expected to arise in practice.

Clause 5.2(3)

Moreover, partial factors comparable to those used in the design Eurocodes should be used (*clause 5.2(3)*): thus, EN 1990 clearly stipulates that design assisted by testing is not a possibility given to designers to reduce strongly partial factors.

CHAPTER 6

Verification by the partial factor method

This chapter is concerned with the verification of building structures and civil engineering works using the partial factor method. The material described in this chapter is covered in *Section 6* of EN 1990, *Eurocode*: *Basis of Structural Design*, and is completed by *Annex A* for various types of construction works. At the present stage, only *Annex A1*, 'Application for buildings', is available, and is discussed in Chapter 7. The material described in this chapter is covered in *Section 6* as follows:

- General *Clause 6.1*
- Limitations *Clause 6.2*
- Design values *Clause 6.3*
- Ultimate limit states *Clause 6.4*
- Serviceability limit states *Clause 6.5*

6.1. General

An assessment of the reliability of buildings and civil engineering works in the Eurocodes is based on the concept of limit states and their verification by the partial factor method. Using this method a structure is considered to be reliable if no relevant limit state is exceeded for all selected design situations when using the design values of the basic variables (actions, material properties and geometrical data) in the design models.

EN 1990 requires consideration of selected design situations and identification of critical load cases. For each of the critical load cases the design values of the effects of actions under consideration should be determined. A load case identifies compatible load arrangements, sets of deformations and imperfections which should be considered simultaneously for a particular verification (*clause 6.1(1)P*).

Clause 6.1(1)P

'*Actions that cannot occur simultaneously, for example due to physical reasons, should not be considered together in combination*' (*clause 6.1(2)*). This rule should be interpreted using good engineering judgement. For example, a maximum snow load cannot physically exist on a heated greenhouse.

Clause 6.1(2)

For the verification of structural reliability the following essential elements are always taken into account:

(1) the various design models for the verification of the ultimate and serviceability limit states
(2) the design values of the appropriate basic variables (actions, material properties and geometrical data), derived from their characteristic or other representative values, and a set of partial factors (γ) and ψ coefficients (*clause 6.1(3)*).

Clause 6.1(3)

In cases where design values of basic variables cannot be derived from characteristic values, in particular because of lack of statistical data, appropriate design values are then determined directly (e.g. design values of actions for accidental design situations), and in such cases conservative values should be chosen (*clause 6.1(4)*).

Clause 6.1(4)

For other cases, e.g. when the design procedure is performed on the basis of tests, the design value may be determined directly from available statistical data (for more details see *Annex D* of EN 1990 and Chapter 10 of this guide). The design values should be selected so that they give the same level of reliability, as implied by the partial factors given or recommended in EN 1990 (*clause 6.1(5)*). EN 1990 firmly states that design assisted by testing should not be considered as a means to lower the reliability level of a construction. It should be used, when appropriate, in order to obtain a better understanding of the statistical properties of a basic variable, and to assess more accurately a design value in accordance with the levels defined in the Eurocodes.

Clause 6.1(5)

6.2. Limitations

The Application Rules in EN 1990 are limited to ultimate limit states and serviceability limit states for structures subjected to static loading and quasi-static loading where the dynamic effects are assessed using equivalent quasi-static loads and dynamic amplification factors, e.g. in the case of wind or traffic loads. Specific rules for non-linear and dynamic analysis and fatigue are not comprehensively covered in EN 1990, but are provided in the design Eurocodes 1 to 9 (*clause 6.2(1)*).

Clause 6.2(1)

6.3. Design values

Figure 6.1 gives a general overview of the system of partial factors used in the Eurocodes (see also *Annex C* to EN 1990 and Chapter 9 of this guide, which give a simplified representation of the partial factor system for the most common ultimate limit states of resistance).

6.3.1. Design values of actions

The design value F_d of an action F can be expressed in general terms as

$$F_d = \gamma_f F_{rep} \qquad (6.1a)$$

F_{rep} represents the value taken into account in the relevant combination of actions. It can be the characteristic value F_k of the action (i.e. the main representative value), the combination value $\psi_0 F_k$ or the frequent or the quasi-permanent values ($\psi_1 F_k$, $\psi_2 F_k$). Therefore, EN 1990 adopts the symbolic representation given in *expression* (*6.1b*) (*clause 6.3.1(1)*):

Clause 6.3.1(1)

$$F_{rep} = \psi F_k \qquad (6.1b)$$

where $\psi = 1$ or ψ_0, ψ_1 or ψ_2. And 'γ_f *is a partial factor for the action which takes account of the possibilities of unfavourable deviations of the action values from the representative values*'.

The system of safety elements (γ factors, ψ factors and characteristic values of actions F_k) is applicable to limit states only where the magnitude of load values governs the reliability (one-dimensional actions). When actions are multidimensional in that they comprise more than one parameter (e.g. fatigue parameters, the stress amplitude $\Delta\sigma$, the number of cycles N and the slope constant of a fatigue strength curve m; see Eurocode 3 and Appendix 1 to Chapter 4 of

Background
In ENV 1991-1, *Basis of Design*, the design values of actions were directly based on the use of γ_F factors incorporating also inaccuracies of the action models (see below). In order to simplify the presentation, it has been decided to use separate factors to cover, on one hand uncertainty on the value of the action itself, and on the other hand uncertainty in modelling the effects of actions.

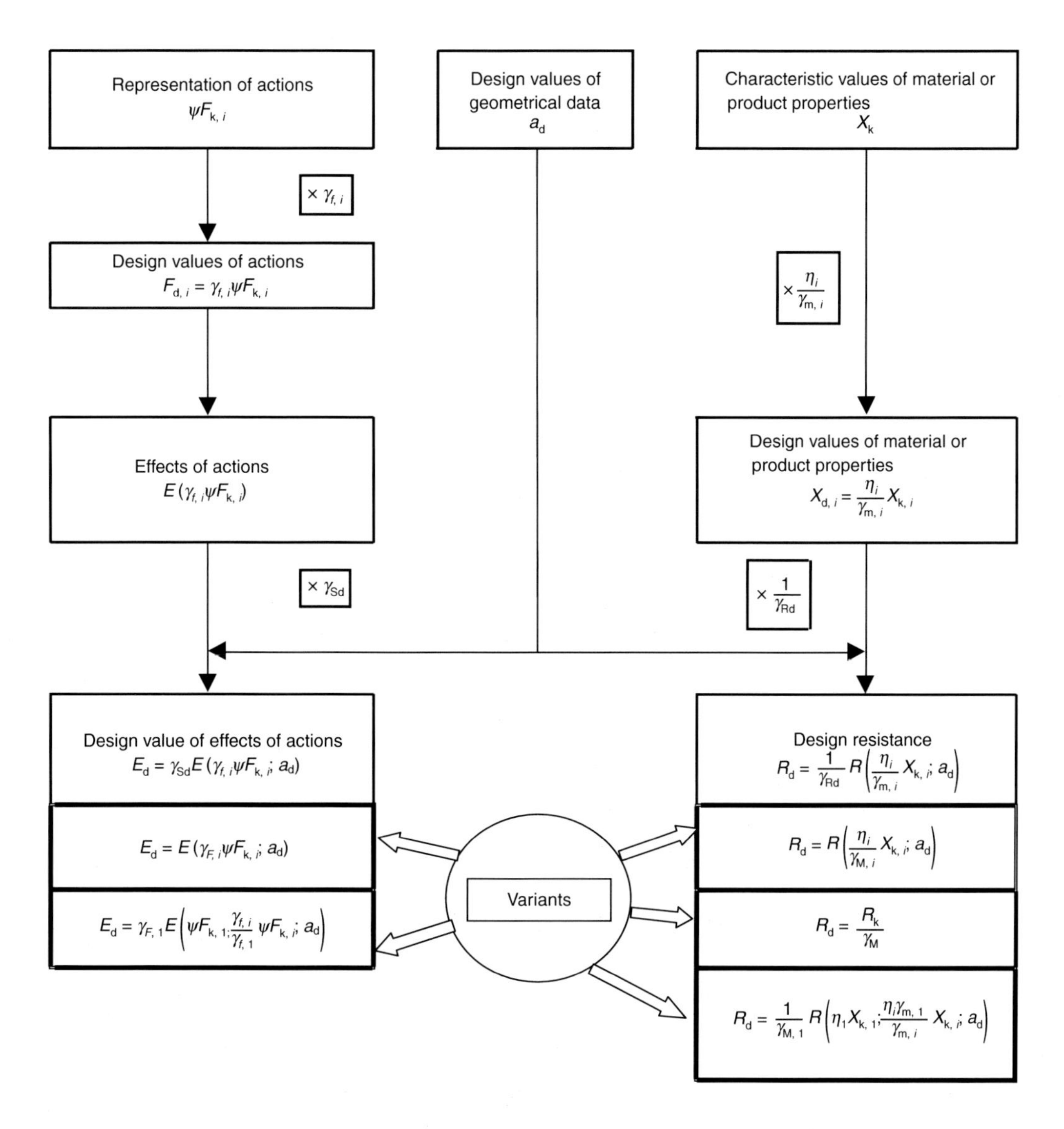

Fig. 6.1. *General overview of the partial factor system in the Eurocodes*

this guide), and when the effects of these parameters are non-linear (e.g. $\sum \Delta\sigma_i^m N_i$), both the representative values and design values of actions depend on the way these parameters influence the limit state. For such cases, detailed rules are given in the design Eurocodes 1 to 9.

In some cases the design values of actions are assessed taking into account the response of the structure. In other cases, e.g. for seismic actions or in the case of ground–structure interaction, the design value may depend on the relevant parameters for the structural behaviour. The question of the design values of actions is then treated in the relevant design Eurocodes (*clause 6.3.1(2)*).

Clause 6.3.1(2)

6.3.2. Design values of the effects of actions

The effects of actions E are the response of the structural members (e.g. internal force, moment, stress or strain) or of the whole structure (e.g. deflection or rotation) to the actions imposed on it, the responses of the structure to the actions being compatible with the model used to define the limit state. The effects of actions E depend on the actions F, the geometrical properties a and, in some cases, the material properties X. For example, when $E(.)$ represents the bending moment in a given cross-section of a structural member: this bending moment may be caused by self-weight, imposed loads, wind actions on the structure, etc.

Clause 6.3.2(1) Where material properties are not involved, and for a specific load case, the expression of the design value E_d of the effects of actions can be expressed in general terms (*clause 6.3.2(1)*), as shown in expression (*6.2*):

$$E_d = \gamma_{Sd} E\{\gamma_{f,i} F_{rep,i};\ a_d\} \qquad i \geq 1 \qquad (6.2)$$

where γ_{Sd} is a partial factor for model uncertainties (models of the effects of actions and, in particular cases, models of actions). a_d represents the design values of geometrical data (see Section 6.3.4).

Clause 6.3.2(2) *Expression* (*6.2*) is not the most frequently used. For the design of common structures, the following simplification (*expression* (*6.2a*)) is adopted by EN 1990 (*clause 6.3.2*(*2*)):

$$E_d = E\{\gamma_{F,i} F_{rep,i};\ a_d\} \qquad i \geq 1 \qquad (6.2a)$$

with

$$\gamma_{F,i} = \gamma_{Sd} \gamma_{f,i} \qquad (6.2b)$$

Expression (*6.2b*) is also commonly met in geotechnical problems (see Eurocode 7).

The decomposition $\gamma_F = \gamma_{Sd}\gamma_f$ may be important when the partial factor design is substituted by more sophisticated numerical simulations of actions and action effects, e.g. by simulation of the dynamic wind effects on buildings, where the magnitude of masses from permanent and variable loads have to be determined together with wind actions. In that case only γ_f applies.

Clause 6.3.2(2) As explained in the note to *clause 6.3.2*(*2*), another expression may be used where relevant, in which a particular $\gamma_{F,1}$ factor is applied to the whole effect of the combination of actions in which the actions are multiplied by appropriate factors:

$$E_d = \gamma_{F,1} E\left\{F_{k,1};\ \frac{\gamma_{f,i}}{\gamma_{f,1}} F_{rep,i};\ a_d\right\} \qquad i > 1 \qquad (D6.1)$$

Expression (D6.1) can be used for partial factor design based on finite-element analysis or for some special geotechnical problems, for example for the calculation of tunnel vaults.

Clause 6.3.2(3)P In *clause 6.3.2(3)P* a distinction is made between favourable and unfavourable permanent actions: the words 'favourable' and 'unfavourable' should be understood with respect to the effect under consideration. In particular, where a variable action acts, permanent actions

Background

As previously explained, numerical values of γ_F factors have been widely unified. For this reason, in some cases, γ_{Sd} does not only cover model uncertainty on effects of actions but also includes an element of safety on the model of one action itself.

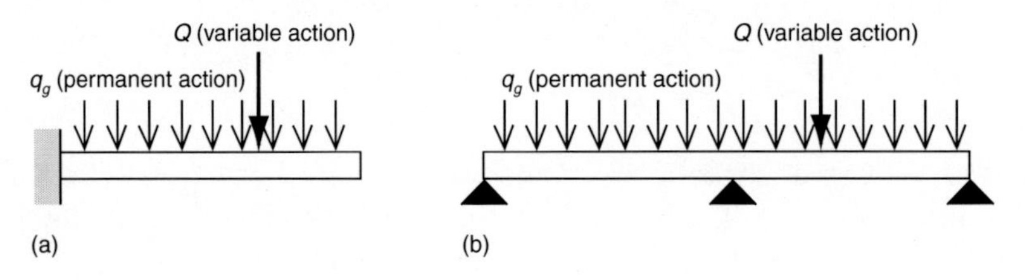

***Fig. 6.2.** Examples of application of permanent and variable actions. (a) q_g and Q act together (unfavourably): the effects of the permanent action q_g should be multiplied by $\gamma_{G,sup}$. (b) Depending on the cross-section under consideration, q_g and Q act together or opposite to each other: the effects of the permanent action q_g should be multiplied by $\gamma_{G,sup}$ or $\gamma_{G,inf}$*

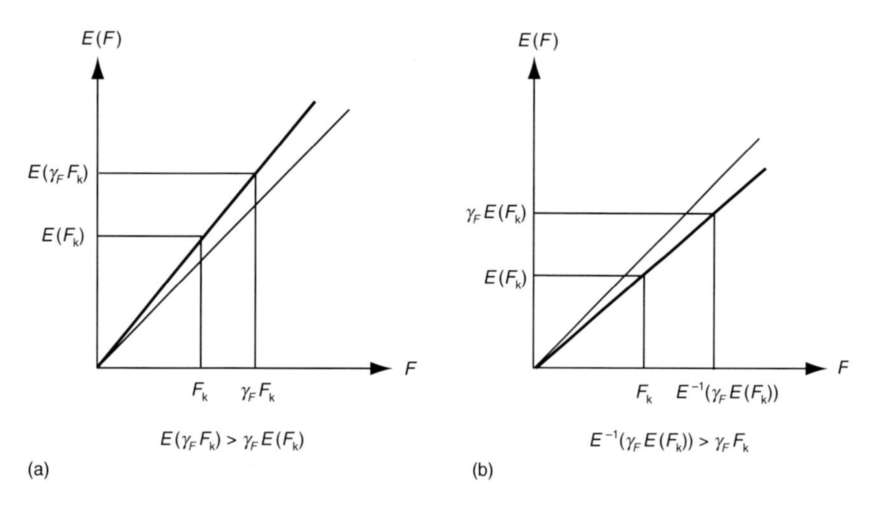

Fig. 6.3. *Application of model factor γ_{Sd} in case of non-linear analysis (single action). (a) Action effect increases more than action. (b) Action effect increases less than action*

should be classified as 'unfavourable' or 'favourable' whether they act 'unfavourably' with, or 'favourably' opposite to, the variable action. In such cases, and if permanent actions are not from the same source (see note 3 to *Table A1.2(B)* in EN 1990), they are multiplied by different partial factors: $\gamma_{G,\,\mathrm{sup}}$ for 'unfavourable' permanent actions and $\gamma_{G,\,\mathrm{inf}}$ for 'favourable' permanent actions (Fig. 6.2).

Specific problems may arise when using the partial factor method in the case of structural non-linear analysis, i.e. when the action effect is not proportional to the action; for non-linear analysis the partial factors should be cautiously applied. In the case of a single predominant action F, EN 1990 proposes the following simplified safe-sided rules (*clause 6.3.2(4)*):

Clause 6.3.2(4)

(1) When the action effect $E(F)$ increases more than the action, the partial factor γ_F should be applied to the representative value of the action (Fig. 6.3(a)):

$$E_\mathrm{d} = E(\gamma_F F_\mathrm{k}) \tag{D6.2}$$

(2) When the action effect $E(F)$ increases less than the action, the partial factor γ_F should be applied to the action effect of the representative value of the action (Fig. 6.3(b)):

$$E_\mathrm{d} = \gamma_F E(F_\mathrm{k}) \tag{D6.3}$$

In practice the situation may be more complex, and, according to EN 1990 (*clause 6.3.2(5)*), more refined methods, given in the relevant EN 1991 to EN 1999 standards (e.g. for prestressed structures), should be used in preference to the previous one. For example, for the case where two actions are involved, the first rule becomes (Fig. 6.4(a)):

Clause 6.3.2(5)

$$E_\mathrm{d} = E(\gamma_G G_\mathrm{k} + \gamma_Q Q_\mathrm{k}) \tag{D6.4}$$

with $\gamma_G = \gamma_{\mathrm{Sd}}\gamma_g$ and $\gamma_Q = \gamma_{\mathrm{Sd}}\gamma_q$.

Concerning the second rule (Fig. 6.4(b)), a more refined approach would involve the model factor γ_{Sd} to the combined effect of actions G and Q taken with their design value, i.e.:

$$E_\mathrm{d} = \gamma_{\mathrm{Sd}} E(\gamma_g G_\mathrm{k};\ \gamma_q Q_\mathrm{k}) \tag{D6.5}$$

6.3.3. Design values of material or product properties

The design value of a resistance may be determined by various means including:

- empirical relationships involving measured physical properties or chemical composition (e.g. composition of a high-strength concrete with silica fume)

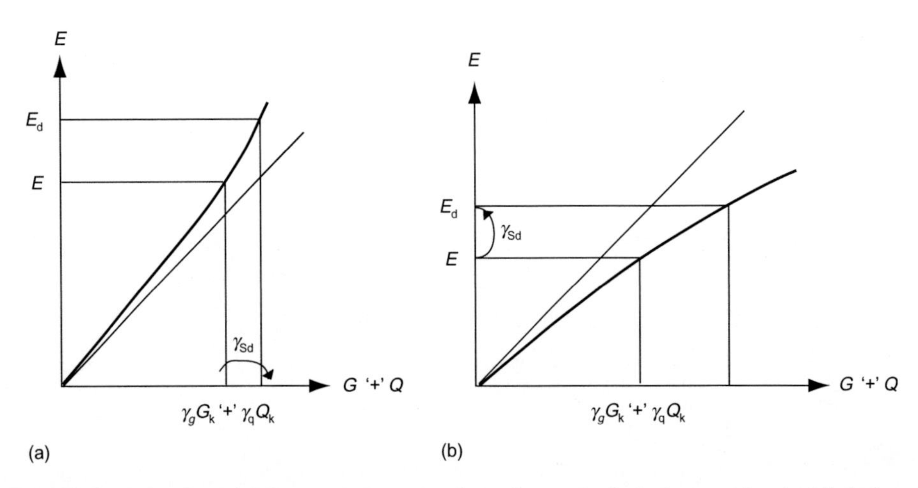

Fig. 6.4. *Application of model factor γ_{Sd} in case of non-linear analysis (two actions). (a) Action effect increases more than action. (b) Action effect increases less than action. '+' denotes 'to be concened with'*

- from previous experience
- from values given in appropriate documents such as European standards.

Generally, the design value X_d of a material or a product property X is determined from the characteristic value X_k using the partial factor for the material or product property γ_m and, if relevant, the conversion factor η in accordance with the relationship (*clause 6.3.3(1)*):

Clause 6.3.3(1)

$$X_d = \eta \frac{X_k}{\gamma_m} \tag{6.3}$$

where η represents the mean value of the conversion factor that takes into account volume and scale effects, the effects of moisture and temperature, etc. The conversion factor may be incorporated in the characteristic value (*clause 6.3.3(2)*).

Clause 6.3.3(2)

From a conceptual point of view, η should also take into account the effects of load duration. In practice, these effects are taken into account separately as, for example, in the case of concrete with factors α_{cc} and α_{ct} (see Eurocode 2) applicable to the characteristic values of the compressive strength,

$$f_{cd} = \alpha_{cc} \frac{f_{ck}}{\gamma_c} \tag{D6.6a}$$

and tensile strength,

$$f_{ctd} = \alpha_{ct} \frac{f_{ctk,\,0.05}}{\gamma_c} \tag{D6.6b}$$

The partial factor γ_m is intended to cover the possibility of unfavourable deviations of the material or product property from its characteristic value and the random part of the conversion factor. Indeed, the conversion factor may be considered as a random variable: its scatter around the mean value is assumed to be taken into account in the γ_m factor.

6.3.4. Design values of geometrical data

The variability of geometrical quantities is usually less significant than the variability of actions and material or product properties, and in many cases is negligible. Consequently, design values of geometrical data are generally represented by the nominal value (*clause 6.3.4(1)*):

Clause 6.3.4(1)

$$a_d = a_{nom} \tag{6.4}$$

The nominal (reference) dimension a_{nom} is the basic dimension which is used in design drawings and documentation. All deviations of the geometric quantities are related to it. The geometrical value a_{nom} comprises not only the geometrical data as lengths and widths of a frame but also represents the so-called 'perfect geometry' in that sway imperfections of the frame or curvature imperfections of the members or inaccuracy of the excavation depth in front of sheet pilings are not considered. Such imperfections are reflected in the 'additive safety elements' Δa as explained below. Where necessary, the design Eurocodes 1 to 9 give appropriate specifications.

Where deviations in the geometrical data have a significant effect on the reliability of a structure (e.g. slender columns or thin silo walls), the geometrical design values are defined by (*clause 6.3.4(2)P*)

Clause 6.3.4(2)P

$$a_d = a_{nom} + \Delta a \qquad (6.5)$$

where Δa takes account of the possibility of unfavourable deviations from the characteristic or nominal values and the cumulative effect of a simultaneous occurrence of several geometrical deviations. It should be noted that Δa is introduced only where the influence of deviations is critical, e.g. imperfections in buckling analysis. Values of Δa are given in Eurocodes 2 to 9.

6.3.5. Design resistance

The general expression of the design resistance of a structural member is (*clause 6.3.5(1)*)

Clause 6.3.5(1)

$$R_d = \frac{1}{\gamma_{Rd}} R\{X_{d,i};\ a_d\} = \frac{1}{\gamma_{Rd}} R\left\{\eta_i \frac{X_{k,i}}{\gamma_{m,i}};\ a_d\right\} \qquad i \geq 1 \qquad (6.6)$$

where γ_{Rd} is a partial factor covering uncertainty in the resistance model, plus geometric deviations if these are not modelled explicitly (see *clause 6.3.4(2)*), and $X_{d,i}$ is the design value of material property i.

Clause 6.3.4(2)

Variations of *expression (6.6)* are given in the design Eurocodes 1 to 9 because the characteristic value of the resistance R_k for a given material, or way of construction, may be expressed in various ways, for example:

(1) as the resistance of a member (e.g. the beam–column resistance), where R_k may be a linear or a non-linear function of many geometrical parameters, material parameters and parameters for structural and geometrical imperfections
(2) as the resistance of a cross-section, generally expressed in terms of a linear or non-linear interaction formula comprising geometrical data and material data compatible with the action effects
(3) as a local resistance in terms of stresses, strains, stress intensity factors (or rotation capacity), etc.

In a general manner, the characteristic value R_k of the resistance of a structural member is a function of one or more parameters which may be expressed in terms of individual characteristic values $X_{k,i}$, or individual nominal values $X_{nom,j}$, so that

$$R_k = R(X_{k,i},\ X_{nom,j},\ a_{nom}) \qquad (D6.7)$$

Depending on the case, X_k, X_{nom}, a_{nom} or R_k may be described as a property of a product in a material or product standard. The particular property may therefore be controlled by testing (see Chapter 10) in order to verify that the definition of R_k as a characteristic value (a given fractile of the distribution of R) is fulfilled.

In some cases the parameter X_k represents a sample property that is verified by testing; however, the value of the *in situ* property of the parameter in the structure may be different from the value measured on samples, and a conversion factor should then be used in R_k.

The following simplification of *expression (6.6)* is used in EN 1990 and EN 1992, for example in the case of concrete structures (*clause 6.3.5(2)*):

Clause 6.3.5(2)

$$R_d = R\left\{\eta_i \frac{X_{k,i}}{\gamma_{M,i}};\ a_d\right\} \qquad i \geq 1 \qquad (6.6a)$$

where

$$\gamma_{M,i} = \gamma_{Rd}\gamma_{m,i} \qquad (6.6b)$$

Clause 6.3.5(3)

In the case of steel structures, the design value R_d is generally obtained directly from the characteristic value of a material or product resistance (*clause 6.3.5(3)*):

$$R_d = \frac{R_k}{\gamma_M} \qquad (6.6c)$$

where both R_k and γ_M are generally determined from test evaluations using *Annex D* of EN 1990. A rigid definition of R_k as a fractile (e.g. the 5% fractile) would often lead to a variety of γ_M factors depending on the resistance considered. Therefore, a unique γ_M factor is used* for a group of resistances, and the fractile of R_k is modified in such a way that the reliability target for R_d is reached.

Clause 6.3.5(4)

For members consisting of different materials that act together in a composite action (e.g. concrete and steel), the resistance R_k may make reference to material properties $X_{k,1}$ and $X_{k,2}$ with different definitions (*clause 6.3.5(4)*). In this case one or both of these properties should be modified, e.g. with

$$X^*_{k,1} = X_{k,1}$$

$$X^*_{k,2} = \frac{X_{k,2}}{\gamma_{m,2}}\gamma_{m,1}$$

so that

$$R_d = \frac{1}{\gamma_{M,1}} R_k\left(\eta_1 X_{k,1},\ \eta_2 \frac{X_{k,2}}{\gamma_{m,2}}\gamma_{m,1},\ a_d\right) \qquad (6.6d)$$

Such an expression may be used, in particular, for finite-element analysis. Deterioration effects (e.g. loss of material due to corrosion) may be considered by introducing a subtractive safety element, for geometrical values for cross-sections, so that

$$a_d = a_{nom} - \Delta a$$

In some cases (e.g. in geotechnical design) R_d is determined without the characteristic value R_k so that

$$R_d = \frac{1}{\gamma_{Rd}} R_k\left(\frac{X_m}{\gamma_m},\ a_d\right) \qquad \text{(D6.8)}$$

6.4. Ultimate limit states

6.4.1. General

To avoid any deviating interpretation of the ultimate limit states, it was decided by the EN 1990 project team, in liaison with experts responsible for *Eurocode 7: Geotechnical Design*, to:

- Avoid the introduction of the former 'cases' or of 'types of limit states'.
- Simply describe the major failure modes in the following way (*clause 6.4.1(1)P*):

Clause 6.4.1(1)P

*This has been adopted by the CEB (now the FIB) in order to apply the same partial factor for bending and for shear.

Background

In ENV 1991-1, three basic 'cases' of ultimate limit state verifications were considered separately as relevant, corresponding to the following definitions:

(1) loss of equilibrium where strength of the material and/or ground are insignificant (case A in ENV 1991-1)
(2) failure of structure or structural elements, including those of the footing, piles, basement walls, etc., where strength of the structural material is decisive (case B in ENV 1991-1)
(3) failure in the ground, where strength of the ground is decisive (case C in ENV 1991-1).

Several guides and background documents gave different interpretations of these various cases, showing that their meaning was not fully clear. More precisely, in some publications, these cases were sometimes confused with load cases, which was inconsistent with the following definition: 'Compatible load arrangements, sets of deformations and imperfections considered simultaneously with fixed variable actions and permanent actions for a particular verification'. Moreover, the sentence (in ENV 1991-1) 'the design should be verified for each case A, B and C separately as relevant', was considered unclear because it was sometimes thought that the most unfavourable of all combinations of actions based on the sets of γ factors corresponding to cases A, B and C had to be taken into account for each particular problem.

a) EQU: Loss of static equilibrium of the structure or any part of it considered as a rigid body, where:
- *minor variations in the value or the spatial distribution of actions from a single source are significant, and*
- *the strengths of construction materials or ground are generally not governing;*

b) STR: Internal failure or excessive deformation of the structure or structural members, including footings, piles, basement walls, etc., where the strength of construction materials of the structure governs;

c) GEO: Failure or excessive deformation of the ground where the strength of soil or rock are significant in providing resistance;

d) FAT: Fatigue failure of the structure or structural members.

The reader should consider that limit states of a structure are idealized states beyond which the structure under consideration does not meet certain structural or functional design requirements. The objective of the verifications is to check that such states cannot be reached or exceeded with a given probability.

The design values are assessed in accordance with *Annex A* (see Chapter 7) (*clause 6.4.1(2)P*).

Clause 6.4.1(2)P

Limit states EQU

Normally, in accordance with the definition, limit states of static equilibrium are independent of the strength of the material. Exceeding the limit state causes, in most cases, immediate collapse. Thus, a loss of static equilibrium is an ultimate limit state. Examples of such limit states are not met very frequently. Figure 6.5 illustrates an example of a bridge deck launched with a counterweight where a loss of static equilibrium may be possible.

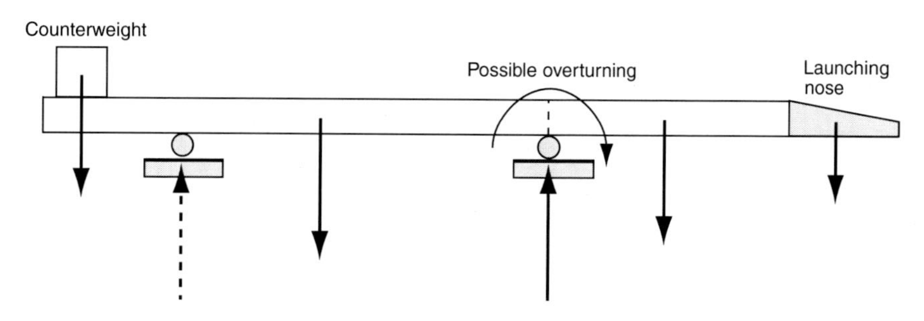

Fig. 6.5. *Example of bridge deck during launching*

In the case of foundations, limit states of static equilibrium nearly always represent the idealization of more complex limit states. Figure 6.6 shows an example of a retaining wall with a footing lying directly on a rocky substratum: a limit state of overturning around point A should be considered for the sizing of the footing because no criterion related to ground resistance can be defined. Indeed, the overturning of a retaining wall is generally the consequence of failure of the ground in contact with its footing.

In most cases, stabilizing devices are used, so it is necessary to check the resistance of these devices. Therefore, even if the primary phenomenon is a loss of static equilibrium (in most cases the beginning of a displacement), the resistance of the stabilizing system has to be verified. In such a case, the designer may have problems as to which combinations of actions to apply. (See Chapter 7 for further guidance.)

Limit states STR

Limit states STR, corresponding to a failure by lack of structural resistance or excessive deformation, are easier to comprehend. Nevertheless, a possible structural failure may be the consequence of a series of undesirable events that give rise to a hazard scenario. It is reasonable for all design situations idealizing the consequences of a particular hazard scenario to be checked with the set of γ factors associated with the first of the events which give rise to the hazard scenario. Therefore, the designer should select the appropriate limit state corresponding to the first event which will govern the combinations of actions.

Limit states GEO

For limit states GEO the strength of soil or rock is significant in providing resistance. Pure geotechnical problems such as slope instability are not covered in EN 1990. In most common cases, limit states GEO are connected with the resistance of foundations (footings, piles, etc.).

The distinction between limit states STR and GEO is necessary because several points of view can be adopted when ground properties are involved in an action or in a resistance. More precisely, the design value of a geotechnical variable (action or resistance) may be assessed either:

- by applying a partial factor to the result of the calculation (application of a theoretical model), or
- by applying partial factors to ground properties before calculating the resistance via the formula.

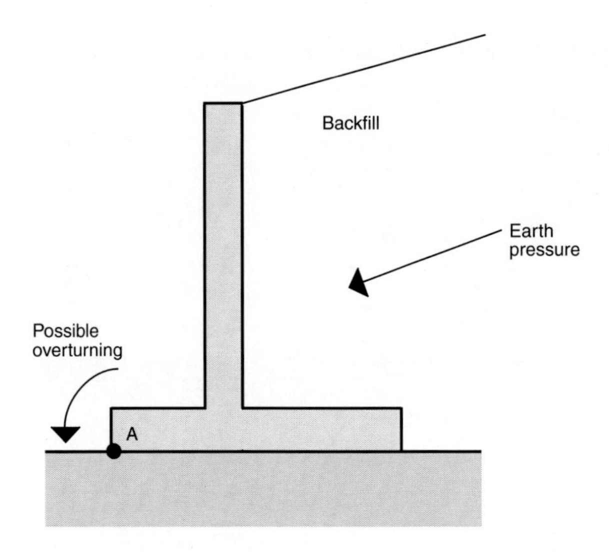

Fig. 6.6. *Retaining wall founded on rock*

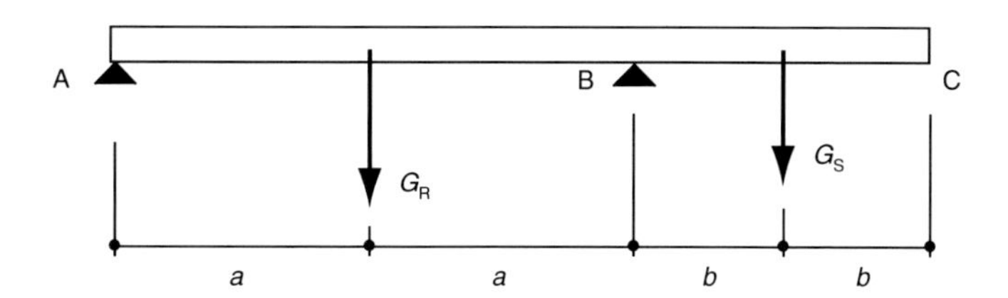

Fig. 6.7. *Beam structure – static equilibrium*

For example, the active pressure $p(z)$ at a depth z behind a retaining wall may be calculated from Rankine's formula:

$$p(z) = k_a z$$

with

$$k_a = \tan^2\left(\frac{\pi}{4} - \frac{\varphi}{2}\right)$$

where φ represents the angle of shearing resistance. It is easy to understand that safety may be introduced either through a suitable choice of this angle, or by applying a partial factor to the result of the calculation of p (see Chapter 7).

Limit states FAT

Fatigue limit states are considered, in the Eurocodes, as ultimate limit states because when fatigue is developing freely, the final step of the process is a structural failure. Nevertheless, the loads which are responsible for fatigue phenomena are not the design loads for ultimate limit states STR or GEO. For example, in the case of steel or composite steel and concrete bridges, the main cause of fatigue phenomena is not the effect of the heaviest lorries but rather of 'frequent' lorries, which apply medium forces with many repetitions. Fatigue verifications depend strongly on the structural material. Therefore, no specific rule is given in EN 1990, but reference is made to EN 1991 for actions and to the design Eurocodes 2 to 9.

6.4.2. Verifications of static equilibrium and resistance

A verification of static equilibrium (*clause 6.4.2.1(P)*), in the case of linearity, which is the most common case, is expressed as follows: *Clause 6.4.2.1(P)*

$$E_{d,\,dst} < E_{d,\,stb} \qquad (6.7)$$

This means that the design effects of destabilizing actions ($E_{d,\,dst}$) are less than the design effects of the stabilizing actions ($E_{d,\,stb}$).

In general, the stabilizing actions are permanent actions, mainly permanent loads (self-weight or actions of counterweights). In some cases, $E_{d,\,stb}$ may also include resistances such as from friction between rigid bodies (*clause 6.4.2(2)*) or material properties (e.g. from anchors). *Clause 6.4.2(2)*

Consider, for example, the simple beam structure shown in Fig. 6.7, where G_R represents the self-weight of the structure between the supports A and B (the 'anchor' part), and G_S, the self-weight of the cantilever BC. Assume also that the supports are unable to carry tensile force. To satisfy *expression (6.7)*,

$$G_{Rd}a > G_{Sd}b \qquad \text{(D6.9)}$$

where

$$G_{Rd} = \gamma_{G,\,inf}G_R \qquad \text{(D6.10)}$$

$$G_{Sd} = \gamma_{G,\,sup}G_S \qquad \text{(D6.11)}$$

When considering a limit state of rupture or excessive deformation of a section, a member or connection, it should be verified that the design value of the effects of actions such as internal forces or moments (E_d) is less than the design value for the corresponding resistance (R_d). The limit state expression is (*clause 6.4.2(3)P*)

Clause 6.4.2(3)P

$$E_d \leq R_d \tag{6.8}$$

This expression may also be applied to cases where the resistance is expressed in terms of a linear or a non-linear interaction formula that refers to various components of action effects.

In some cases, e.g. for earthquake-resistant structures or in plastic design, it is required that particular structural parts develop yielding mechanisms before the whole structure attains the ultimate limit state. In that case the structural parts intended to yield should be designed so that

$$E_d \leq R_{yd,\,inf} \tag{D6.12a}$$

and the other parts shall be capacity designed with

$$R_{yd,\,sup} < R_d \tag{D6.12b}$$

where $R_{yd,\,inf}$ and $R_{yd,\,sup}$ represent a lower-bound estimate and an upper-bound estimate of the yield strength expected in the structural parts intended to yield.

6.4.3. Combination of actions (fatigue verifications excluded)

General

Clause 6.4.3.1(1)P

The general principle adopted in EN 1990 is as follows: In accordance with *clause 6.4.3.1(1)P* '*for each critical load case, the design values of the effects of actions* (E_d) *shall be determined by combining the values of actions that are considered to occur simultaneously*'. The meaning of this principle is not immediately apparent. For a given construction, several actions, considered as several natural or man-made phenomena, apply permanently. For example, a building is permanently subject to actions due to self-weight, loads on floors, wind, snow, thermal actions, etc. However, for the verifications only critical load cases need to be taken into account, and these critical load cases are closely linked to the design values selected for actions.

Therefore, for the application of this principle, EN 1990 proposes the following rule: '*each combination of actions should include a leading variable action or an accidental action*' (*clause 6.4.3.1(2)*). However, this rule may not always be systematically followed (see Chapter 7).

Clause 6.4.3.1(2)

In order to help the designer, EN 1990 provides two further principles. The first one is (*clause 6.4.3.1(4)P*):

Clause 6.4.3.1(4)P

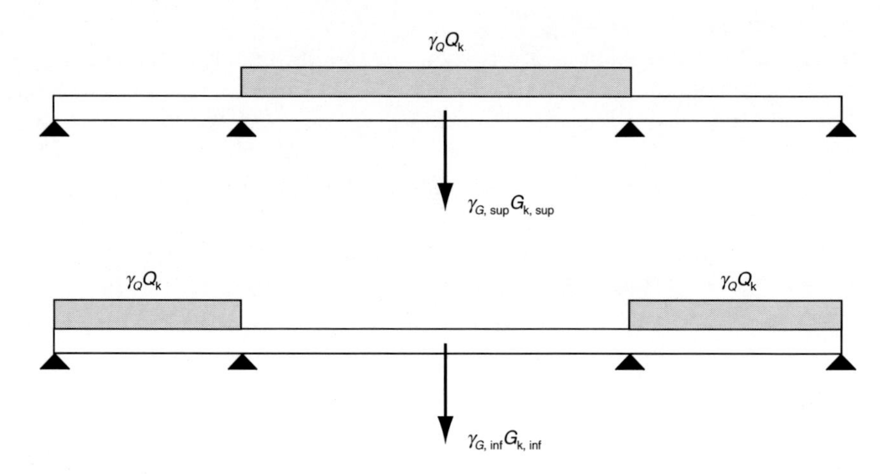

Fig. 6.8. Example of a continuous beam

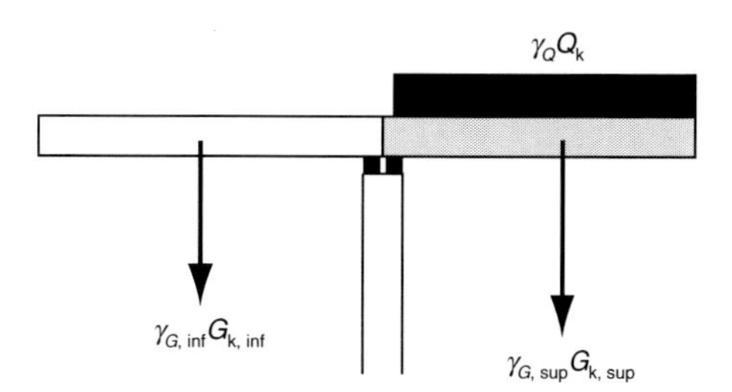

Fig. 6.9. *Bridge deck built by the cantilever method: risk of loss of static equilibrium*

> *Where the results of a verification may be very sensitive to variations of the magnitude of a permanent action from place to place in the structure, the unfavourable and the favourable parts of this action shall be considered as individual actions. This applies in particular to the verification of static equilibrium and analogous limit states, see 6.4.2(2).*

This clause is very important. It allows the designer to consider a clearly identified permanent action (e.g. self-weight of a continuous beam) as a single action: in a combination of actions, this permanent action may be considered either as a favourable or an unfavourable action. For example, Fig. 6.8 shows a three-span continuous beam for which the results of the verification of cross-sections are not very sensitive to variations in the magnitude of self-weight from place to place in the structure.

For the assessment of extreme values of the design bending moment at mid-span of the centre span, the design variable load (represented by a uniformly distributed load) may be applied to the centre span (for the maximum value) or to the side spans (for the minimum value). In the first case, the design self-weight of the beam will be the most 'unfavourable' ($\gamma_{G,\,sup} G_{k,\,sup}$), and in the second case, it will be the least 'unfavourable' ($\gamma_{G,\,inf} G_{k,\,inf}$).

Figure 6.9 illustrates the case of a prestressed concrete bridge deck built by the cantilever method. In this case the self-weight of the two arms of the bridge deck under construction may be considered as two individual actions because the results of a verification concerning static equilibrium are now very sensitive to variations in the magnitude in self-weight from place to place in the structure. As a consequence, the self-weight of one arm is taken into account with its minimum characteristic value and the self-weight of the second one is taken into account with its maximum characteristic value.

The second principle for combinations of actions states (*clause 6.4.3.1(5)*):

Clause 6.4.3.1(5)

> *Where several effects of one action (e.g. bending moment and normal force due to self-weight) are not fully correlated, the partial factor applied to any favourable component may be reduced.*

For example, in the case of an eccentrically loaded column the partial factor applicable to any favourable component may be reduced by up to 20%. Guidance for such reduction is given in the various design Eurocodes 2 to 9 or in their National Annexes. This second principle is also very important: it draws the designer's attention to the fact that safety should be investigated for all the aspects of the design.

'*Imposed deformations should be taken into account where relevant*' (*clause 6.4.3.1(6)*): these imposed deformations include uneven settlements of foundations or parts of foundations, shrinkage for concrete structures, temperature changes, etc.

Clause 6.4.3.1(6)

Combinations of actions for persistent or transient design situations (fundamental combinations)

The general format of effects of actions proposed by EN 1990 is (*clause 6.4.3.2(1)*)

Clause 6.4.3.2(1)

$$E_d = \gamma_{Sd} E\{\gamma_{g,j} G_{k,j};\ \gamma_p P;\ \gamma_{q,1} Q_{k,1};\ \gamma_{q,i} \psi_{0,i} Q_{k,i}\} \qquad j \geq 1; i > 1 \qquad (6.9a)$$

The design value of the effect of actions using this format is calculated via the following procedure:

(1) assessment of characteristic values of actions
(2) assessment of design values of individual actions
(3) calculation of the combined effect of individual actions taken into account with their design values
(4) application of the model uncertainty factor γ_{Sd} in order to obtain the design value of the effect of actions.

In *expression* (*6.9a*) it is assumed that a number of variable actions are acting simultaneously. $Q_{k,1}$ is the leading variable action: this means that, for the effect under consideration (e.g. bending moment in a cross-section of a structural member), the variable action Q_1 is applied in order to obtain the most unfavourable effect and is therefore taken into account with its characteristic value $Q_{k,1}$. Other variable actions should be taken into account simultaneously, together with the leading variable action, if this is physically possible: these variable actions are called accompanying variable actions and are taken into account with their combination value $\psi_{0,i} Q_{k,i}$. For example, in a building structure, several variable loads can act simultaneously: imposed loads on floors, wind, temperature, etc. The rule, based on the selection of one particular variable action as the leading variable action of the combination of actions, is generally adopted in all design Eurocodes. Nevertheless, a slight deviation is allowed when using *expressions* (*6.10a*) and (*6.10b*) given in *clause 6.4.3.2* as explained below. When the leading action is not obvious, i.e. when the most critical combination of actions cannot be identified easily, it has to be understood that each variable action should be considered in turn as the leading one.

Clause 6.4.3.2

In the most common cases, temperature changes, shrinkage and uneven settlements may be considered as non-leading. Also, in relevant load cases, permanent actions that increase the effect of the variable actions (i.e. produce unfavourable effects) are represented by their upper design values, those that decrease the effect of the variable actions (i.e. produce favourable effects) are represented by their lower design values.

In many cases, the combination of effects of actions is directly based on the design values of all actions (*clause 6.4.3.2.*(*2*)):

Clause 6.4.3.2.(2)

$$E_d = E\{\gamma_{G,j} G_{k,j};\ \gamma_P P;\ \gamma_{Q,1} Q_{k,1};\ \gamma_{Q,i}\psi_{0,i} Q_{k,i}\} \qquad j \geq 1;\ i > 1 \qquad (6.9b)$$

The values of the γ and ψ factors for actions are given in *Annex A* to EN 1990 (see Chapter 7 in the case of buildings), and the partial factors for properties of materials and products are given in the design Eurocodes (EN 1992 to EN 1999).

Two expressions of the combination of actions in the braces in *expression* (*6.9b*) are proposed in EN 1990 (*clause 6.4.3.2*(*3*)). The most classical expression is

Clause 6.4.3.2(3)

$$\sum_{j\geq 1} \gamma_{G,j} G_{k,j} \text{ '+' } \gamma_P P \text{ '+' } \gamma_{Q,1} Q_{k,1} \text{ '+' } \sum_{i>1} \gamma_{Q,i}\psi_{0,i} Q_{k,i} \qquad (6.10)$$

where '+' denotes 'to be combined with', Σ denotes 'the combined effect of' and P represents action due to prestressing. In most common cases, where there is no action due to prestressing, all factors $\gamma_{Q,i}$ are equal and expression (*6.10*) becomes

$$\sum \gamma_{G,j,\sup} G_{k,j,\sup} \text{ '+' } \sum \gamma_{G,j,\inf} G_{k,j,\inf} \text{ '+' } \gamma_Q \left\{ Q_{k,1} \text{ '+' } \sum_{i>1} \psi_{0,i} Q_{k,i} \right\} \qquad \text{(D6.13)}$$

However, for the STR and GEO limit states discussed earlier, EN 1990 also allows (if permitted by the National Annex) the less favourable of the two following expressions:

$$\begin{cases} \sum_{j\geq 1} \gamma_{G,j} G_{k,j} \text{ '+' } \gamma_P P \text{ '+' } \gamma_{Q,1}\psi_{0,1} Q_{k,1} \text{ '+' } \sum_{i>1} \gamma_{Q,i}\psi_{0,i} Q_{k,i} & (6.10a) \\ \sum_{j\geq 1} \xi_j \gamma_{G,j} G_{k,j} \text{ '+' } \gamma_P P \text{ '+' } \gamma_{Q,1} Q_{k,1} \text{ '+' } \sum_{i>1} \gamma_{Q,i}\psi_{0,i} Q_{k,i} & (6.10b) \end{cases}$$

where ξ is a reduction factor for unfavourable permanent actions. It is normally chosen within the range 0.85–1.00 (see Chapter 7). A discussion on the practical consequences of these two expressions can be found in Chapter 7. In *expression (6.10a)* all variable actions are taken into account with their combination value ($\psi_0 Q_k$). In *expression (6.10b)*, one variable action is identified as a leading action (the other variable actions are taken into account as accompanying actions), but a reduction factor is applied to the unfavourable permanent actions. *Expressions (6.10a)* and *(6.10b)* mean that the magnitude level corresponding to characteristic values of permanent and variable actions is such that the probability attached to a combination of actions where permanent unfavourable actions and the leading variable action are taken into account with their characteristic value is very low. A more accurate explanation is given in Chapter 7, based on reliability methods. *Expressions (6.10a)* and *(6.10b)* will always give a lower design value for load effect than the use of *expression (6.10)*. *Expression (6.10a)* will be more unfavourable when the variable action is greater than the permanent action while *expression (6.10b)* will be more unfavourable when the permanent action is greater than the variable action.

EN 1990 underlines that if the relationship between actions and their effects is not linear (*clause 6.4.3.2(4)*), *expression (6.9a)* or *(6.9b)* should be applied directly, depending upon the relative increase of the effects of actions compared with the increase in the magnitude of actions.

Clause 6.4.3.2(4)

The choice between *expressions (6.10)* or *(6.10a)* and *(6.10b)* will be stated in the National Annex (see Chapter 7).

Combinations of actions for accidental design situations

The general format of effects of actions for the accidental design situations is analogous to the general format for STR/GEO ultimate limit states. Here, the leading action is the accidental action, and the most general expression of the design value of the effect of actions is the following (*clause 6.4.3.3(1)*):

Clause 6.4.3.3(1)

$$E_d = E\{G_{k,j};\ P;\ A_d;\ (\psi_{1,1} \text{ or } \psi_{2,1})Q_{k,1};\ \psi_{2,i}Q_{k,i}\} \qquad j \geq 1;\ i > 1 \qquad (6.11a)$$

which can also be expressed as (*clause 6.4.3.3(2)*)

Clause 6.4.3.3(2)

$$\sum_{j \geq 1} G_{k,j} \text{ '+' } P \text{ '+' } A_d \text{ '+' } (\psi_{1,1} \text{ or } \psi_{2,1})Q_{k,1} \text{ '+' } \sum_{i>1} \psi_{2,i}Q_{k,i} \qquad (6.11b)$$

This combination considers that:

- accidents are unintended events such as explosions, fire or vehicular impact, which are of short duration and have a low probability of occurrence
- a certain amount of damage is generally acceptable in the event of an accident
- accidents generally occur when structures are in use (see also Chapter 2 of this guide).

Hence, to provide a realistic accidental combination, accidental actions are applied directly; with the frequent and quasi-permanent combination values used for the main (if any) and other variable actions, respectively (*clause 6.4.3.3(3)*).

Clause 6.4.3.3(3)

Regarding the representative value (frequent or quasi-permanent) of a possible main variable action, discretion is left to national authorities for the reason that all accidental situations or events cannot be similarly treated. For example, in the case of fire, it seems logical to adopt a frequent value of imposed loads in a staircase together with the design accidental action. In other cases, the choice may be different. When the main variable action is not obvious, each variable action should be considered in turn as the main action.

The combinations for accidental design situations either involve an explicit design value of accidental action A_d (e.g. impact) or refer to a situation after an accidental event ($A_d = 0$). For fire situations A_d refers to the design value of the indirect thermal action as determined by EN 1991-1-2 (*clause 6.4.3.3(4)*).

Clause 6.4.3.3(4)

Combinations of actions for seismic design situations

In the Eurocode system, seismic actions have not been amalgamated with most common accidental actions because differing levels of magnitude, depending upon the serviceability or safety requirements, can be defined by a national authority or a client. For example, in the case of railway bridges, the appropriate authority may require continuation of normal rail traffic (including high-speed passenger trains) after an earthquake of a relatively short return period (e.g. 50 years). However, more or less limited damage may be accepted for a more severe earthquake (e.g. over 500 years return period). In any case, the general format of effects is given by the following expression (*clause 6.4.3.4(1)*):

Clause 6.4.3.4(1)

$$E_d = E\{G_{k,j};\ P;\ A_{Ed};\ \psi_{2,i}Q_{k,i}\} \qquad j \geq 1;\ i \geq 1 \qquad (6.12a)$$

Clause 6.4.3.4(2)

that can be expressed, in common cases, as *clause (6.4.3.4(2))*:

$$\sum_{j \geq 1} G_{k,j} \text{ '+' } P \text{ '+' } A_{Ed} \text{ '+' } \sum_{i \geq 1} \psi_{2,i}Q_{k,i} \qquad (6.12b)$$

6.4.4. Partial factors for actions and combinations of actions

Clause 6.4.5

This short clause (*clause 6.4.5*) reminds the designer that γ and ψ factors are found in *Annex A* to EN 1990 (see Chapter 7 for the case of buildings), which refers to the various parts of EN 1991 and to National Annexes.

6.4.5. Partial factors for material and products

Similarly to the previous clause, the γ factors applicable to properties of materials and products are found in the design Eurocodes 2 to 9, which may refer to National Annexes (*clause 6.4.5*).

Clause 6.4.5

6.5. Serviceability limit states

6.5.1. Verifications of serviceability

From a general point of view, verifications of serviceability limit states are expressed as (*clause 6.5.1(1)P*)

Clause 6.5.1(1)P

$$E_d \leq C_d \qquad (6.13)$$

where:

C_d *is the limiting design value of the relevant serviceability criterion.*

E_d *is the design value of the effects of actions specified in the serviceability criterion, determined on the basis of the relevant combination.*

It should be mentioned that there are differences in serviceability criteria, depending on the type of limit state and the structural material under consideration. For example, the serviceability criteria may refer to deformations, to crack widths for concrete structures, or to vibration frequencies for sway structures, independently of their structural materials.

6.5.2. Serviceability criteria

Serviceability requirements related with deformations are generally defined in the design Eurocodes 2 to 9, or for the particular project, or by the national authority, in accordance with *Annex A* to EN 1990 (see Chapter 7) (*clause 6.5.2(1)*).

Clause 6.5.2(1)

6.5.3. Combination of actions

Three categories of combinations of actions are proposed in EN 1990: characteristic, frequent and quasi-permanent. The appropriate combinations of actions should be selected depending on the serviceability requirements and performance criteria imposed for the particular project, the client or the relevant national authority (*clause 6.5.3(1)*).

Clause 6.5.3(1)

The characteristic combination (in the past the wording 'rare combination' was also used) is expressed as follows (*clause 6.5.3(2)*):

Clause 6.5.3(2)

$$E_d = E\{G_{k,j};\ P;\ Q_{k,1};\ \psi_{0,i}Q_{k,i}\} \qquad j \geq 1;\ i > 1 \qquad (6.14a)$$

or, in common cases,

$$\sum_{j\geq 1} G_{k,j} \text{ `+' } P_k \text{ `+' } Q_{k,1} \text{ `+' } \sum_{i>1} \psi_{0,i} Q_{k,i} \qquad (6.14b)$$

This characteristic combination of actions is built on the same pattern as the fundamental combination of actions for STR/GEO ultimate limit states: all γ factors are generally equal to 1, and this is an aspect of the semi-probabilistic format of structural verifications.

The characteristic combination is normally used for irreversible limit states, e.g. the exceedance of some cracking limits in concrete structures.

The frequent combination

$$E_d = E\{G_{k,j};\ P;\ \psi_{1,1}Q_{k,1};\ \psi_{2,i}Q_{k,i}\} \qquad j \geq 1;\ i > 1 \qquad (6.15a)$$

in which the combination of actions in braces can be expressed as

$$\sum_{j\geq 1} G_{k,j} \text{ `+' } P \text{ `+' } \psi_{1,1} Q_{k,1} \text{ `+' } \sum_{i>1} \psi_{2,i} Q_{k,i} \qquad (6.15b)$$

is normally used for reversible limit states such as the quasi-permanent combination of actions.

The quasi-permanent combination (also used for reversible limit states), which is used for the assessment of long-term effects (e.g. effects due to creep and shrinkage in concrete structures) is written as

$$E_d = E\{G_{k,j};\ P;\ \psi_{2,i}Q_{k,i}\} \qquad j \geq 1;\ i \geq 1 \qquad (6.16a)$$

or (simplified)

$$\sum_{j\geq 1} G_{k,j} \text{ `+' } P \text{ `+' } \sum_{i\geq 1} \psi_{2,i} Q_{k,i} \qquad (6.16b)$$

Guidance on the selection of the representative value of the prestressing action (i.e. P_k or P_m) is given in the design Eurocodes 1 to 9 for the type of prestress under consideration.

6.5.4. Partial factors for materials

'For serviceability limit states the partial factors γ_M for the properties of materials should be taken as 1,0 except if differently specified in EN 1992 to EN 1999' (*clause 6.5.4*).

Clause 6.5.4

Further reading

See the list at the end of Chapter 7.

CHAPTER 7

Annex A1 (normative) – Application for buildings

This chapter is concerned with the definition of combinations of actions and requirements for the verification of building structures. The material described in this chapter is covered in *Annex A1*, 'Application for buildings', of EN 1990, *Eurocode*: *Basis of Structural Design*. This annex, which completes *Section 6* (see Chapter 6), is normative. The material described in this chapter is covered in *Annex A1* of EN 1990 as follows:

- Field of application — *Clause A1.1*
- Combinations of actions — *Clause A1.2*
- Ultimate limit states — *Clause A1.3*
- Serviceability limit states — *Clause A1.4*

7.1. Field of application

Clause A1.1(1) states

Clause A1.1(1)

> *Annex A1 gives rules and methods for establishing combinations of actions for buildings. It also gives the recommended design values of permanent, variable and accidental actions and ψ factors to be used in the design of buildings.*

The note to *clause A1.1(1)* recommends that the design working life needs be defined (see Chapter 2): in general, this design working life is not normally directly used in calculations, but it has to be defined for some problems related, for example, to fatigue or corrosion of steel.

7.2. Combinations of actions

7.2.1. General

Clause A1.2.1(1)

Effects of actions that cannot exist simultaneously due to physical or functional reasons (see Chapter 6) should not be considered together in combinations of actions (*clause A1.2.1(1)*). This application rule is a matter of engineering judgement. Of course, in most cases, several variable actions exist simultaneously in a building: imposed loads on floors, wind actions, temperature changes, etc. The general rules applicable for the establishment of combinations of actions are explained in Chapter 6 (see Section 6.4.3), and a comprehensive application of these rules may lead to a large number of load combinations. To aid simplicity for the design, EN 1990 allows (*clause A1.2.1(1)*, note 1) the combinations of actions to be based on not more than two variable actions.

Background

In ENV 1991-1, *Basis of Design*, the following simplified combinations were permitted as an alternative to the fundamental combination :

(1) Design situation with one variable action only:

$$\sum_{j\geq 1} \gamma_{G,j} G_{k,j} \text{ '+' } [1.5] Q_{k,1}$$

(2) Design situation with two or more variable actions:

$$\sum_{j\geq 1} \gamma_{G,j} G_{k,j} \text{ '+' } [1.35] \sum_{i\geq 1} Q_{k,i}$$

The simplified formats have not been kept for the following reasons:

- they were not correct from a conceptual point of view
- they could not be considered as enveloping normal formats because they were not systematically safe-sided
- they did not really lead to simpler calculations than normal combinations of actions.

For example, if we consider a problem with one permanent action (e.g. self-weight, G_k) and two independent variable actions (e.g. floor-imposed loads $Q_{k,1}$ and wind actions $Q_{k,2}$), the simplified formats led to the consideration of the following combinations:

$1.35G_k + 1.5Q_{k,1}$
$1.35G_k + 1.5Q_{k,2}$
$1.35G_k + 1.35Q_{k,1} + 1.35Q_{k,2}$

In fact, the general method (based now on *expression* (*6.10*) in EN 1990) is used only for verification:

$1.35G_k + 1.5Q_{k,1} + 1.05Q_{k,2}$ $(\psi_{0,2} = 0.7)$

and

$1.35G_k + 0.9Q_{k,1} + 1.5Q_{k,2}$ $(\psi_{0,2} = 0.7)$

See Table 7.1 for ψ factors

The suggested limitation to using two variable actions only is acceptable in common cases (e.g. a normal six-storey residential building) due to the high levels of characteristic and combination values of variable actions and the low probability of the combined significant effects of additional actions. Indeed, the probability of occurrence of a fundamental combination (*expression* (*6.10*)) with more than two variable actions taken with their characteristic (for the leading action) and combination (for the accompanying actions) values would be very low. Nevertheless, EN 1990 draws the designer's attention to the fact that the use of the proposed simplification may depend on the use, the form and the location of the building. It is stressed that this simplification may produce unacceptable low levels of safety when used simultaneously with *expressions* (*6.10a*) and (*6.10b*).

The Eurocode reminds designers what combinations of actions should be used when verifying ultimate limit states (*clause A1.2.1*(*2*)) or serviceability limit states (*clause A1.2.1*(*3*)), but modifications of some combinations are allowed for geographical reasons in the National Annex (*clause A1.2.1*(*1*), note 2).

Clause A1.2.1(2)
Clause A1.2.1(3)
Clause A1.2.1(1)

EN 1990 does not give γ factors for prestressing. These factors are defined in the relevant design Eurocodes, and in particular in EN 1992 (*clause A1.2.1*(*4*)).

Clause A1.2.1(4)

7.2.2. Values of ψ factors

Recommended values of ψ factors for the more common actions are given in Table 7.1 (which reproduces *Table A1.1* of EN 1990). They are in accordance with values given in other parts of EN 1991, and can be altered in the National Annex. Moreover, for countries not mentioned in the table (i.e. countries outside the EU), specific adjustments are recommended (*clause A1.2.2*(*1*)).

Clause A1.2.2(1)

Table 7.1. *Recommended values of ψ factors for buildings (*Table A1.1 *of EN 1990)*

Action	ψ_0	ψ_1	ψ_2
Imposed loads in buildings, category (see EN 1991-1-1)			
Category A: domestic, residential areas	*0,7*	*0,5*	*0,3*
Category B: office areas	*0,7*	*0,5*	*0,3*
Category C: congregation areas	*0,7*	*0,7*	*0,6*
Category D: shopping areas	*0,7*	*0,7*	*0,6*
Category E: storage areas	*1,0*	*0,9*	*0,8*
Category F: traffic area, vehicle weight ≤ 30kN	*0,7*	*0,7*	*0,6*
Category G: traffic area, 30kN < vehicle weight ≤ 160kN	*0,7*	*0,5*	*0,3*
Category H: roofs	*0*	*0*	*0*
*Snow loads on buildings (see EN 1991-1-3)**			
Finland, Iceland, Norway, Sweden	*0,70*	*0,50*	*0,20*
Remainder of CEN Member States, for sites located at altitude H > 1000 m a.s.l.	*0,70*	*0,50*	*0,20*
Remainder of CEN Member States, for sites located at altitude H ≤ 1000 m a.s.l.	*0,50*	*0,20*	*0*
Wind loads on buildings (see EN 1991-1-4)	*0,6*	*0,2*	*0*
Temperature (non-fire) in buildings (see EN 1991-1-5)	*0,6*	*0,5*	*0*
NOTE The ψ values may be set by the National Annex.			
(*) For countries not mentioned below, see relevant local conditions.			

7.3. Ultimate limit states

7.3.1. Design values of actions in persistent and transient design situations

Three sets of design values of actions (sets A, B and C) are defined for persistent and transient design situations, depending on the limit state under consideration (*clause A1.3.1(1)*). Numerical values for γ and ψ factors are normally given in the National Annex. However, EN 1990 recommends values for γ and ψ which may probably be widely adopted. These values are given in notes to EN 1990, and are included in *Tables A1.2(A)* to *A1.2(C)* (reproduced here as Tables 7.3(A) to 7.3(C)), corresponding to sets A, B and C, respectively.

Clause A1.3.1(1)

Concerning permanent actions, the reader is reminded that the use of upper and lower characteristic values (see Chapter 4) is intended for all limit states which appear to be very sensitive to variations in magnitude of these actions (*clause A1.3.1(2)*). Of course, some engineering judgement is necessary to recognize the cases where a limit state is very or not very sensitive to such variations. This rule is intended mainly for limit states of static equilibrium (EQU).

Clause A1.3.1(2)

As explained in Chapter 6, four limit states are identified, depending on the way to introduce safety in the assessment of geotechnical and non-geotechnical actions and in geotechnical resistances: EQU, STR, GEO and FAT.

The correspondence between limit states and sets of design values is shown in Table 7.2 (*clauses A1.3.1(3)* and *A1.3.1(4)*).

Clause A1.3.1(3)
Clause A1.3.1(4)

For GEO limit states or STR limit states involving geotechnical actions, three approaches are defined* (*clause A1.3.1(5)*), and sets of design values are given for each approach in EN 1990.

Clause A1.3.1(5)

*EN 1997 also introduces the limit states UPL (loss of equilibrium of the structure or the ground due to uplift by water pressure) and HYD (hydraulic heave, internal erosion and piping in the ground caused by hydraulic gradients).

These limit states (EQU, STR and GEO) are schematically illustrated in Fig. 7.1.

The choice of approach 1, 2 or 3 is made by the appropriate National Annex. EN 1990 does not give any design value for limit states due to fatigue (FAT) or for limit states associated with pure geotechnical, hydraulic or buoyancy failure (*clauses A1.3.1(6)* and *A1.3.1(7)*), which are treated in EN 1997, *Geotechnical Design*, and the handbook for EN 1997.

Clause A1.3.1(6)
Clause A1.3.1(7)

7.3.2. EQU limit states

The static equilibrium of a structure or of any part of it (considered as a rigid body) is verified using the design values of actions in Table 7.3(A) (set A), which reproduces *Table A1.2(A)* of EN 1990.

As can be seen from Table 7.3(A), the combination of actions is based on *expression (6.10)* of EN 1990, with one leading variable action, accompanying variable actions and permanent actions which may be 'unfavourable' if they act together with the variable actions, or 'favourable' if they act opposite to the variable actions.

As already explained, EN 1990 gives only recommended values for γ factors in notes 1 and 2 to *Table A1.2(A)*: these γ factors may be confirmed or altered by the National Annex.

Table 7.2. *Limit states and sets of design values*

Limit state	Set of partial factors
EQU – static equilibrium	Set A (Table 7.3(a))
STR – resistance of building structures not involving geotechnical actions	Set B (Table 7.3(b))
STR – resistance of building structures involving geotechnical actions GEO – failure or excessive deformation of the ground	*Approach 1* Set C (Table 7.3(c)) for all actions, and set B for all actions, the most unfavourable *Approach 2* Set B for all actions *Approach 3* Set B for actions on/from the structure, and set C for geotechnical actions

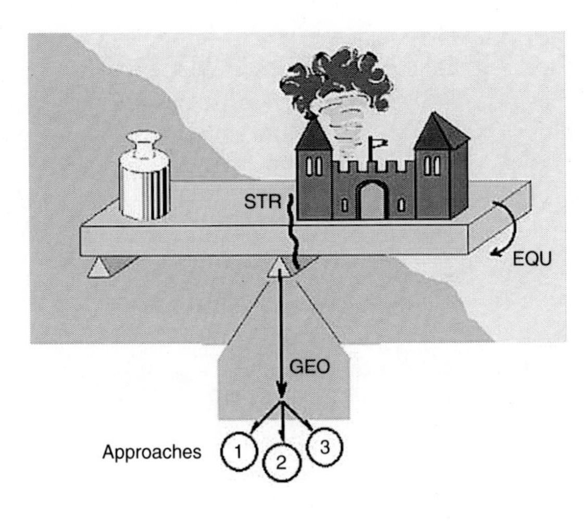

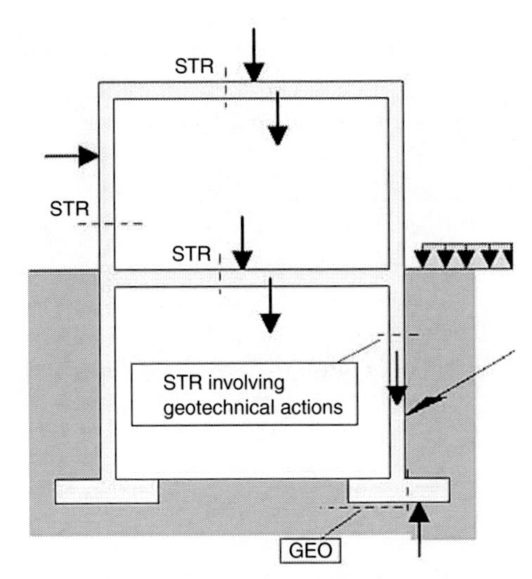

Fig. 7.1. *Examples of limit states EQU, STR and GEO*

Table 7.3(A). *Design values of actions (EQU) (set A) (Table A1.2(A) of EN 1990)*

Persistent and transient design situations	*Permanent actions*		*Leading variable action (*)*	*Accompanying variable actions*	
	Unfavourable	*Favourable*		*Main (if any)*	*Others*
(Eq. 6.10)	$\gamma_{Gj,sup} G_{kj,sup}$	$\gamma_{Gj,inf} G_{kj,inf}$	$\gamma_{Q,1} Q_{k,1}$		$\gamma_{Q,i} \psi_{0,i} Q_{k,i}$

(*) Variable actions are those considered in Table A1.1

NOTE 1 The γ values may be set by the National Annex. The recommended set of values for γ are:
$\gamma_{Gj,sup} = 1,10$
$\gamma_{Gj,inf} = 0,90$
$\gamma_{Q,1} = 1,50$ *where unfavourable (0 where favourable)*
$\gamma_{Q,i} = 1,50$ *where unfavourable (0 where favourable)*

NOTE 2 In cases where the verification of static equilibrium also involves the resistance of structural members, as an alternative to two separate verifications based on Tables A1.2(A) and A1.2(B), a combined verification, based on Table A1.2(A), may be adopted, if allowed by the National annex, with the following set of recommended values. The recommended values may be altered by the National annex.
$\gamma_{Gj,sup} = 1,35$
$\gamma_{Gj,inf} = 1,15$
$\gamma_{Q,1} = 1,50$ *where unfavourable (0 where favourable)*
$\gamma_{Q,i} = 1,50$ *where unfavourable (0 where favourable)*
provided that applying $\gamma_{Gj,inf} = 1,00$ both to the favourable part and to the unfavourable part of permanent actions does not give a more unfavourable effect.

The numerical γ values recommended in *Table A1.1(A)* need explanation. With the set of recommended γ values given in note 1, the combination of actions reads:

$$1.10\sum G_{k,j,\mathrm{sup}} \text{ '+' } 0.90\sum G_{k,j,\mathrm{inf}} \text{ '+' } 1.50Q_{k,1} \text{ '+' } 1.50\sum_{i\geq 2} \psi_{0,i}Q_{k,i}$$

or, in a more 'user-friendly' way

$$1.10G_{\mathrm{unfav}} \text{ '+' } 0.90G_{\mathrm{fav}} \text{ '+' } 1.50Q_{k,1} \text{ '+' } 1.50\sum_{i\geq 2} \psi_{0,i}Q_{k,i}$$

The identification of favourable and unfavourable permanent actions is based on the two rules evoked previously: '*where the results of a verification are very sensitive to variations of the magnitude of a permanent action from place to place in a structure, the unfavourable and the favourable parts of this action shall be considered as individual actions*' (*clause 6.4.3.1*) and the rule concerning the use of the upper and lower characteristic values of permanent actions (as explained in Chapter 4). In many cases, nominal values are taken as characteristic values.

Clause 6.4.3.1

Where static equilibrium is not directly ensured, a stabilizing system is normally provided. For such a case, a verification with respect to ultimate limit states STR/GEO is necessary. In that case, an alternative set of recommended values is given which may be used, if allowed by the National Annex, to verify both relevant EQU and STR limit states.

With the set of recommended values given in note 2 of *Table A1.2(A)* of *clause A1.3* of EN 1990, the combination of actions is

Clause A1.3

$$1.35\sum G_{k,j,\mathrm{sup}} \text{ '+' } 1.15\sum G_{k,j,\mathrm{inf}} \text{ '+' } 1.50Q_{k,1} \text{ '+' } 1.50\sum_{i\geq 2} \psi_{0,i}Q_{k,i}$$

or, in a more 'user-friendly' way

$$1.35G_{\mathrm{unfav}} \text{ '+' } 1.15G_{\mathrm{fav}} \text{ '+' } 1.50Q_{k,1} \text{ '+' } 1.50\sum_{i\geq 2} \psi_{0,i}Q_{k,i}$$

There is no scientific interpretation of the proposed set of design values: they have been

Background

The partial factors 1.10 and 0.90 may be interpreted in the following way. In accordance with reliability methods, where permanent actions are unfavourable, their design value derives from the formula

$$G_{\mathrm{d,\,sup}} = G_{\mathrm{m}}(1 - \alpha_{\mathrm{E}}\beta V_G) = G_{\mathrm{m}}(1 + 0.7 \times 3.8 \times V_G)$$

Where permanent actions are favourable they may be treated as resistances, and their design value derives from the formula

$$G_{\mathrm{d,\,inf}} = G_{\mathrm{m}}(1 - \alpha_{\mathrm{R}}\beta V_G) = G_{\mathrm{m}}(1 - 0.8 \times 3.8 \times V_G)$$

V_G is the coefficient of variation of the permanent action under consideration. In EN 1990, note 2 of *clause 4.1.2(1)P* (see Chapter 4) suggests that the coefficient of variation of permanent actions can be in the range 0.05 to 0.10. These values apply more to the effects of permanent actions (including model uncertainties) than to the actions themselves (for which there is no model uncertainty). In static equilibrium problems (EQU), the permanent actions are represented directly (and not as effects of actions) in the expression of the limit state, and these actions are mainly due to self-weight. This explains why a lower range can be adopted for V_G, such as 0.02 to 0.05 (0.02 corresponds to bridge construction sites with high level control). For example, for $V_G = 0.05$, $G_{\mathrm{d,\,sup}} = 1.13G_{\mathrm{m}}$ and $G_{\mathrm{d,\,inf}} = 0.85G_{\mathrm{m}}$, which gives an interpretation of the recommended partial factors.

It should also be noted that the set of partial factors recommended in note 1 of *Table A1.2(A)* of EN 1990 is inconsistent because factors 1.10 and 0.9 do not include any model uncertainty factor whereas the factor 1.50 for variable actions includes a model uncertainty factor; however, this has no real importance in most cases.

adjusted in order to give an acceptable combination to be used both for EQU and STR ultimate limit states. A detailed example explaining EQU is developed later in this chapter, in Section 7.5.1.

7.3.3. STR limit states

Design of structural members not involving geotechnical actions is normally verified using the design values of actions from set B (Table 7.3(B) (*Table A1.2(B)* in EN 1990)).

The presentation of *Table A1.2(B)* of EN 1990 may appear somewhat elaborate, and needs a detailed explanation.

First, it should be noted that *Table A1.2(B)* actually proposes the following three different sets of design values (the decision of which one to use is left to the National Annex):

- *expression (6.10)*
- the less favourable of *expressions (6.10a)* and *(6.10b)*
- the less favourable of *expressions (6.10a)* 'modified' and *(6.10b)*

Expression (6.10a) 'modified' is the combination of actions which includes the permanent actions shown below:

$$\sum \gamma_{G,j,\mathrm{sup}} G_{\mathrm{k},j,\mathrm{sup}} \text{ `+' } \sum \gamma_{G,j,\mathrm{inf}} G_{\mathrm{k},j,\mathrm{inf}}$$

Using the set of recommended values given in note 2 of *Table A1.2(B)*, the combinations of actions read

$$1.35 \sum G_{\mathrm{k},j,\mathrm{sup}} \text{ `+' } \sum G_{\mathrm{k},j,\mathrm{inf}} \text{ `+' } 1.50 Q_{\mathrm{k},1} \text{ `+' } 1.50 \sum_{i \geq 2} \psi_{0,i} Q_{\mathrm{k},i}$$

for *expression (6.10)*, and

$$1.35 \sum G_{\mathrm{k},j,\mathrm{sup}} \text{ `+' } \sum G_{\mathrm{k},j,\mathrm{inf}} \text{ `+' } 1.50 \sum_{i \geq 1} \psi_{0,i} Q_{\mathrm{k},i}$$

$$1.15 \sum G_{\mathrm{k},j,\mathrm{sup}} \text{ `+' } \sum G_{\mathrm{k},j,\mathrm{inf}} \text{ `+' } 1.50 Q_{\mathrm{k},1} \text{ `+' } 1.50 \sum_{i \geq 2} \psi_{0,i} Q_{\mathrm{k},i}$$

for *expressions (6.10a)* and *(6.10b)*.

Table 7.3(B). *Design values of actions (STR/GEO) (set B)* (Table A1.2(B) *of EN 1990)*

Persistent and transient design situations	*Permanent actions*		*Leading variable action (*)*	*Accompanying variable actions (*)*	
	Unfavourable	*Favourable*		*Main (if any)*	*Others*
(Eq. 6.10)	$\gamma_{Gj,sup} G_{kj,sup}$	$\gamma_{Gj,inf} G_{kj,inf}$	$\gamma_{Q,1} Q_{k,1}$		$\gamma_{Q,i} \psi_{0,i} Q_{k,i}$

Persistent and transient design situations	*Permanent actions*		*Leading variable action (*)*	*Accompanying variable actions (*)*	
	Unfavourable	*Favourable*	*Action*	*Main*	*Others*
(Eq. 6.10a)	$\gamma_{Gj,sup} G_{kj,sup}$	$\gamma_{Gj,inf} G_{kj,inf}$		$\gamma_{Q,1} \psi_{0,1} Q_{k,1}$	$\gamma_{Q,i} \psi_{0,i} Q_{k,i}$
(Eq. 6.10b)	$\xi \gamma_{Gj,sup} G_{kj,sup}$	$\gamma_{Gj,inf} G_{kj,inf}$	$\gamma_{Q,1} Q_{k,1}$		$\gamma_{Q,i} \psi_{0,i} Q_{k,i}$

(*) Variable actions are those considered in Table A1.1

NOTE 1 The choice between 6.10, or 6.10a and 6.10b will be in the National Annex. In case of 6.10a and 6.10b, the National Annex may in addition modify 6.10a to include permanent actions only.

NOTE 2 The γ and ξ values may be set by the National annex. The following values for γ and ξ are recommended when using expressions 6.10, or 6.10a and 6.10b.
$\gamma_{Gj,sup} = 1{,}35$
$\gamma_{Gj,inf} = 1{,}00$
$\gamma_{Q,1} = 1{,}50$ *where unfavourable (0 where favourable)*
$\gamma_{Q,i} = 1{,}50$ *where unfavourable (0 where favourable)*
$\xi = 0{,}85$ *(so that $\xi \gamma_{Gj,sup} = 0{,}85 \times 1{,}35 \cong 1{,}15$).*
See also EN 1991 to ENV 1999 for γ values to be used for imposed deformations.

NOTE 3 The characteristic values of all permanent actions from one source are multiplied by $\gamma_{G,sup}$ if the total resulting action effect is unfavourable and $\gamma_{G,inf}$ if the total resulting action effect is favourable. For example, all actions originating from the self weight of the structure may be considered as coming from one source; this also applies if different materials are involved.

NOTE 4 For particular verifications, the values for γ_G and γ_Q may be subdivided into γ_g and γ_q and the model uncertainty factor γ_{Sd}. A value of γ_{Sd} in the range 1,05 to 1,15 can be used in most common cases and can be modified in the National Annex.

Background – interpretation of recommended values of γ factors

The traditional interpretation of the recommended numerical values of γ factors is given in *CEB Bulletins* 127 and 128, $\gamma_F = \gamma_{Sd}\gamma_f$:

Action	γ_f	γ_{Sd}	γ_F
Permanent unfavourable	1.125	1.20	$\approx$1.35
Permanent favourable	0.875	1.20	$\approx$1.00
Variable (unfavourable)	1.35	1.10	$\approx$1.50

This interpretation is the result of very accurate studies. It shows that a unique value of a γ_{Sd} factor has no scientific justification, and results from engineering judgement.

It should be noted that EN 1990 does not give recommended values for *expression* (*6.10a*) 'modified'.

It is clear that the two possibilities of *expression* (*6.10*) or *expressions* (*6.10a*) and (*6.10b*) are not equivalent in that they do not lead to the same reliability level.

When using appropriate statistical data for permanent and variable actions for determining the γ and ψ_0 values, these values would be functions of the ratio between permanent and variable actions. A good approximation to these functions would result from the use of the two combination *expressions* (*expressions* (*6.10a*) and (*6.10b*)) which allow each action including the permanent actions G to be either a 'leading' action $\gamma_F F_k$ or an accompanying action $\gamma_F \psi_0 F_k$. *Expression* (*6.10*) presumes that the permanent actions $\gamma_G G$ and one variable action $\gamma_Q Q_{k,1}$ should always act together as design values.

Background – reliability levels attached to the three procedures

The three alternative procedures for combinations of actions provided in *Annex A1* of EN 1990 have been investigated and also compared with combination rules given in British standards (BS 5950 and BS 8110) by using probability-based reliability methods.

In order to characterize the differences resulting from the three procedures, an elementary model was used, based on the following limit state function:

$$g(\underline{X}) = \theta_R R - \theta_E(G + Q + W)$$

where $\underline{X}$ denotes the vector of basic variables (random variables entering the right-hand side of this equation), θ_R denotes the factor expressing the uncertainty of the resistance model, θ_E denotes the factor expressing the uncertainty of the loading model, R denotes a resistance, G denotes a permanent action, Q denotes imposed loads on building floors (as defined in EN 1990) and W denotes wind action.

Appropriate probabilistic models have been selected for the six basic variables. Parameters concerning the resistance of reinforced concrete (in particular the mean and standard deviation) have been determined by considering the bending resistance of a reinforced concrete section with the reinforcement ratio of 1%. The reinforcement steel S500 (having a mean of 560 MPa and a standard deviation of 30 MPa), and the concrete C20 (having a mean of 30 MPa and a standard deviation of 5 MPa) have been assumed for the determination of the parameters. The following four cases of combination of actions were investigated for both steel and concrete structural members.

(1) permanent action G and imposed load Q only
(2) permanent action G and wind action W only
(3) permanent action G with imposed load Q dominant and wind action W accompanying for $k = 0.5$ and 0.8
(4) permanent action G with wind action W dominant and imposed load Q accompanying for $k = 2.00$ and 10.0

where $k = W/Q$.

The following figures show two examples of the variation of the reliability index β as a function of the load ratio

$$\chi = \frac{Q+W}{G+W+Q}$$

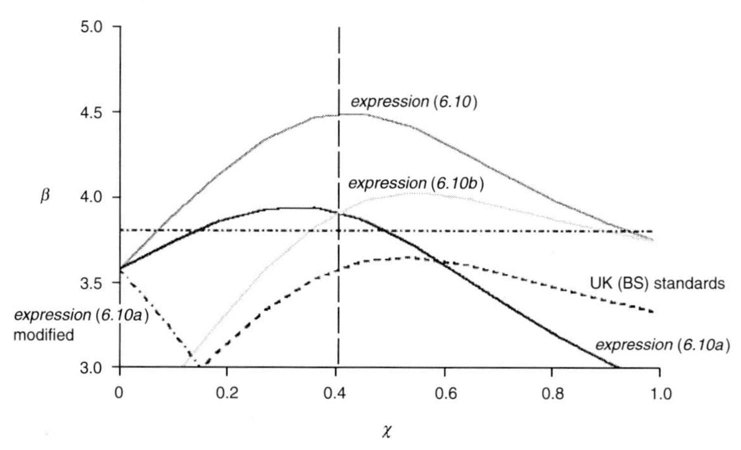

Reliability index β for a steel element, with permanent load G, imposed load Q dominant and accompanying wind load W (k = 0.5)

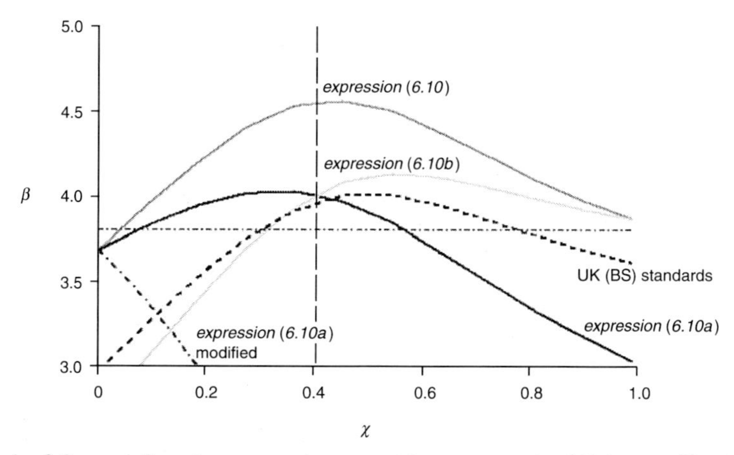

Reliability index β for a reinforced concrete element, with permanent load G, imposed load Q dominant and accompanying wind load W (k = 0.5)

The calculations show that:

(1) *Expression (6.10)*, when used with the partial factors recommended by EN 1990, gives for most practical cases of load ratio χ reliability levels above those desired ($\beta = 3.8$). The use of *expressions (6.10a)* and *(6.10b)* gives lower reliability levels than obtained with *expression (6.10)*, but still in most cases above those desired ($\beta = 3.8$).

(2) Modified *expression (6.10a)* used together with *expression (6.10b)* from EN 1990 leads to a lower reliability level than desired ($\beta = 3.8$), particularly when the load ratio χ is less than 0.5.

(3) The combination rules in BS 5950 and BS 8110 lead to similar results as obtained with *expression (6.10)* from EN 1990, when considering one variable action only. However, the use of the UK combination rules when two variable actions are being considered together leads to a substantially lower reliability than EN 1990 *expression (6.10)* or *expressions (6.10a)* and *(6.10b)*, in particular for low load ratios χ.

(4) The use of *expression (6.10a)* used together with *expression (6.10b)* leads to a more uniform distribution of β, as the function of the load ratio χ, than *expression (6.10)*.

In general, *expression (6.10a)* will be the more unfavourable when the variable action is greater than the permanent action while *expression (6.10b)* will be the more unfavourable when the permanent action is greater than the variable action. As an example it can be easily shown that for thick concrete slabs *expression (6.10a)* is decisive, while for very thin concrete slabs and steel and timber beams *expression (6.10b)* is decisive.

Hence the joint combination rules given by *expressions (6.10a)* and *(6.10b)* on one side and that given by *expression (6.10)* on the other differ in the estimation of different risks from permanent actions (realistic persistent actions) and variable actions (assessed from extreme value distributions) and represent different levels of reliability that are offered to regulatory bodies for choice, through the National Annex as EN 1990 does not recommend a unique approach.

Attention is drawn to note 4 of *Table A1.2(B)*, which allows identification of a model factor. All structural analyses are based on models (structural models and models of actions) which are only approximations. This has been clearly stated in the *Basic Note* on model uncertainties, adopted by the CEB (*CEB Bulletin* 170, 1985).

It is clear that it is not possible to define an exact unique value for factor γ_{Sd} intended to cover individually all structural analysis uncertainties: the value would be very different from one structure to another, and even from one structural member cross-section to another. For this reason, EN 1990 proposes a value of γ_{Sd} within the range 1.05 to 1.15 that can be used for most common cases and can be modified in the National Annex. This approach can be adopted when considering non-linear problems. In many cases, the value of 1.15 is the most appropriate.

The use of *expression (6.10)* is, perhaps, economically less favourable than the use of *expressions (6.10a)* and *(6.10b)*, but, in the case of concrete structures, its use automatically covers the verification of several of the serviceability limit states.

7.3.4. STR/GEO limit states

Resistance of structural members (footings, piles, basement walls, etc.) involving geotechnical actions and the resistance of the ground should be verified using one of the three approaches (to be chosen in the National Annex) in Table 7.2:

- Approach 1: applying in separate calculations design values from Table 7.3(C) (*Table A1.2(C)* of EN 1990) and Table 7.3(B) (*Table A1.2(B)* of EN 1990) to the geotechnical actions as well as the other actions on/from the structure
- Approach 2: applying design values from Table 7.3(B) (*Table A1.2(B)* of EN 1990) to the geotechnical actions as well as the other actions on/from the structure

Table 7.3(C). *Design values of actions (STR/GEO) (set C) (Table A1.2(C) of EN 1990)*

Persistent and transient design situation	*Permanent actions*		*Leading variable action (*)*	*Accompanying variable actions (*)*	
	Unfavourable	*Favourable*		*Main (if any)*	*Others*
(Eq. 6.10)	$\gamma_{Gj,sup}G_{kj,sup}$	$\gamma_{Gj,inf}G_{kj,inf}$	$\gamma_{Q,1}Q_{k,1}$		$\gamma_{Q,i}\psi_{0,i}Q_{k,i}$

(*) Variable actions are those considered in Table A1.1

NOTE The γ values may be set by the National annex. The recommended set of values for γ are:
$\gamma_{Gj,sup} = 1,00$
$\gamma_{Gj,inf} = 1,00$
$\gamma_{Q,1} = 1,30$ *where unfavourable (0 where favourable)*
$\gamma_{Q,i} = 1,30$ *where unfavourable (0 where favourable)*

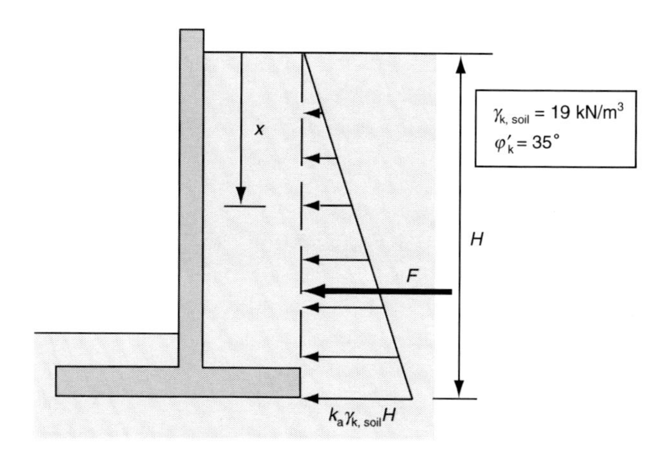

Fig. 7.2. *Example of geotechnical action*

- Approach 3: applying design values from Table 7.3(C) (*Table A1.2(C)* of EN 1990) to the geotechnical actions and, simultaneously, applying partial factors from Table 7.3(B) to the other actions on/from the structure.

The three design approaches differ in the way in which they distribute partial factors between actions, the effects of actions, material properties and resistances. EN 1997, *Geotechnical Design*, states that this is in part due to the differing approaches in the way in which allowance is made for uncertainties in modelling the effects of actions and resistances.

Let us consider a very basic example. Figure 7.2 shows a cantilever retaining wall with a horizontal backfill. The active earth pressure may be calculated on the virtual back of the wall from Rankine's theory, assuming that this pressure is horizontal. No surcharge is applied to the backfill. At depth x, the pressure is

$$q(x) = k_a \gamma_{k,\,soil} x$$

and

$$k_a = \tan^2\left(\frac{\pi}{4} - \frac{\varphi'_k}{2}\right)$$

where φ'_k is the characteristic value of the angle of shearing resistance of the backfill, $\gamma_{k,\,soil}$ is the characteristic value of the backfill density and k_a is the coefficient of active earth pressure. The resulting assumed horizontal force F is

$$F = \tfrac{1}{2} k_a \gamma_{k,\,soil} H^2$$

In this formula, F is a function of φ'_k and $\gamma_{k,\,soil}$: $F = F(\gamma_{k,\,soil}, \varphi'_k)$.

The following describes the application of safety factors to the resulting force F, in order to obtain its design value.

In the first case, a γ_F global factor is applied as for other permanent actions, k_a being assessed from the characteristic value of the angle of shearing resistance φ'_k and the characteristic value of ground density $\gamma_{k,\,soil}$: $F_d = \gamma_F F(\gamma_{k,\,soil}, \varphi'_k)$.

In the second case, a γ_φ factor is directly applied to the shearing resistance. Thus the design value of the angle of shearing resistance is

$$\varphi'_d = \tan^{-1}\left(\frac{\tan\varphi'_k}{\gamma_\varphi}\right)$$

and

$$F_d = F(\gamma_{k,\,soil}, \varphi'_d)$$

The numerical comparison is established as follows. In the first case, taking $\gamma_\varphi = 1.25$ and $\varphi'_k = 35°$:

$$k_a = \tan^2\left(\frac{\pi}{4} - \frac{\varphi'_k}{2}\right) = 0.27$$

If F is 'unfavourable' regarding the limit state under consideration, and if the same γ factor is applied as for other permanent actions (1.35), then $1.35k_a = 0.37$.

In the second case, $\varphi'_d = 29.3°$, and thus $k_a = 0.34$.

The two methods are not equivalent, but, in this case, lead to comparable results.

The three design approaches can now be explained.

Design approach 1

In the first approach, partial factors from set B (Table 7.3(B)) are applied to both structural and geotechnical actions. No partial material factors are applied to the geotechnical parameters. No partial factors are applied to the calculation of geotechnical resistance with the exception of pile foundation design where some partial resistance factors are applied in specific cases.

In the second calculation, partial factors from set C (Table 7.3(C)) are applied in the majority of geotechnical cases. In this set, the structural and geotechnical actions are unfactored except for the case of variable unfavourable actions. Partial material factors are applied to the characteristic values of geotechnical parameters. This set follows a material factor approach.

In the case of piles and anchors, particular partial factors are applied for the second calculation: the actions are unfactored and partial factors are applied to resistances, which are derived using unfactored geotechnical properties.

This set follows a resistance factor approach. EN 1997 states that for the calculation of design values giving rise to unfavourable actions on the pile and where the strength of the ground is involved in other ways, such as developing negative skin friction or resisting lateral loading, partial material factors will be applied together with partial resistance factors where appropriate.

Design approach 2

This is a resistance factor approach where partial factors from set B (Table 7.3(B)) are applied to the representative values of structural actions and/or action effects and to the characteristic values of geotechnical actions and/or action effects as well as to the characteristic values of the resistance of the ground. No material factors are applied to characteristic geotechnical parameters.

Design approach 3

This is a combined resistance factor/material factor approach where:

- partial factors from set B (Table 7.3(B)) are applied to the representative values of structural actions and/or action effects
- partial factors from set C (Table 7.3(C)) are applied to the representative values of geotechnical actions, and
- partial material factors are applied to characteristic geotechnical parameters, which are then used in the derivation of the geotechnical actions/action effects as well as the ground resistance.

7.3.5. Synthesis

Considering the various sets of recommended values, it is possible to establish Table 7.4 which proposes a synthesis of the various recommended partial factors for actions. The alternative expression, *expression* (*6.10a*), 'modified' has not been incorporated in this table because the values recommended by the Eurocode are not relevant for this expression.

Table 7.4. *Sets of recommended values for partial factors*

Limit state		$\xi\gamma_{G,j,sup}$	$\gamma_{G,j,inf}$	$\psi\gamma_{Q,k,1}$	$\psi\gamma_{Q,k,i}$, $i > 1$	Comments
EQU – static equilibrium						
	Usual set of partial factors	1.10	0.90	1.50	$1.50\psi_{0,i}$	Loss of equilibrium of the structure or any part of it, considered as a rigid body (*clause 3.3(4)P*): no geotechnical action, no geotechnical property
	Alternative set of partial factors	1.35	1.15	1.50	$1.50\psi_{0,i}$	Recommended where the verification of static equilibrium involves the resistance of structural members
STR – resistance of building structures with no geotechnical actions						
National choice	*Expression (6.10)*	1.35	1.00	1.50	$1.50\psi_{0,i}$	
	Expression (6.10a)	1.35	1.00	$1.50\psi_{0,1}$	$1.50\psi_{0,i}$	The less favourable (of 6.10a and 6.10b)
	Expression (6.10b)	1.15	1.00	1.50	$1.50\psi_{0,i}$	
STR – resistance of building structures with geotechnical actions **GEO – failure or excessive deformation of ground**						
National choice	Approach 1					Applicable to all actions
	Expression (6.10)	1.35	1.00	1.50	$1.50\psi_{0,i}$	
	or					
	expression (6.10a/b)	1.35	1.00	$1.50\psi_{0,1}$	$1.50\psi_{0,i}$	The less favourable (of the bracketed sets above, and expression (6.10) below)
		1.15	1.00	1.50	$1.50\psi_{0,i}$	
	and					
	expression (6.10)	1.00	1.00	1.30	$1.30\psi_{0,i}$	
	Approach 2					Applicable to all actions
	Expression (6.10)	1.35	1.00	1.50	$1.50\psi_{0,i}$	
	or					
	expression (6.10a/b)	1.35	1.00	$1.50\psi_{0,1}$	$1.50\psi_{0,i}$	
		1.15	1.00	1.50	$1.50\psi_{0,i}$	
	Approach 3					
	Expression (6.10)	1.35	1.00	1.50	$1.50\psi_{0,i}$	For non-geotechnical actions
	or					
	expression (6.10a/b)	1.35	1.00	$1.50\psi_{0,1}$	$1.50\psi_{0,i}$	
		1.15	1.00	1.50	$1.50\psi_{0,i}$	
	Expression (6.10)	1.00	1.00	1.30	$1.30\psi_{0,i}$	For geotechnical actions

Clause A1.3.2

7.3.6. Design values of actions in the accidental and seismic design situations

In general, accidental actions are characterized by a very low probability of occurrence during the lifetime of the structure. As far as they are man-made they result from abnormal conditions of use (e.g. explosions, impact from vehicles or ships, or fire) and often are of short duration. Accidental actions may also arise from extremely rare natural or climatic phenomena such as earthquakes, tornadoes or heavy snowfalls.

Due to the character of accidental situations their application belongs to the general safety scenario and depends on the probability of occurrence, the importance of the building and failure consequences. Their use is therefore decided by the regulatory bodies.

The partial factors for actions for the ultimate limit states in the accidental and seismic design situations (*expressions* (*6.11a*) to (*6.12b*)) are normally taken equal to 1.0 but, in general, not only are the safety elements for actions modified for accidental load combinations but so also are the partial factors for resistances.

Seismic actions are singled out because of their different treatment as accidental actions or 'normal' actions according to the 'seismic climate' in various seismic regions, where the return period of seismic events differs significantly (e.g. differences in Central Europe or in the Mediterranean area).

Clause A1.3.2

The combinations of actions are described in Table 7.5 (reproducing *Table A1.3* in *clause A1.3.2* of EN 1990).

A degree of damage is generally acceptable in the event of an accident; and accidents generally occur when structures are in use. Hence, to provide a realistic accidental load combination, accidental loads are applied directly with the frequent and quasi-permanent combination values used for the main and other variable actions, respectively.

The combinations for accidental design situations either involve an explicit design value of accidental action A_d (e.g. impact) or refer to a situation after an accidental event ($A_d = 0$). For fire situations A_d refers to the design value of the indirect thermal action as determined in EN 1991, Part 1-2.

For the main accompanying variable action, the National Annex should be followed as to whether to use the frequent or the quasi-permanent value. This rule is mainly intended for fire design situations: it is easy to understand that, in the case of a fire, crowding of people, for example on staircases, is normally foreseeable and that the use in calculations of the quasi-permanent value of imposed loads on floors may give an unacceptable level of safety.

Seismic design situation are analogous to accidental design situations, but increasingly frequently, for example for the design of railway bridges, two levels of seismic action are taken into account, corresponding to different return periods: one related to ultimate limit

Table 7.5. *Design values of actions for use in accidental and seismic combinations of actions* (Table A1.3 *of EN 1990)*

Design situation	*Permanent actions*		*Leading accidental or seismic action*	*Accompanying variable actions (**)*	
	Unfavourable	*Favourable*		*Main (if any)*	*Others*
Accidental (*) *(Eq. 6.11a/b)*	$G_{kj,sup}$	$G_{kj,inf}$	A_d	ψ_{11} or $\psi_{21} Q_{k1}$	$\psi_{2,i} Q_{k,i}$
Seismic *(Eq. 6.12a/b)*	$G_{kj,sup}$	$G_{kj,inf}$	$\gamma_I A_{Ek}$ or A_{Ed}		$\psi_{2,i} Q_{k,i}$

(*) In the case of accidental design situations, the main variable action may be taken with its frequent or, as in seismic combinations of actions, its quasi-permanent values. The choice will be in the National annex, depending on the accidental action under consideration. See also EN 1991-1-2.

(**) Variable actions are those considered in Table 7.1 (Table A1.1 of EN 1990).

Table 7.6. *Design values of actions for use in the combination of actions (Table A1.4 of EN 1990)*

	Permanent actions G_d		*Variable actions* Q_d	
Combination	*Unfavourable*	*Favourable*	*Leading*	*Others*
Characteristic	$G_{kj,sup}$	$G_{kj,inf}$	$Q_{k,1}$	$\psi_{0,i}Q_{k,i}$
Frequent	$G_{kj,sup}$	$G_{kj,inf}$	$\psi_{1,1}Q_{k,1}$	$\psi_{2,i}Q_{k,i}$
Quasi-permanent	$G_{kj,sup}$	$G_{kj,inf}$	$\psi_{2,1}Q_{k,1}$	$\psi_{2,i}Q_{k,i}$

state verifications and the other related to serviceability limit states concerned with specific comfort criteria for passengers.

7.3.7. Fatigue

Fatigue is not treated in *Annex A1* to EN 1990. All rules relating to fatigue problems are given in the design Eurocodes 2 to 9. For fatigue assessments the safety factors are dependent on whether prewarning mechanisms exist or not, so that damage preceding failure can be detected and preventive measures undertaken.

If sufficient prewarning signals can be detected under normal conditions of use the structure is classified as damage-tolerant, otherwise the structure is classified as not damage-tolerant.

For damage-tolerant structures the partial factors on actions for the fatigue assessment may be taken as $\gamma_F = 1.00$. The structure may be fully used even when the design fatigue life is exceeded, as long as no prewarning signals are observed.

When the structure is not damage-tolerant the safety factors to be applied depend on whether the loading is monitored or not.

In the case of a monitored load, the safety factor to be applied to the fatigue damage should be at least 1.35, and the structure should also be taken out of service when the cumulative fatigue damage reaches its limit when no prewarning signals are apparent. In the case of a non-monitored load the safety factor should be at least 2.00, and the structure should be taken out of service when the calculated service life (e.g. 50 years) is exceeded.

Methods for the determination of damage tolerance and notes on how inspection and control measures influence the safety factor are given in EN 1992 to EN 1999.

7.4. Serviceability limit states

Clause A1.4

7.4.1. Partial factors for actions

For serviceability limit states the partial factors for actions are normally taken as 1.0: this aspect is a main feature of the semi-probabilistic format. In some cases, different values may be defined in the design Eurocodes 1 to 9. In EN 1990 the serviceability combinations of actions are presented in *Table A1.4* (reproduced here as Table 7.6).

The combinations given in Table 7.6 can be written as follows:

- characteristic combination:

$$\sum G_{k,j,\mathrm{sup}} \text{ `+' } \sum G_{k,j,\mathrm{inf}} \text{ `+' } Q_{k,1} \text{ `+' } \sum_{i>1} \psi_{0,i}Q_{k,i}$$

- frequent combination:

$$\sum G_{k,j,\mathrm{sup}} \text{ `+' } \sum G_{k,j,\mathrm{inf}} \text{ `+' } \psi_{1,1}Q_{k,1} \text{ `+' } \sum_{i>1} \psi_{2,i}Q_{k,i}$$

- quasi-permanent combination:

$$\sum G_{k,j,\mathrm{sup}} \text{ `+' } \sum G_{k,j,\mathrm{inf}} \text{ `+' } \psi_{2,1}Q_{k,1} \text{ `+' } \sum_{i>1} \psi_{2,i}Q_{k,i}$$

Table 7.7. Examples of limiting values of vertical deflections

Serviceability requirement	Combination of actions					
	Characteristic combination		Frequent combination		Quasi-permanent combination	
Deflection (see Fig. 7.3):	w_{tot}	w_{max}	w_{max}	α	w_{max}	w_z
Function of the structure						
Irreversible limit states (limit deformations to control cracking of particular elements)						
Elements supporting bearing walls without reinforcement	$\leq L/300$	–	–	–	–	$\leq L/300$
Elements supporting partition walls						
Brittle (not reinforced)	$\leq L/500$	–	–	–	–	$\leq L/300$
Reinforced	$\leq L/300$	–	–	–	–	$\leq L/300$
Removable	$\leq L/300$	–	–	–	–	$\leq L/150$
Ceilings						
Plastered	$\leq L/250$	–	–	–	–	–
False	$\leq L/250$	–	–	–	–	–
Flooring						
Rigid (e.g. ceramic tiles)	$\leq L/500$	–	–	–	–	–
Flexible (e.g. vinyl floor covering)	$\leq L/250$	–	–	–	–	–
Irreversible limit states (limit deflection to ensure drainage of water)						
Roof covering						
Rigid	$\leq L/250$	–	–	–	–	–
Flexible	$\leq L/125$	–	–	–	–	–
Drainage slope of roof element (Fig. 7.3(c))	–	–	–	$\geq 2\%$	–	–
Reversible limit states (Limit deformations for functioning)						
Fit for use for wheeled furniture or equipment	–	–	$\leq L/300$	–	–	–
Fit for use for overhead cranes on tracks	–		$\leq L/600$ ≤ 25 mm	–	–	–
Appearance of the structure						
Reversible limit states (limit deformations for appearance)					$\leq L/300$	

Table 7.8. Examples of limiting values of horizontal deflections

Serviceability requirement	Combination of actions		
	Characteristic combination	Frequent combination	Quasi-permanent combination
Deflection (see Fig. 7.3(b))	Δu_i	Δu_i	Δu_i
Function of the structure			
Irreversible limit states			
No cracking in bearing walls without reinforcement	$\leq \Delta H/300$	–	–
No cracking in partitions	$\leq \Delta H/300$	–	–
Reversible limit states			
Fit for use of cranes on tracks		$\leq \Delta H/400$	–
Appearance of the structure			
Reversible limit states			$\leq \Delta H/250$

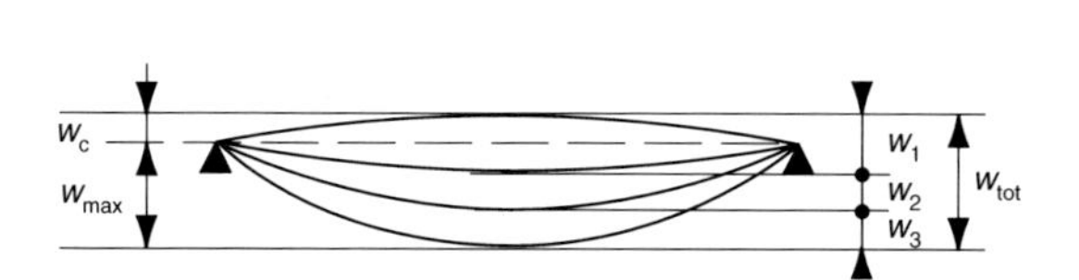

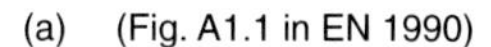

(a) (Fig. A1.1 in EN 1990)

w_c precamber in the unloaded structural member
w_1 initial part of the deflection under permanent loads of the relevant combination of actions according to *expressions* (*6.14a*) to (*6.16b*)
w_2 long-term part of the deflection under permanent loads
w_3 additional part of the deflection due to the variable actions of the relevant combination of actions according to *expressions* (*6.14a*) to (*6.16b*)
w_{tot} total deflection as the sum of w_1, w_2, w_3
w_{max} remaining total deflection taking into account the precamber

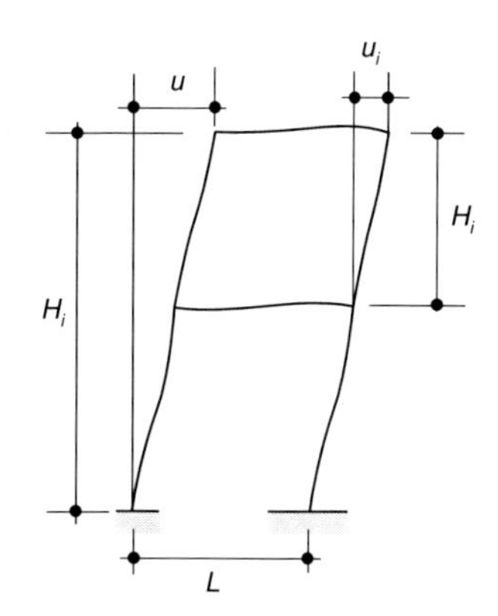

(b) (Fig. A1.2 in EN 1990)

u overall horizontal displacement over the building height H
u_i horizontal displacement over a strorey height H_i

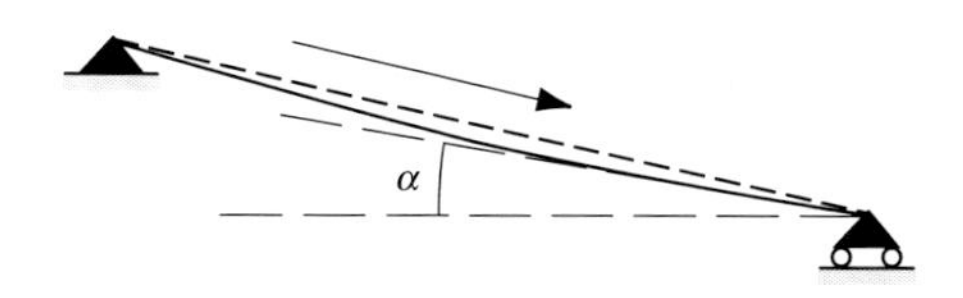

(c)

α drainage slope after deflection

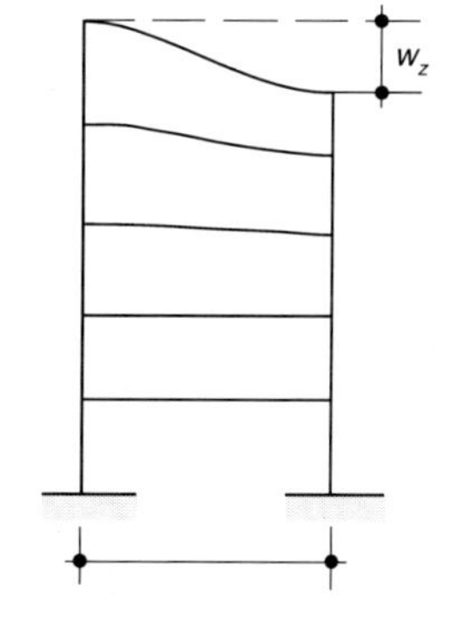

(d)

w_z relative vertical displacement between supports (e.g. due to excessive deformation of a supporting beam or of the foundation)
L span of a beam or twice the length of a cantilever

Fig. 7.3. *Definition of vertical deflections and horizontal displacements*

7.4.2. Serviceability criteria

Serviceability criteria for buildings as for other civil engineering works are not always easy to define because they are dependent upon requirements which are partly subjective: floor stiffness, differential floor levels, storey sway and/or building sway and roof stiffness. Stiffness criteria may be expressed in terms of limits for vertical deflections and for vibrations, or in terms of limits for horizontal displacements (*clause A1.4.2*(*1*)). *Clause A1.4.2(1)*

The Eurocode does not provide numerical serviceability criteria, but indicates that these should be agreed with the client for a particular project and may be defined in the National Annex (*clause A1.4.2*(*2*)). The main reason for this is that serviceability criteria are normally expressed in terms of deflections or displacements and should be defined independently of *Clause A1.4.2(2)* the structural materials. However, it has not yet been possible to harmonize among all materials.

Clause A1.4.2(3)P No further comments are necessary for *clause A1.4.2(3)P*.

7.4.3. Deformations and horizontal displacements

Tables 7.7 and 7.8 give some examples of limiting values of vertical and horizontal deflections with the notation defined in Fig. 7.3. Note that EN 1990 gives definitions corresponding only to Figs 7.3(a) and 7.3(b) (*clause A1.4.3(2)*). *Clause A1.4.3(2)*

Clause A1.4.3(3) No further comments are necessary for *clause A1.4.3(3)*.

When considering the appearance of the structure the quasi-permanent combination (*expression (6.16b)* of EN 1990) should be used (*clause A1.4.3(4)*). *Clause A1.4.3(4)*

Clause A1.4.3(5) No further comment is necessary for *clause A1.4.3(5)*.

The assessment of long-term deformations due to shrinkage, relaxation or creep should be performed using permanent actions and quasi-permanent values of the variable actions (*clause A1.4.3(6)*). *Clause A1.4.3(6)*

Clause A1.4.3(7) No further comment is necessary for *clause A1.4.3(7)*.

7.4.4. Vibrations

Clause A1.4.4 Without giving any numerical limiting value, *clause A1.4.4* of EN 1990 states that the design should take into account:

a) the comfort of the user;
b) the functioning of the structure or its structural members (e.g. cracks in partitions, damage to cladding, sensitivity of building contents to vibrations).

In general, the problem is to define more or less severe limiting values for the lowest frequencies of vibrations of the structure or structural members which should be kept above these limiting values, depending upon the function of the building and the source of the vibration (*clause A1.4.4(2)*). *Clause A1.4.4(2)*

Clause A1.4.4(3) No further comment is necessary for *clause A1.4.4(3)*.

Possible sources of vibration that should be considered include walking (as for footbridges), synchronized movements by people (dance, etc.), machinery, ground-borne vibrations from traffic, and wind action. These and other sources should be specified for each project and agreed with the client (*clause A1.4.4(4)*). *Clause A1.4.4(4)*

7.5. Examples

7.5.1. Static equilibrium

Consider a simply supported beam with a cantilever part (Fig. 7.4). Two actions will be considered, represented by uniformly distributed loads: the self-weight of the beam q_g and a free variable action q_q. For the investigation of a possible loss of equilibrium, the variable action is applied only to the cantilever part.

Clause 6.4.3.1(4)P *Clause 6.4.3.1(4)P* of EN 1990 states:

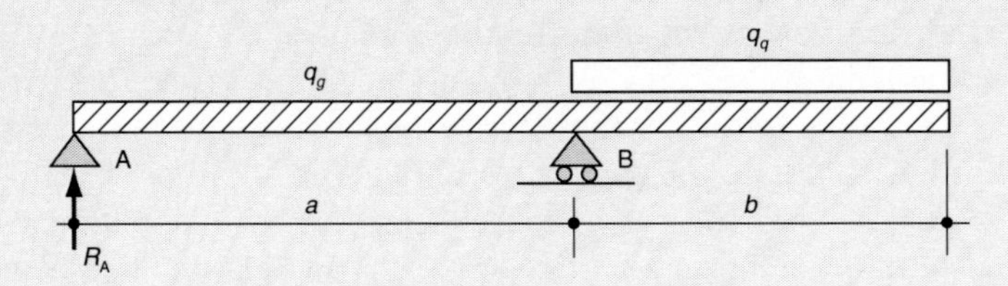

Fig. 7.4. *Simply supported beam with cantilever part*

***Table 7.9.** Example of static equilibrium*

Limit state	Application of actions and partial factors	Reaction at support A and verification of the limit state
EQU	$0.90q_g$ (span a, A–B); $1.50q_q$, $1.10q_g$ (span b)	Values recommended in Table 7.3(A), note 1 $R_{A1} = \frac{1}{2}aq_g(0.35 - 0.75x)$ EQU verified if $x \leq 0.47$
EQU	$1.15q_g$ (span a, A–B); $1.50q_q$, $1.35q_g$ (span b)	Values recommended in Table 7.3(A), note 2 $R_{A2} = \frac{1}{2}aq_g(0.475 - 0.75x)$ EQU verified if $x \leq 0.63$
Anchor placed at A to ensure stability		
STR (for anchor)	$1.35q_g$ (spans a and b); $1.50q_q$ (span b)	Values recommended in Table 7.2(B) for *expression (6.10)* (the factor 1.35 for permanent actions is the most unfavourable) $R_{A3} = \frac{1}{2}aq_g(0.675 - 0.75x)$ The reaction is negative if $x > 0.90$
STR (for anchor)	$1.15q_g$ (spans a and b); $1.5q_q$ (span b)	Values recommended in Table 7.2(B) for *expression (6.10a)* (the most unfavourable) $R_{A4} = \frac{1}{2}aq_g(0.575 - 0.75x)$ The reaction is negative if $x > 0.77$

where the results of a verification may be very sensitive to variations of the magnitude of a permanent action from place to place in the structure, the unfavourable and the favourable parts of this action shall be considered as individual actions.

This applies in particular to the verification of static equilibrium and analogous limit states.

Expressed generally the vertical reaction at support A is

$$R_A = \tfrac{1}{2}aq_g(\gamma_{G,1} - \beta^2\gamma_{G,2} - \beta^2 x\gamma_Q)$$

with $\beta = b/a$ and $x = q_q/q_g$, and the static equilibrium is considered verified if $R_A \geq 0$. In the following, we assume $\beta^2 = 0.5$. Where static equilibrium is not ensured, the example assumes that an anchor is placed at A: this anchor should be designed for an appropriate resistance (STR limit state) and an appropriate stability in the ground (GEO limit state). In the following only the STR limit state is considered. The various partial factors are applied as shown in Table 7.9.

The functions representing the magnitude of R_A are shown in Fig. 7.5.

The conclusions that can be drawn from this example are:

(1) The two sets of partial factors given in notes 1 and 2 in Table 7.3(A) are not, of course,

equivalent. The second set is less pessimistic than the first one for the verification of static equilibrium, but the difference appears acceptable.

(2) If static equilibrium is ensured by an anchor at A, this anchor should normally be designed considering an STR limit state for the anchor itself and probably a GEO limit state for the anchor–ground interaction. For the STR limit state the combinations of actions given in Table 7.3(B) should normally be used (*expression* (*6.10*) or *expressions* (*6.10a*) and (*6.10b*)); however, Fig. 7.5 shows that there is a range of values of x for which the anchor cannot be designed.

(3) The design rules have to be adjusted for particular projects, but, if the verification of static equilibrium involves the resistance of stability devices, it is recommended that the alternative set of partial factors given in Table 7.3(A), note 2, is used.

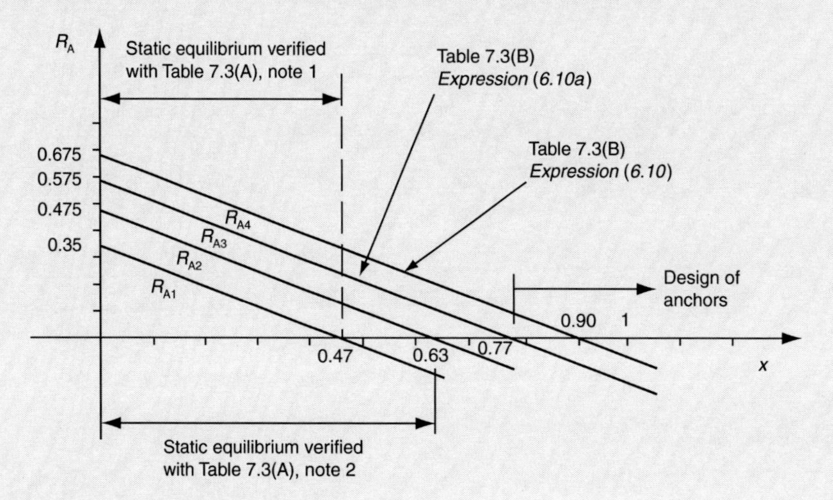

Fig. 7.5. *Variation of* R_A *as a function of* x

7.5.2. Example of a spread foundation

Let us now consider the simple spread foundation represented in Fig. 7.6. The concrete footing is assumed rigid, so that the ground response can be considered as linear.

The forces and moments caused by permanent and variable actions at the centre O are F_v (the vertical force), F_h (the horizontal force) and M (the moment).

The assessment of the width B of the footing results from the consideration of two possible GEO limit states corresponding respectively to the capacity of the ground vertical bearing resistance and to a failure by sliding. For the sake of simplicity, only the limit state of vertical bearing capacity will be considered.

Assuming that $M \leq \frac{1}{6}BF_v$ the calculation of pressure under the footing gives

$$q_{sup} = \frac{F_v}{B} + 6\frac{M}{B^2}$$

$$q_{inf} = \frac{F_v}{B} - 6\frac{M}{B^2}$$

In order to compare the ground pressure to the ground resistance, a 'reference' pressure, q_{ref}, is introduced which will be compared with the design value q_d:

$$q_{ref} = \frac{3q_{sup} + q_{inf}}{4} = \frac{F_v}{B} + 3\frac{M}{B^2}$$

The width of the footing can be obtained from the formula

$$B = \frac{F_{d,v}}{2q_d} + \sqrt{\left(\frac{F_{d,v}}{2q_d}\right)^2 + \frac{3M_d}{q_d}}$$

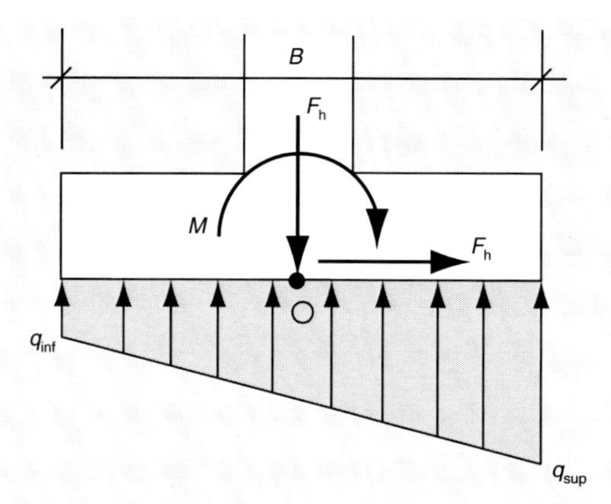

Fig. 7.6. *Example of a spread foundation*

Table 7.10. *Characteristic values of actions transmitted to the footing*

Characteristic value	Permanent action (kN)	Variable action (kN)
$F_{k,v}$	380	125
M_k	70	20

Table 7.11. *Design values of actions transmitted to the footing*[a]

Set	$F_{d,v}$	M_d
B	*Equation (6.10)* 1.35 × 380 + 1.50 × 125 = 700.5	*Equation (6.10)* 1.35 × 70 + 1.50 × 20 = 124.5
	Equations (6.10a) and *(6.10b)* 1.35 × 380 + 1.05 × 125 = **644.25** or 1.15 × 380 + 1.50 × 125 = 624.5	*Equations (6.10a)* and *(6.10b)* 1.35 × 70 + 1.05 × 20 = **115.5** or 1.15 × 70 + 1.50 × 20 = 110.5
C	1.00 × 380 + 1.30 × 125 = 542.5	1.00 × 70 + 1.30 × 20 = 96.0

[a] Less favourable values are in bold

where $F_{d,v}$ and M_d are the design values of the vertical force and of the moment, respectively. The characteristic (subscript k) values of actions transmitted to the inner face of the footing are given in Table 7.10.

The design values arising from the three approaches, using the set of γ factors, are given in Table 7.11.

7.5.3. STR limit states in a continuous beam

For the continuous beam shown in Fig. 7.7 some elementary load cases will be considered, with a permanent action (self-weight, G) and only one variable action (Q). The characteristic values are denoted G_k and Q_k.

Figure 7.8 shows the line of influence of the bending moment at support 1 (the positive part of the line of influence is above the beam axis). The minimum algebraic negative bending moment is obtained when the variable action is applied to spans corresponding to negative parts of the line of influence. The fundamental combination, based on *expression (6.10)*, is

$$\gamma_{G,\sup} G_k + \gamma_Q Q_k$$

or, with the recommended values for partial factors,

$$1.35G_k + 1.50Q_k$$

The maximum algebraic negative bending moment at support 1 is obtained when the variable action is applied to span 2–3, corresponding to the positive part of the line of influence. The fundamental combination, based on *expression (6.10)*, is

$$\gamma_{G,\mathrm{inf}} G_k + \gamma_Q Q_k$$

or, with the recommended values for partial factors,

$$1.00G_k + 1.50Q_k$$

Figure 7.9 shows the line of influence of the bending moment at mid-span of the second span (1–2). The maximum positive bending moment is obtained when the variable action is applied to the parts of the beam corresponding to the positive parts of the line of influence. The fundamental combination, based on *expression (6.10)*, is

$$\gamma_{G,\mathrm{sup}} G_k + \gamma_Q Q_k$$

or, with the recommended values for partial factors,

$$1.35G_k + 1.50Q_k$$

The minimum positive bending moment at mid-span of the second span (1–2) is obtained when the variable action is applied to spans 0–1 and 2–3, corresponding to the negative parts of the line of influence. The fundamental combination, based on *expression (6.10)*, is

$$\gamma_{G,\mathrm{inf}} G_k + \gamma_Q Q_k$$

or, with the recommended values for partial factors,

$$1.00G_k + 1.50Q_k$$

Figure 7.10 shows the line of influence of the shear force in a cross-section of span 1–2. The maximum positive shear force is obtained when the variable action is applied to the parts of the beam corresponding to the positive parts of the line of influence. However, in this case the effect of the permanent action depends on the location of the cross-section,

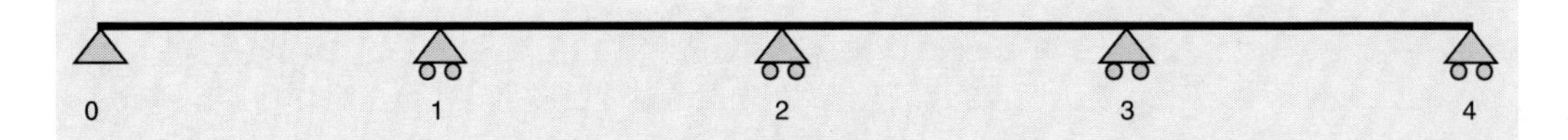

Fig. 7.7. Continuous beam

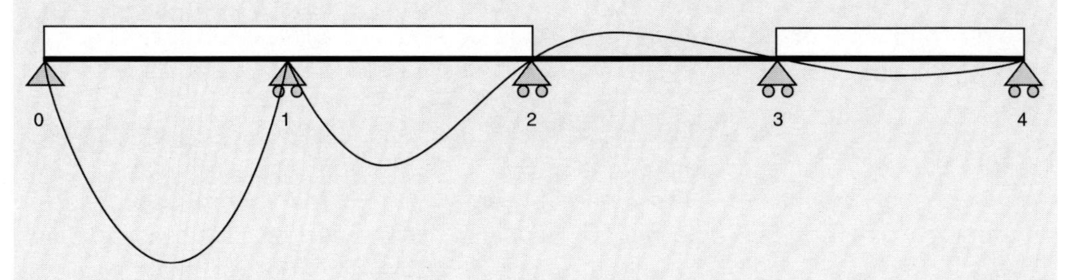

Fig. 7.8. Application of the variable action to the negative parts of the line of influence of the bending moment at support 1

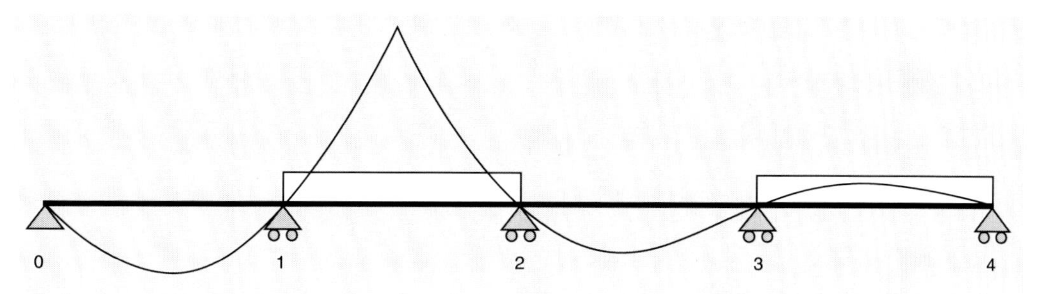

Fig. 7.9. *Application of the variable action to the positive parts of the line of influence of the bending moment at mid-span of span 1–2*

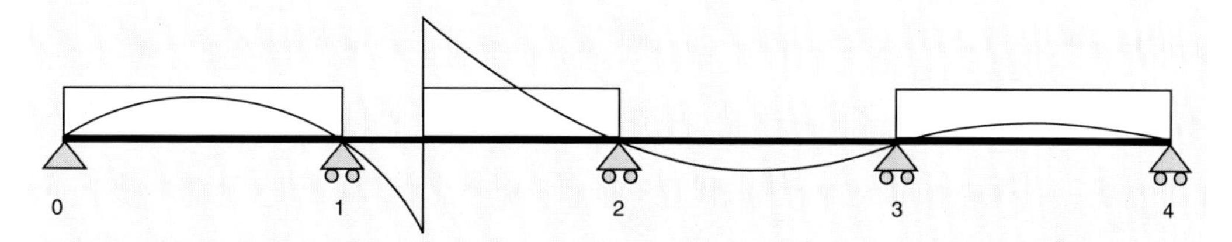

Fig. 7.10. *Application of the variable action to the positive parts of the line of influence of the shear force in span 1–2*

the geometry and the mechanical properties of the beam. For this reason, except for obvious cases, the fundamental combination for the design, based on *expression (6.10)*, is the more unfavourable of the following two expressions:

$$\gamma_{G,\,\text{sup}} G_k + \gamma_{Q,} Q_k \qquad \text{or} \qquad \gamma_{G,\,\text{inf}} G_k + \gamma_Q Q_k$$

or, with the recommended values for partial factors,

$$1.35G_k + 1.50Q_k \qquad \text{or} \qquad 1.00G_k + 1.50Q_k$$

respectively.

Analogous considerations may be developed for the minimum algebraic shear force for the same cross-section.

In conclusion, these examples show that, even for simple structures, the problem of combinations of actions cannot always be solved easily. For a typical building with a few floors, when considering two variable actions (e.g. imposed loads and wind forces) acting together with permanent actions, the number of load cases can be very large, and if simplified methods are not used it is necessary to use a good software.

7.5.4. STR limit states in a framed structure

For the frame shown in Fig. 7.11 some load cases will be considered to investigate the overall stability for the structure. We will assume that the building is to be used as an office.

The examples of load cases are based on the consideration of only two variable actions, as permitted by *clause A1.2.1(1)*, note 1: imposed loads and wind actions.

Clause A1.2.1(1)

Notation

Characteristic loads/m:

G_{kr}, self-weight for the roof
G_{kf}, self-weight for floors
Q_{kr}, imposed load for the roof
Q_{kf}, imposed floor loads

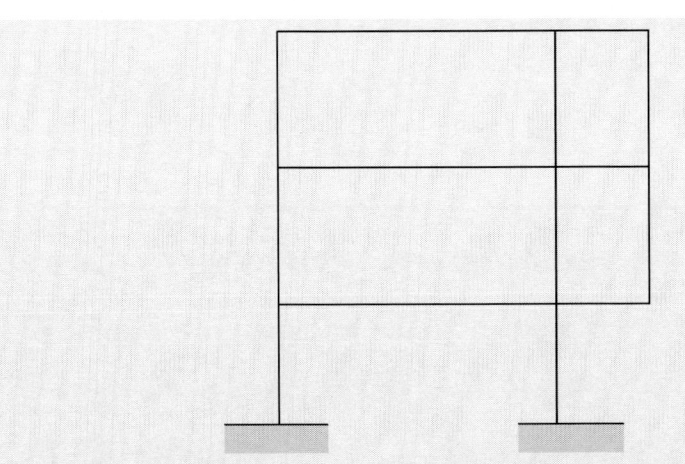

Fig. 7.11. Frame configuration

Characteristic load/frame:

W_k, wind loads – roof or floor

Load cases

The fundamental combination of actions that should be used is, for example, *expression (6.10)* from *clause 6.4.3.2*:

Clause 6.4.3.2

$$\sum_{j \geq 1} \gamma_{G,j} G_{k,j} \text{ '+' } \gamma_P P \text{ '+' } \gamma_{Q,1} Q_{k,1} \text{ '+' } \sum_{i>1} \gamma_{Q,i} \psi_{0,i} Q_{k,i} \qquad (6.10)$$

As the stability of the structure will be sensitive to a possible variation of self-weights, it will be necessary to allow for this in accordance with *Table A1.25(B)* of EN 1990. The values of partial factors are the values recommended in *Annex A1* of EN 1990. Thus,

$\gamma_{G,\text{inf}} = 1.0$
$\gamma_{G,\text{sup}} = 1.35$
$\gamma_Q = 1.5$
$\psi_0 = 0.7$ for imposed loads (offices) (from *Table A1.1*)
$\psi_0 = 0.6$ for wind action for buildings (from *Table A1.1*)

Depending on the cross-section of structural elements under consideration, the effects of self-weight are multiplied globally by 1.00 or 1.35 (see *Table A1.2(B)*, note 3, in EN 1990). The variable action is a free action as is applied on the unfavourable parts of the line of influence corresponding to the effect under consideration (see Section 6.4.3 of this guide).

Load case 1

Treat the wind action as the dominant action (Fig. 7.12).

Load case 2

Treat the imposed load on the roof as the dominant load (Fig. 7.13).

Load case 3

Treat the imposed load on the floors as the dominant load (Fig. 7.14).

Load case 4

Consider the case without wind loading, treating the imposed floor loads as the primary load (Fig. 7.15).

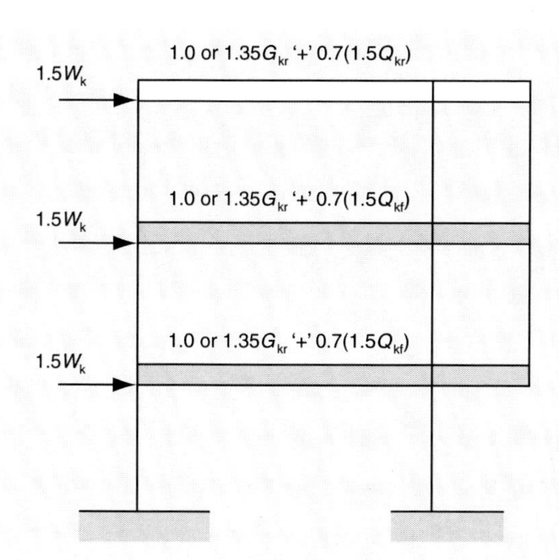

Fig. 7.12. *Load case 1*

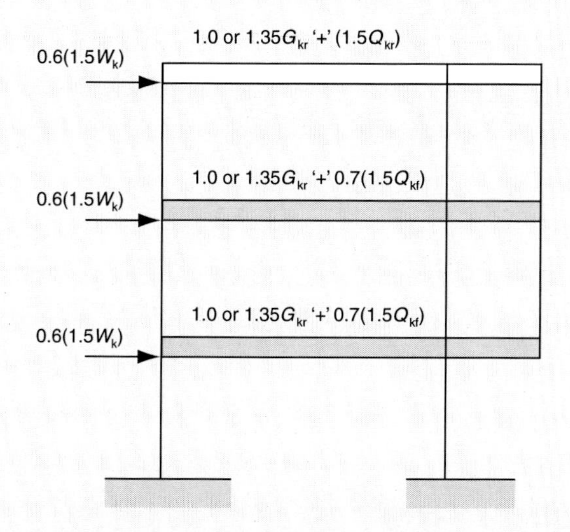

Fig. 7.13. *Load case 2*

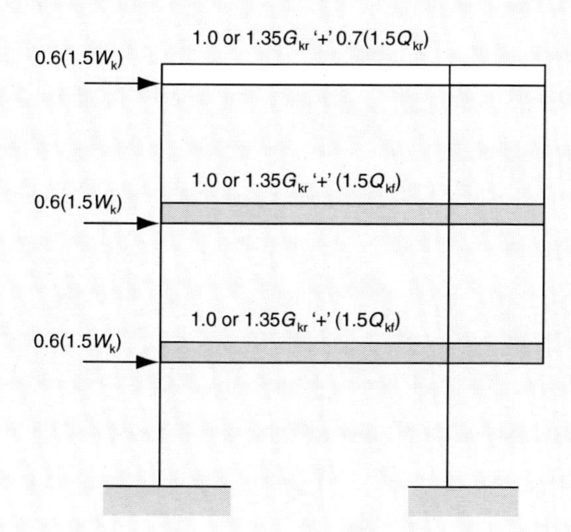

Fig. 7.14. *Load case 3*

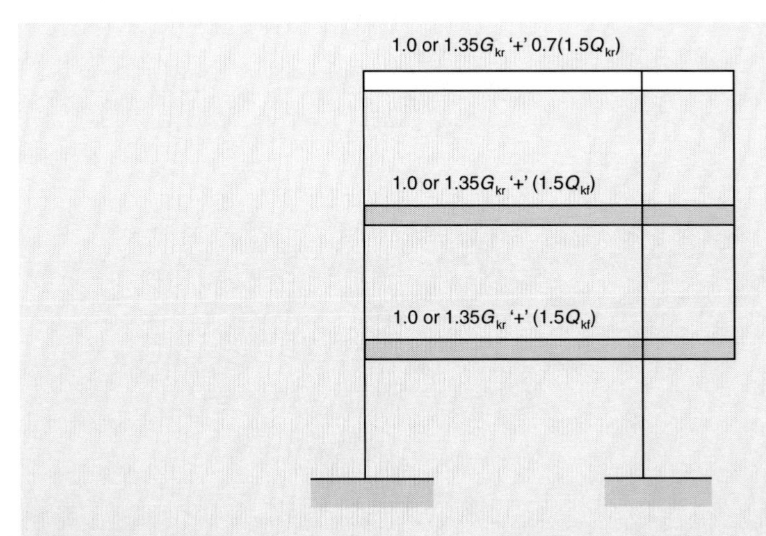

Fig. 7.15. Load case 4

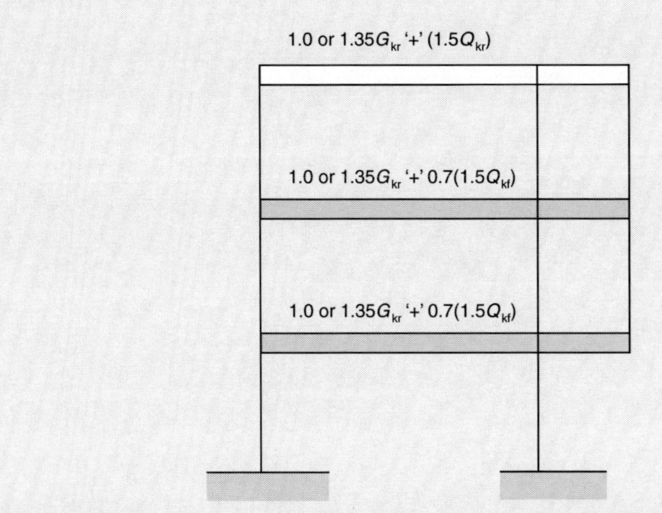

Fig. 7.16. Load case 5

Load case 5
Consider the case without wind loading, treating the imposed roof load as the primary load (Fig. 7.16).

Note: when the wind loading is reversed, another set of arrangements will need to be considered.

Appendix: vibration considerations for serviceability limit states

Vibration criteria can apply to three categories of 'receiver' (see ISO 10137):[16]

(1) human occupants – including those of adjacent property
(2) building contents – including those of adjacent property
(3) building structure – including that of adjacent property.

From the reaction of people to vibrations, vibration criteria can be further classified as those pertaining to:

(1) sensitive occupation, such as hospital operating rooms
(2) regular occupation, such as offices and residential areas
(3) active occupation, such as assembly areas or places of heavy industrial work.

Vibration criteria arising from human occupation are given in terms of acceptance criteria according to ISO 2631.[17–19] These criteria include the relevant acceleration–frequency line for a selected exposure time and direction of vibration.

The vibration criteria selected for the contents of buildings should allow the satisfactory functioning of sensitive instruments or manufacturing processes. Because of the great variety of such equipment and processes it is not possible to present any fixed levels of vibration amplitude that will ensure satisfactory operation. Limits for the movements of machines are usually specified by considering the maximum deflection and frequency.

The vibration criteria selected for building structures should avoid the development of minor damage to structural and non-structural elements. The permissible levels of vibration effects depend on the type of structure, and its age, importance and other aspects. The corresponding limits not covered by acceleration–frequency lines or deflection–frequency lines may be expressed in terms of maximum stress, maximum stress range or maximum deformation. These limits should be specified in the design specifications.

For example, when conditions for human comfort need to be specified, they should be given in terms of an acceleration criteria according to ISO 2631.[17] The acceptance criteria should include a relevant acceleration–frequency line for the selected exposure time and direction of vibration. For continuous and shock-induced vibrations in buildings (traffic and pile driving), see ISO 2631, Part 2,[18] for the range from 1 to 80 Hz, and for vibration caused by wind see ISO 2631, Part 3,[19] for the range from 0.01 to 1 Hz.

Further reading

British Standards Institution (1985) *Structural Use of Concrete. Part 1: Code of Practice for Design and Construction*. BSI, Milton Keynes, BS 8110.

British Standards Institution (1990) *Structural Use of Steel Work in Building. Part 1: Code of Practice for Design in Simple and Continuous Construction: Hot Rolled Sections*. BSI, Milton Keynes, BS 5950.

British Standards Institution (1996) *Loading for Buildings*. BSI, Milton Keynes, BS 6399: Part 1.

Building Research Establishment (1997) *Response of Structures Subject to Dynamic Crowd Loads. Digest 426*. BRE Watford.

Calgaro, J. A. (1996) *Introduction aux Eurocodes – Sécurité des Constructions et Bases de la Théorie de la Fiabilité*. Presses de l'Ecole Nationale des Ponts et Chaussées, Paris.

Euro-International Concrete Committee (1985) *Basic Notes on Model Uncertainties – State-of-the-art Report. CEB Bulletin 170*. FIB, Lausanne.

Euro-International Concrete Committee (1991) *Reliability of Concrete Structures – Final Report of Permanent Commission I. CEB Bulletin 202*. FIB, Lausanne.

European Committee for Standardization (1994) *Basis of Design*. CEN, Brussels, ENV 1991-1.

European Committee for Standardization (2001) *Eurocode: Basis of Structural Design*. CEN, Brussels, EN 1990

Finnish Ministry of the Environment, Housing and Building Department (2000) *Probabilistic Calibration of Partial Safety Factors (Eurocode and Finnish Proposal)*. Helsinki.

Holický, M. and Marková, J. (2000) Verification of load factors for concrete components by reliability and optimization analysis: background documents for implementing Eurocodes. *Progress in Structural Engineering and Materials* **2**, No. 4, 502–507.

International Organization for Standardization (1985) *Evaluation of Human Exposure to Whole-body Vibration, Part 1: General Requirements*. ISO, Geneva, ISO 2631:1.

International Organization for Standardization (1985) *Evaluation of Human Exposure to Whole-body Vibration, Part 3: Evaluation of Exposure to Whole-body z-axis Vertical Vibration in the Frequency Range 0.1 to 0.63 Hz*. ISO Geneva, ISO 2631:3.

International Organization for Standardization (1989) *Evaluation of Human Exposure to Whole-body Vibration, Part 2: Continuous and Shock-induced Vibrations in Buildings (1–80 Hz)*. ISO Geneva, ISO 2631:2.

International Organization for Standardization (1992) *Bases for Design of Structures – Serviceability of Structures against Vibration*. ISO, Geneva, ISO 10137.

International Organization for Standardization (1997) *General Principles on Reliability for Structures*. ISO, Zurich, ISO 2394.

Joint Committee on Structural Safety (2001) *Probabilistic Model Codes* (working document). JCSS, Zurich.

Mathieu, H. (1979) *Manuel Sécurité des Structures. CEB Bulletins 127* and *128*. FIB, Lausanne.

SAKO and Joint Committee of NKB and INSTA-B (1999) *Basis of Design of Structures. Proposal for Modification of Partial Safety Factors in Eurocodes*. SAKO, Helsinki.

Sorensen, J. D., Hansen, S. O. and Nielsen, T. A. (2001) Partial safety factors and target reliability level in Danish codes. *Proceedings of Safety, Risk, and Reliablity*, pp. 179–184. IABSE, Malta.

Tursktra, C. J. (1970) *Application of Bayesian Decision Theory. Study No. 3: Structural Reliability and Codified Design*. Solid Mechanics Division, University of Waterloo, Ontario.

Vrouwenfelder, T. (2001) JCSS Probabilistic model code. *Proceedings of Safety, Risk, and Reliability*, pp. 65–70. IABSE, Malta.

CHAPTER 8

Management of structural reliability for construction works

This chapter is concerned with the reliability management aspects of EN 1990, *Eurocode: Basis of Structural Design*. The material described in this chapter is covered by *Annex B*, in the following clauses:

- Scope and field of application *Clause B1*
- Symbols *Clause B2*
- Reliability differentiation *Clause B3*
- Design supervision differentiation *Clause B4*
- Inspection during execution *Clause B5*
- Partial factors for resistance properties *Clause B6*

8.1. Scope and field of application

Annex B provides additional guidance to *clause 2.2* (reliability management), which is one of the principal requirements in EN 1990. This chapter also applies to appropriate clauses in EN 1991 to EN 1999 (*clause B1*(*1*)), where reliability differentiation rules are specified for a few particular aspects.

Clause 2.2

Clause B1(1)

Clause B1(*2*) explains the layout and style of *Annex B* and its links to *clause 2.2* of EN 1990 and requires no comment in this guide.

Clause B1(2)
Clause 2.2

Annex B is an informative annex and is formulated in a such a way so as to provide a framework to allow different reliability levels, to be used if desired; it provides guidance on the methods which can be adopted at the national level to use these concepts (*clause B1*(*3*)).

Clause B1(3)

With reference to *clauses B1*(*2*) and *B1*(*3*) the main tools selected in *Annex B* for the management of structural reliability of construction works are:

Clause B1(2)
Clause B1(3)

- differentiation by values of β factors
- alteration of partial factors
- design supervision differentiation
- measures aimed to reduce errors in design and execution of the structure, and gross human errors
- adequate inspection and maintenance according to procedures specified in the project documentation.

Background
The purpose of reliability differentiation is the socio-economic optimization of the resources to be used to build construction works, taking into account all the expected consequences of failure and the cost of construction.

8.2. Symbols

The subscript 'FI' is used to indicate a factor applicable for reliability differentiation; 'F' indicates a partial factor for an action, and 'I' an importance factor, similar to the factor introduced in EN 1998. A detailed explanation of the reliability index β is given in *Annex C* of EN 1990 and Chapter 9 of this guide (*clause B2*).

Clause B2

8.3. Reliability differentiation

8.3.1. Consequence clauses

For the purpose of reliability differentiation, *Annex B* of EN 1990 establishes consequences classes (CC) (*clause B2(1)*). *Annex B* defines quantitatively three consequences of failure or malfunction of a structure which are defined as follows:

Clause B2(1)

- Consequences class CC3: high consequence for loss of human life, or economic, social or environmental consequences very great
- Consequences class CC2: medium consequence for loss of human life, economic, social or environmental consequences considerable
- Consequences class CC1: low consequences for loss of human life, and economic, social or environmental consequences small or negligible.

Examples for CC3, CC2 and CC1 are given in Table 8.1.

Table 8.1. *Consequence class matrix*

	Consequences of failure[a]		
Frequency of use	Low[b]	Medium[c]	High[d]
Low	CC1	CC2	CC3
Medium	CC2	CC2	CC3
High	Not applicable	CC3	CC3

[a] Consequences of failure include the consideration of:

- loss of human life (sometimes called the safety of people)
- environment and social consequences (e.g. when a failure causes an environmental catastrophe)
- economic consequences (e.g. the cost of replacement of a building and its contents and the cost of the loss of its use)
- the value of the loss of human life

[b] Includes agricultural buildings where people do not normally enter, sheds and greenhouses
[c] Includes hotels, schools, residential bridges and access bridges (e.g. to farms)
[d] Includes grandstands, theatres, significant high-rise buildings and bridges

Background
The CIB[15] defines 'risk' and 'acceptable risk' as follows.

Risk
Risk is a measure of the danger that undesired events represent for humans, the environment or economic values. Risk is expressed in the probability and consequences of the undesired events. Risk is often estimated by the mathematical expectation of the consequences of an undesired event: it is then the product 'probability × consequences'.

Acceptable risk
Acceptable risk is a level of risk which is generally not seriously perceived by an individual or society, and which may be considered as a reference point in criteria of risk. Cultural, social, psychological, economic and other aspects will influence societal risk perception.

The concept of 'acceptable' risk of human death resulting from structural failure raises very sensitive questions, concerning public perception.[15] Fatalities due to accidents, taken from recent figures[16] (Table 8.2) are considered to reflect the public perception of acceptability of fatalities for different types of accident and exposure to serious hazards.

As can be seen from Table 8.2 the public demands a very high level of reliability in buildings. Partial factor design is based on the consideration of limit states which are, in most common cases, classified into ultimate and serviceability limit states, idealizing undesirable phenomena. The design is such that their probability of occurrence in 50 years is less than an 'acceptable' value. Figure 8.1 shows the usual ranges of values for the ultimate and serviceability limit states associated with a probability of failure over a 50 year period.

Table 8.2. *'Accepted' risks of death due to exposure to various hazards*

Hazard	Risk ($\times 10^{-6}$ p.a.)[a]	Hazard	Risk ($\times 10^{-6}$ p.a.)[a]
Building hazards		Occupations (UK)	
Structural failure (UK)	0.14	Chemical and allied industries	85
Building fires (Australia)	4	Ship building and marine engineering	105
		Agriculture	110
		Construction industries	150
		Railways	180
		Coal mining	210
		Quarrying	295
		Mining (non-coal)	750
		Offshore oil and gas (1967–76)	1 650
		Deep sea fishing (1959–78)	2 800
Natural hazards (USA)		Sports (USA)	
Hurricanes (1901–72)	0.4	Cave exploration (1970–78)	45
Tornadoes (1953–71)	0.4	Glider flying (1970–78)	400
Lightning (1969)	0.5	Scuba diving (1970–78)	420
Earthquakes (California)	2	Hang gliding (1977–79)	1 500
		Parachuting (1978)	1 900
General accidents (USA 1969)		All causes (UK, 1977)	
		Whole population	12 000
Poisoning	20	Woman aged 30 years	600
Drowning	30	Man aged 30 years	1 000
Fires and burns	40	Woman aged 60 years	10 000
Falls	90	Man aged 60 years	20 000
Road accidents	300		

[a] Risk expressed as the probability of death for typical exposed person per calendar year

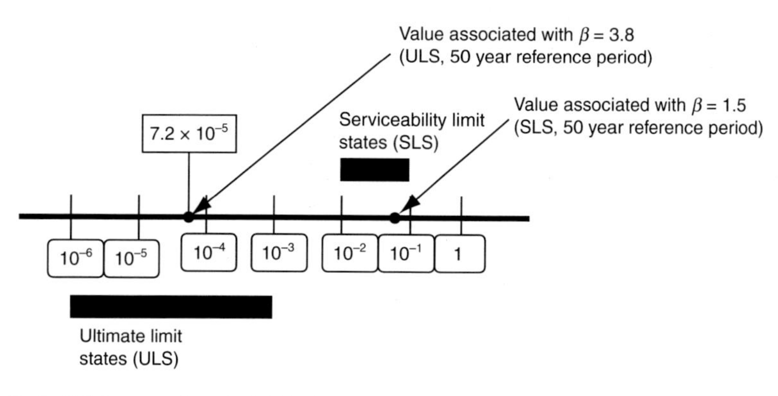

Fig. 8.1. *Probabilities associated with limit states*

EN 1990, as all other Eurocodes, uses the concept of partial factor design and, embodied in the values of the partial factors, there are implicit 'acceptable' or 'accepted' risk levels. However, 'risk' and 'risk analysis' are not defined in EN 1990. This is because the word 'risk' has a different meaning to an engineer, an insurance specialist, or an economist, etc. In the same way, the term 'risk analysis' has no meaning if the procedure to carry out an analysis is not accurately defined. For example, there is no universal methodology for performing a risk analysis for a heavy vehicle or ship impacting a bridge pier.

Clause B3.1(2)

Thus, the criterion for classification in EN 1990 is the importance in terms of consequences of failure of the structure or structural members (*clause B3.1(2)*). It is widely accepted that the reliability level of a structure should be higher the greater the consequences of failure. The selection of the consequence class and different levels of reliability requires consideration of a number of appropriate aspects, including:

- frequency of use
- the cause and/or mode of attaining a limit state
- the possible consequences of failure in terms of risk to life, injury and potential economic losses
- political requirements and public aversion to failure
- the expense and procedures necessary to reduce the risk of failure.

Table 8.1, a matrix indicating appropriate consequence classes, complements *Table B1* of EN 1990, and will aid the selection of a consequence class for a construction works, structural member or component.

Clause B3.1(3)

Within a particular construction works, different structural members or components may have to be designated with the same, higher or lower consequences of failure (*clause B3.1(3)*). As an example, consider a medium-sized hotel building, whose public rooms are used for conferences, meetings and social events (e.g. weddings). It could be that the public rooms have large spans, where the implications of their collapse (i.e. consequences of failure) would be high. In this case, the client's representative (i.e. the designer) or checking authority may designate the elements supporting the public rooms CC3, and the structural elements supporting hotel bedrooms as CC2. The hotel building as a whole would usually be classed CC2 or CC3, depending on its consequences of failure.

8.3.2. Differentiation by β values

Clause B3.2(1)
Clause B3.2(2)

In *Annex B* of EN 1990, three reliability classes (RC), which are defined by the β reliability index concept (*clause B3.2(1)*), are associated with the three consequences classes (*clause B3.2(2)*). Consequences classes CC1, CC2 and CC3 are associated with reliability classes RC1, RC2 and RC3, respectively.

Clause C5(1)

The reliability index β is a function of the probability of failure, and is explained in Chapter 9 of this guide. The relationship between the probability of failure P_f and β is given in Table 8.3 (see *clause C5(1)* and Fig. 8.1).

Table 8.3. *Relationship between* P_f *and* β

P_f	β
10^{-1}	1.28
10^{-2}	2.32
10^{-3}	3.09
10^{-4}	3.72
10^{-5}	4.27
10^{-6}	4.75
10^{-7}	5.20

Table 8.4. *Consequences and reliability classes, and values for the reliability index* β

		Values for β					
		Ultimate limit states		Fatigue		Serviceability	
Consequences class	Reliability class	1 year reference period[a]	50 year reference period[a]	1 year reference period	50 year reference period	1 year reference period	50 year reference period
CC3	RC3	5.2	4.3				
CC2	RC2	4.7	3.8		1.5–3.8	2.9	1.5
CC1	RC1	4.2	3.3				
(1)	(2)	(3)	(4)	(5)	(6)	(7)	(8)

[a] The values for β are recommended minimum values in columns 3 and 4

Table 8.4 establishes a link between consequences classes, reliability classes and values for the reliability index β. It includes information from *Table B2* of EN 1990, which is concerned with ultimate limit states only. Table 8.4 is extended to include fatigue and serviceability limit states.

Clause B3.2(3)

According to the note to *Table B2* of EN 1990 (*clause B3.2(3)*) a design using EN 1990 with the recommended values of partial factors given in *Annex A1* (application for buildings) and the other design Eurocodes with the recommended material resistance factors is generally considered to lead to a structure with a β value greater than 3.8 for a 50 year reference period and corresponding to RC2 and CC2.

EN 1990 recognizes that risks associated with structural failure, related to the present time, are reasonable, and its recommendations are based on this recognition, thus associating the medium-class consequences (i.e. CC2) with a minimum probability of failure of 7.2×10^{-5} in 50 years, corresponding to $\beta = 3.8$ (see Fig. 8.1).

The probability of failure and its corresponding β index are only notional values that do not necessarily represent actual failure rates (which depend mainly on human errors). They are used as operational values for code calibration purposes and comparison of reliability levels of structures.

Many investigations have been performed (e.g. see *CEB Bulletin* 202)[17] to determine β factors, corresponding to ultimate limit states for structures or structural elements designed using various codes and realistic data concerning actions and resistances. These investigations consistently show a significant scatter of β values. A comparable scatter would probably be found when using the Eurocode suite. This is due to the fact that all codified models (e.g. models for actions, resistances and structural analysis), including numerical values, are unavoidably approximate in order to simplify the design in the most common cases and be more or less appropriate for each particular case. Figure 8.2 is a histogram of the relative frequency of β values for an assumed large number of calculations.

The difference between bridges and buildings is due to the higher levels of design supervision, the control of material quality and inspection during execution that is generally given to the design and execution of bridges. This is an example of reliability differentiation by the requirements for quality levels.

A certain proportion of construction works may have a β value less than 3.8 in 50 years. Many engineers consider that this value should be a target value for the calibration of the whole system of actions–resistances–partial factors. Considering the case of buildings, the average value of the β factor (see Fig. 8.2) could be lowered but with a corresponding reduction in the scatter, so that the proportion of construction works below $\beta = 3.8$ would remain approximately the same. Such a lowering of the average β index value can be obtained by using *expressions* (*6.10a*) and (*6.10b*) of EN 1990 for combinations of actions applicable to ultimate limit states of resistance instead of the classical expression (*expression* (*6.10*)) of EN 1990. See also Chapters 6 and 7 of this guide.

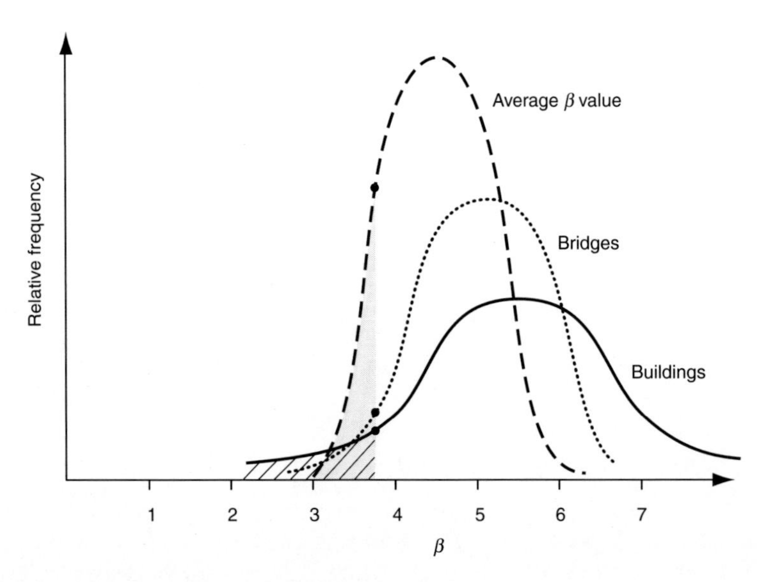

Fig. 8.2. *Frequency of β values for construction works*

The number of verification rules for serviceability limit states in the Eurocodes is limited, and it has been assumed that the reliability levels for the ultimate limit states will not be reduced, thus indirectly covering some of the serviceability limit state verifications. Use of *expressions* (*6.10a*) and (*6.10b*), however, will reduce safety levels and therefore make it necessary to consider the verification for the serviceability limit states more thoroughly than when *expression* (*6.10*) is used.

The normal reliability level can be maintained by the adoption of higher quality levels in design and execution. Other means have been used in the Eurocodes. For example, the adjusting factors α and β of traffic loads given in EN 1991-2 are normally intended to keep reliability levels constant under different traffic conditions, but they might also be used to define reliability classes (to be applied, for example, to existing bridges).

8.3.3. Differentiation by measures relating to partial factors

Clause B3.3(1)

A reliability differentiation can be envisaged by distinguishing classes of γ_F factors to be used in the fundamental combinations of actions for persistent design situations. *Clause B3.3*(*1*) suggests the use of a multiplication factor K_{FI} applicable to γ factors of unfavourable actions: equal to 1.0 for the medium reliability class (RC2), it can be taken equal to 0.9 for reliability class RC1 and 1.1 for reliability class RC3. Attention is drawn to the fact that a simultaneous use of *expression* (*6.10b*) with $\xi = 0.85$ and $K_{FI} = 0.9$ would lead to a global $\gamma = 1$ applicable for unfavourable permanent actions; an application of *Annex B* to EN 1990 should not use all 'favourable' possibilities in reducing reliability levels, but if this is done it should be with extreme caution.

Clause B3.3

On the other hand, instead of applying the K_{FI} factor of 1.1 to γ_F for actions which are unfavourable for CC3 structures, it is normally preferable to apply other measures, e.g. higher levels of quality control (note to *Table B3*, *clause B3.3*).

Clause B3.3(2)

Reliability differentiation may also be applied through the partial factors of resistance γ_M (see Section 8.6 and also *Eurocode 3*: *Design of Steel Structures*, which describes a reliability differentiation in relation to a fatigue verification (*clause B3.3*(*2*)).

Experience suggests that a differentiation of partial factors with the limits given in *Table B3* of *Annex B* has no significant influence on the reliability level of the structure; however, any lowering of factors for economic reasons must be compensated for by a higher level of quality control.

Clause B3.3(3)

Clause B3.3(*3*) recognizes that the reliability classes of construction works may be linked to the requirements for quality levels of the design (DSL; see Section 8.4) and execution process (IL; see Section 8.5).

Background

Due, largely, to increased competition among material producers, there has been a tendency within the construction industry to reduce safety margins (in particular partial factors) for both actions and material resistance. This together with other rules that can lower safety levels and the increased use of IT packages for analysis will result in buildings which will become more slender, with reduced robustness; and hence a much reduced reserve strength in comparison to buildings designed about 10 years ago. This trend is becoming very apparent among, for example, product manufacturers.

The Eurocodes permit the choice of various factors, for example:

- reliability differentiation
- different load combination expressions through a National Annex
- safety factors through a National Annex
- imposed load values
- α_{cc} factors for the value of the design compressive strength of concrete resistance at the ultimate limit state
- γ_M factors for materials, etc.

If all these factors are chosen with the primary objective of economy, this would lead to structures or structural elements with a lowered level of safety and structures with reduced reserve strengths, and thus the risk of failure and collapse is increased.

Clause 2.2(6) (see Chapter 2) states that the different measures to reduce the risk of failure may be interchanged to a limited extent provided that the required reliability level is maintained. Chapter 2 of this guide cites an example where during a refurbishment it may be necessary to compensate for a slightly lower partial factor by a high level of quality management. Other situations include where for reasons of economy a lower K_{FI} may be chosen but compensated for by a higher level of design supervision and quality control, in particular for high-volume factory-produced standard units (e.g. lighting columns or standard beams) (*clause B3.3(4)*).

Clause 2.2(6)

Clause B3.3(4)

8.4. Design supervision differentiation

For measures relating to quality management and measures aimed at reducing errors in design and execution of the structure and gross human errors, *Annex B* of EN 1990 introduces the concept of design supervision levels (DSL).

Experience shows that:

- gross errors are caused by human factors (e.g. violation of accepted rules for design and execution)
- almost every serious failure is caused by errors in design and execution
- gross errors can only be avoided by quality control levels for design and supervision.

The design supervision levels (DSL3, DSL2 and DSL1, corresponding respectively to CC3, CC2 and CC1) represent the various organizational quality control steps taken to ensure the reliability of a structure, which may be used together with other measures, such as classification of designers and checking authorities (*clause B4(1)*).

Clause B4(1)

Clause 2.2(5) allows these design supervision levels to be related to the reliability classes or to be chosen on the basis of the importance of the structure (i.e. consequence classes) and in accordance with the national requirements or design brief. The three design supervision levels are shown in Table 8.5 (based on *Table B4* of EN 1990) and should be implemented through appropriate quality management measures (*clause B4(2)*).

Clause 2.2(5)

Clause B4(2)

Differentiation is made on the basis of supervision of the design at the design stage of the structure, thus if the quality control measures are more stringent such as third-party checking then a higher reliability class can be expected than for normal supervision (i.e. self-checking).

Clause B4(3)

Clause B4(3) goes further, to say that design supervision differentiation may also include a classification of designers and/or design inspectors (checkers, controlling authorities, etc.) depending on their competence and experience, and their internal organization, for the relevant type of construction works being designed because the type of construction works, the materials used and the structural forms adopted can affect the classification. For example, EU member states or clients could specify that certain design consultants with expertise in certain fields and a proven track record should provide the extended supervision (i.e. third-party supervision).

Clause B4(4)

Clause B4(4) points out that design supervision differentiation can consist of:

- a more refined detailed assessment of the nature and magnitude of actions to be restricted by the structure or
- a system of design load management actively or passively to restrict these actions.

A more detailed understanding of the action creating a hazard in a structure and then actively or passively controlling it (e.g. warning systems for load exceedance on floors in intelligent buildings) is a part of design supervision differentiation.

8.5. Inspection during execution

Clause B5(1)

Clause B5(1) introduces inspection classes (IL) which are differentiated on the basis of the level of inspection during execution (Table 8.6).

Annex B recommends inspection levels to be linked to the reliability classes previously defined. It also states that the inspection levels should define the subjects to be covered by

Table 8.5. *Design supervision levels*

Design supervision level	Characteristics	Minimum recommended requirements for checking of calculations, drawings and specification
DSL3 (relating to RC3/CC3)	Extended supervision	Third-party checking: checking performed by an organization different from that which prepared the design
DSL2 (relating to RC2/CC2)	Normal supervision	Checking by personnel different from those originally responsible and in accordance with procedure of the organization
DSL1 (relating to RC2/CC1)	Normal (basic) supervision	Self-checking: checking performed by the person who prepared the design

For examples see Table 8.1, footnotes b, c and d

Table 8.6. *Inspection levels (IL)*

Inspection level	Characteristics	Requirements
IL3 (relating to RC3/CC3)	Extended inspection	Third-party inspection
IL2 (relating to RC2/CC2)	Normal inspection	Inspection in accordance with the procedures of the organization
IL1 (relating to RC1/CC1)	Normal (basic) inspection	Self-inspection

For examples see Table 8.1, footnotes b, c and d

Table 8.7. *Examples of design supervision levels for activities (to be regarded as a guide only)*

Activity	Normal (basic) supervision	Normal supervision	Extended supervision
Basis for design as related to the intended function and use of the structure	✓	✓	✓
Basis for evaluation of soil conditions			✓
Assumptions for actions, and calculation models for actions	✓	✓	✓
Calculation model(s) for structural design (calculation of action effects)		✓	✓
Relevance of assumed material properties	✓		✓
Assessment of design values of soil parameters	✓	✓	✓
Identification of critical components, areas and cross-sections		✓	✓
Checks of global equilibrium	✓	✓	✓
Checks of structural calculations by independent calculations		✓	✓
Compliance of calculations with drawings	✓	✓	✓
Specification of relevant requirements for inspection of execution		✓	✓

Table 8.8. *Execution activities: examples of inspection classes with regard to concrete construction (to be regarded as a guide only)*

Activity	Normal (basic) inspection 1	Normal inspection 2	Extended inspection 3
Scaffolding, formwork	Random sampling	Major scaffolding and formwork to be inspected before concreting	All scaffolding and formwork to be inspected
Ordinary reinforcement	Random checking	Major reinforcement to be inspected before concreting	All reinforcement to be inspected before concreting
Prestressing steel	Not applicable	All prestressing steel to be inspected before concreting	
Embedded items	According to project specification		
Erection of precast elements	According to project specification		
Delivery and casting of concrete	Occasional checks	Occasional checks	Check of entire process
Curing and finishing of concrete	None	Occasional checks	Check of entire process
Stressing of prestressing steel	Not applicable	According to project specification	
Documentation of inspection	Not required	Required	

The inspection of execution also consists of documentation of product properties using EN 206, etc.

the inspection of products and execution of works including stating the scope of the inspection, thus the inspection rules will vary from one structural material to another, and reference should be made to the relevant CEN execution standards. Tables 8.7 and 8.8 give examples of activities to be checked for the three inspection levels for both the design and execution stages.

8.6. Partial factors for material properties

Clause B2.6(1)

Clause B2.6(1) also recommends that a partial factor product property, or a member resistance, can be reduced if an inspection class higher than that required according to Table 8.6 and/or more severe requirements are used during the manufacture of a product or supervision during execution.

As stated in Section 8.4, a differentiation in partial factors has a significant impact on the cost of a product and the cost of the construction works, and as such is desired by many parts of the construction industry including product manufacturers, clients and organizations involved in PFI (private finance initiatives). Such a differentiation must be justified by increased inspection, thus increasing the probability of reaching the target properties.

Resistance product properties which are of particular importance for structural safety are geometry and strength of materials.

Further reading

Euro-International Concrete Committee (1991) *CEB–FIP Model Code 90. CEB Bulletins 203–205*. FIB, Lausanne.

Menzies, J. B. (1995) Hazards, risks and structural safety. *Structural Engineer* **73**, No. 21.

Reid, S. G. (1999) Perception and communication of risk, and the importance of dependability. *Structural Safety* **21**, 373–384.

SAKO (1995) *NKB Committee and Work Reports 1995:03 E: Basis of Design of Structures – Classification and Reliability Differentiation of Structures*. SAKO, Helsinki.

Tietz, S. B. (1998) Risk analysis – uses and abuses. *Structural Engineer* **76**, No. 20.

CHAPTER 9

Basis for partial factor design and reliability analysis

This chapter is concerned with the basis for partial factor design and with the general concept of reliability analysis. The material described in this chapter is covered in the informative *Annex C* of EN 1990, *Eurocode*: *Basis of Structural Design* in 10 clauses:

- Scope and field of application — *Clause C1*
- Symbols — *Clause C2*
- Introduction — *Clause C3*
- Overview of reliability methods — *Clause C4*
- Reliability index β — *Clause C5*
- Target values of reliability index β — *Clause C6*
- Approach for calibration of design values — *Clause C7*
- Reliability verification formats in Eurocodes — *Clause C8*
- Partial factors in EN 1990 — *Clause C9*
- ψ_0 factors — *Clause C10*

This chapter includes seven numerical examples illustrating general calculation procedures described in *Annex C* of EN 1990. The appendix to this chapter includes five Mathcad* sheets that can be used to apply general procedures and, in particular, to verify the example calculations.

9.1. Scope and field of application

The Eurocodes are based on the partial factor method (as described in *Section 6* and *Annex A* of EN 1990). Detailed information and theoretical backgrounds for the partial factor method are provided in *Annex C* (*clause C1(1)*). *Clause C1*(*2*) states that *Annex C* provides information on structural reliability methods, on the application of these methods for determination of design values and partial factors by calibration, and on the design verification formats used in the Eurocodes.

Clause C1(1)
Clause C1(2)

9.2. Symbols

The symbols and terms (*clause C2*) used in *Annex C* mostly coincide with the traditional notation used in structural reliability. It should, however, be noted that alternative terms can

Clause C2

---

*Mathcad is a software package that performs calculations and produces documents containing text, equations and graphs.

be found in ISO 2394 and other literature on structural reliability. For example the symbol g used in *Annex C* for the 'performance function' is often called the 'limit state function' or the 'state function', or, in some simple cases, the 'reliability (safety) margin'. Another important term, 'survival probability' P_s, is often called 'reliability' (see also ISO 2394[8]). Some terms used in *Annex C*, for example '*probabilistic*, *semi-probabilistic*, *deterministic methods*' and classification of '*level I, II and III reliability methods*', may be used in the literature in slightly different ways. Additional terms (such as '*design value method*', used previously in ENV 1991-1 but not in EN 1990) may be found in ISO 2394 and other literature.

Clause C2

Supplementary symbols and terms to those given in *clause C2* will be introduced in this chapter in order to provide more comprehensive background information. For example $\varphi(X)$ will be used for the probability density function of a variable X, and $\underline{X}$ for a vector of all basic variables (this symbol is also used in Chapter 10 of this guide and in *Annex D* of EN 1990).

9.3. Introduction

Clause C3(1)

Basic variables, denoted in general by a vector $\underline{X}$, include three fundamental categories of variables entering load and resistance models in any design verification (*Section 4* and *Annex C, clause C3(1)*):

- action variables F
- resistance variables R
- geometric properties a.

Clause 3.4(1)P
Clause C3(1)

As a rule, each category consists of a number of variables, for example actions F may consist of several permanent actions G and variable actions Q. In verification of a structure all basic variables can be substituted by their design values, which are used in structural and load models to verify that no limit state is exceeded (*clauses 3.4(1)P* and *C3(1)*).

Clause C3(2)

The design values of basic variables are determined from their characteristic values using partial and ψ factors (*Section 6*). Numerical values of these factors can be determined using two basic procedures mentioned in *clause C3(2)*:

(1) calibration to past experience
(2) application of probabilistic reliability theory.

Clause C3(3)
Clause C6

As a rule, both procedures for determination of γ and ψ factors are combined in order to increase the credibility of obtained results. When probabilistic reliability theory is applied, then the values of γ and ψ factors should be determined in such a way (*clause C3(3)*) that the reliability level is as close as possible to the target reliability given in *clause C6*. Thus, the reliability level of a structure should be neither lower (for safety reasons) nor significantly greater (for economic reasons) than the target level as both cases may lead to undesirable consequences. It should be mentioned that the γ and ψ factors are mostly determined using procedure 1, calibration to past experience, based on statistical evaluation of experimental data and field observations. However, structural reliability methods now provide increasingly efficient background information on all reliability elements used in Eurocodes.

9.4. Overview of reliability methods

Clause C4(1)
Clause C2
Clause C4(1)
Clause C4(2)
Clause C4(3)

The overview of reliability methods (*clause C4(1)*) given in *Figure C1* of EN 1990 is essentially the same as in the previous version (ENV 1991-1), and need not be discussed in detail here. However, as already mentioned in *clause C2*, EN 1990 uses slightly different terminology from ISO 2394.[8] It is a consequence of the fact that the terminology used in *clauses C4(1)*, *C4(2)* and *C4(3)* (probabilistic, deterministic methods, levels I, II and III) and methodology (FORM, semi-probabilistic methods) are still not fully harmonized in reliability theory. In particular, the term 'semi-probabilistic methods (level I)' is not generally accepted and may even be confusing, as it is not defined in EN 1990. Most likely it refers to the 'design values method' as defined in the previous document ENV 1991-1 and in ISO 2394.

As already mentioned above, the present generation of Eurocodes is still mostly calibrated to previous experience (*clause C4(4)*) using procedure 1 described above. Nevertheless, this procedure is increasingly effective when combined with other calibration procedures indicated in *Figure C1*, e.g. using full probabilistic or semi-probabilistic (design value) methods. As mentioned in Chapter 3, in accordance with *clause 3.5(5)* a design directly based on probabilistic methods may be used as an alternative. Although specific conditions for the use of probabilistic methods should be given by the relevant authority, *Annex C* of EN 1990 should provide a basis.

Clause C4(4)

Clause 3.5(5)

9.5. Reliability index β

The traditionally used reliability index β is one of the most frequently used reliability measures of structures (*clause C5(1)*). It should be underlined that it is a quantity fully equivalent to the probability of failure P_f (whatever method is used for its determination), for which

Clause C5(1)

$$\beta = -\Phi^{-1}(P_f) \qquad (C.1)$$

where $\Phi^{-1}(P_f)$ denotes the inverse distribution function of the standardized normal distribution of the probability P_f (*clause C5(1)*). Note the negative sign on the right-hand side of *equation (C.1)*, introduced to keep β positive for $P_f < 0.5$.

The probability P_f can be generally expressed through the performance function g (*clause C5(2)*) as

Clause C5(2)

$$P_f = \text{Prob}(g \leq 0) = \int_{g \leq 0} \varphi(\underline{X})\,\mathrm{d}\underline{X} \qquad (C.2a)$$

Holds, where $\varphi(\underline{X})$ is the joint probability density function of the vector of all the basic variables $\underline{X}$. The integral in *equation (C.2a)* indicates how the probability P_f can be determined, provided that the joint probability density function $\varphi(\underline{X})$ is known (it may be a quite complicated or unknown function). In some special cases the integration indicated in *equation (C.2a)* can be done analytically; in other cases, when the number of basic variables is small (up to 5), various types of numerical integration may be effectively applied.

In general, the failure probability P_f may be computed using

- exact analytical integration
- numerical integration methods
- approximate analytical methods (first-order reliability method (FORM), second-order reliability method (SORM), methods of moments)
- simulation methods

or by a combination of these methods.

The above-mentioned general concepts may be well illustrated by considering two cumulative variables, the action effect E and the resistance R. In this fundamental case of structural reliability the concept of performance function (reliability or safety margin) g is

$$g = R - E \qquad (C.2b)$$

In this case, calculation of the failure probability P_f can be performed without any specialized software. First, assume that R and E are mutually independent variables with a normal distribution with means μ_R and μ_E and standard deviations σ_R and σ_E, respectively. Then the reliability margin g also has normal distribution, with the following mean and standard deviation:

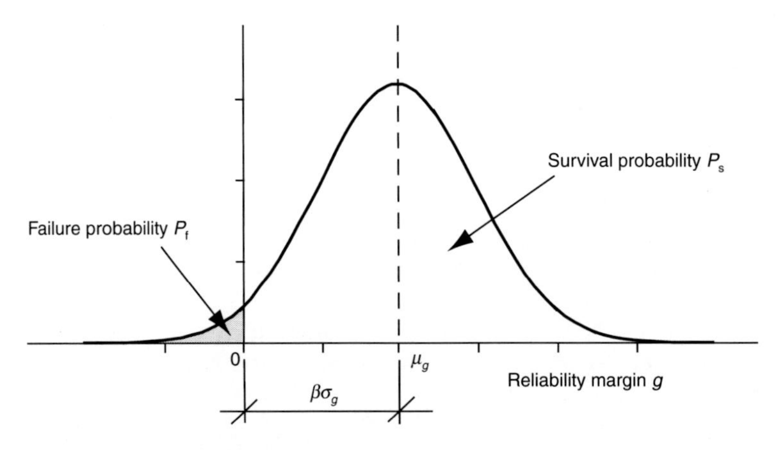

***Fig. 9.1.** Distribution of the reliability margin g*

$$\mu_g = \mu_R - \mu_E \tag{D9.1}$$

$$\sigma_g = (\sigma_R^2 + \sigma_E^2)^{1/2} \tag{D9.2}$$

The distribution of the reliability margin g is indicated in Fig. 9.1, which also shows the failure probability $P_f = P\{g \leq 0\}$ (probability of the event $g \leq 0$) and survival probability (reliability) $P_s = P\{g > 0\}$ (probability of the event $g > 0$).

Thus, the structural failure corresponds to the event described by the inequality $g \leq 0$. As g has a normal distribution (see Fig. 9.1) the failure probability P_f can be easily determined using transformation of g to the standardized normal variable u, given as $u = (g - \mu_g)/\sigma_g$. The distribution function of standardized normal variable $\Phi(u)$ is well known (see *Annex C*), and detailed tables of this variable are available in the technical literature or in electronic form.

For the critical value of the performance function $g = 0$, the standardized variable has the value $u = -\mu_g/\sigma_g$. The probability P_f (the probability of a negative performance function $g \leq 0$) is then given by the standardized normal distribution function at the critical point $u = -\mu_g/\sigma_g$ corresponding to the reliability margin $g = 0$. Thus,

$$P_f = \Phi(-\mu_g/\sigma_g) \tag{D9.3}$$

where Φ denotes the standardized normal distribution function.

It follows from *equations* (*C.1*) and (*C.6*) that in the considered fundamental case, based on the assumption of a normal distribution for both the load effect E and the resistance R, the reliability index β is (*clause C5*(*3*))

Clause C5(3)

$$\beta = \mu_g/\sigma_g \tag{C.2c}$$

In this case the reliability index β is the distance of the mean μ_g of the reliability margin g from the origin (zero), taking the standard deviation σ_g of g as a unit measure.

However, the above result is valid only under the limiting assumptions of the normal distribution of both fundamental variables R and E. In a more general case, when R and E have a general 'non-normal' distribution, the probability of failure P_f cannot be determined using equation (D9.3).

When E and R have an arbitrary probability distribution, then equation (D9.3) and *equation* (*C.2c*) can be used as first estimates only. In this case, however, the probability of failure P_f may be still determined without any specialized software using the following integration formula:

$$P_f = \int_{-\infty}^{+\infty} \varphi_E(x)\Phi_R(x)\,dx \tag{D9.4}$$

where $\varphi_E(x)$ denotes the probability density function of the load effect E, and $\Phi_R(x)$ a distribution function of the resistance R. The reliability index β can then be determined from the failure probability P_f using *equation (C.1)*. Examples 9.1, 9.2 and 9.3 illustrate practical applications of the above formulae.

Example 9.1

Consider a steel rod (hanger) made from S235 steel ($f_{yk} = 235$ MPa) exposed to a permanent load $G_k = 1$ MN. The minimum cross-sectional area A follows from the design criteria:

$$A = G_k\gamma_G/(f_{yk}/\gamma_M) = 1 \times 1.35/(235/1.10) = 0.006319 \text{ m}^2$$

Note that the design value of the load effect is $E_d = G_d = 1 \times 1.35 = 1.35$ MN, the design value of the resistance is $R_d = Af_{yk}/\gamma_M = 0.006319 \times 235/1.10 = 1.35$ MN.

In reliability analysis, basic variables representing the load G and yield strength f_y are considered as random variables, while the cross-sectional area A is taken as a deterministic variable (its variability is traditionally included in the variability of the yield strength f_y). The performance function g defined by *equation (C.3)* can now be written as

$$g = R - E = Af_y - G \quad \text{(D9.5)}$$

A first estimate of the reliability index may be obtained assuming the normal distribution for both E and R. Furthermore, it is assumed that the mean of the permanent load is equal to the characteristic value $\mu_E = G_k = 1$ MN, and the standard deviation is given as $\sigma_E = 0.1\mu_E = 0.1$ MN (coefficient of variation 10%). The mean value of resistance is given by the cross-sectional area A and the mean of the yield strength, which is taken as 280 MPa, thus $\mu_R = 0.006319 \times 280 = 1.769$ MN (the mean yield strength of 280 MPa follows from long-term experience with S235 steel). Finally, the standard deviation $\sigma_R = 0.08\mu_R = 0.1416$ MN (the coefficient of variation of the yield strength including variation of the cross-sectional area is assumed to be 8%).

The mean and standard deviation of the performance function g given by *equation (C.3)* follow from *equations (C.4)* and *(C.5)*:

$$\mu_g = \mu_R - \mu_E = 1.769 - 1.00 = 0.769 \quad \text{(D9.6)}$$

$$\sigma_g = (\sigma_R^2 + \sigma_E^2)^{1/2} = (0.1416^2 + 0.1^2)^{1/2} = 0.173 \quad \text{(D9.7)}$$

The reliability index follows from *equation (C.7)*:

$$\beta = \mu_g/\sigma_g = 0.769/0.173 = 4.44 \quad \text{(D9.8)}$$

The probability of failure follows from *equation (C.1)* as $P_f = 4.5 \times 10^{-6}$. However, the obtained values for the reliability index and failure probability should be considered as first estimates only.

Example 9.2

The simplified calculation of the reliability index in Example 9.1 may be easily improved assuming more realistic theoretical models. A more realistic estimate of the reliability level of the hanger considered in Example 9.1 can be found by assuming that the resistance R has a log-normal distribution with the lower bound at zero. Then using integration (*expression (C.8)*), assuming that the normal distribution for E yields the failure probability $P_f = 6.2 \times 10^{-7}$, the reliability index $\beta = 4.85$ can be determined using *equation (C.1)*. (Note that Mathcad sheet 1 in the appendix to this chapter shows this integration procedure for two assumptions concerning the distribution of the action effect E: the normal and gamma distributions.) A satisfactory approximation can, however, be obtained even without integration approximating the reliability margin g by the three-parameter log-normal distribution (this procedure is also included in Mathcad sheet1).This approximation, assuming the normal distribution for E, leads to the failure probability $P_f = 4.4 \times 10^{-7}$ and the reliability index $\beta = 4.91$ (slightly greater than the correct value $\beta = 4.85$).

Example 9.3
Another possibility for improving the reliability analysis of the rod (hanger) in Example 9.1 is to include the effect of model uncertainty. Note that the results in Examples 9.1 and 9.2 were obtained neglecting both the load and resistance model uncertainty. If these effects are taken into account, the performance function g given by *equation* (*C.2b*) may be generalized as

$$g = R - E = \theta_R A f_y - \theta_E G \qquad \text{(D9.9)}$$

where θ_R and θ_E denote random variables describing the uncertainty in the load and resistance model. Calculation of the failure probability P_f is now slightly more complicated, but can still be done without specialized software. Mathcad sheet 1 (see the appendix) shows this calculation. It appears that under reasonable assumptions for variables θ_R and θ_E the reliability index β may decrease considerably (by about 1.0) compared with the case when no model uncertainty is considered, and the performance function g is given by *equation* (*C.9*).

9.6. Target value of the reliability index β

Clause C6(1)

The target values of the reliability index β given in *clause C6*(*1*) were mainly derived from a number of recent reliability studies of structural components made from different materials. However, it should be mentioned that the obtained reliability indexes depend on many factors (type of component, loading conditions and material) and, consequently, have a wide scatter. It appears that the results of any reliability study depend significantly on the assumed theoretical models used to describe the basic variables. Moreover, these models are not yet unified and have not been used systematically. Still, the recommended values of the reliability index may be considered as reasonable average values for reliability levels characterizing existing structures.

Another possibility for specifying the target reliability index or the target failure probability is the minimum requirement for human safety from the individual or societal point of view when the expected number of fatalities is taken into account. This approach is described briefly in ISO 2394. Without going into detail it starts from an accepted lethal accident rate of 10^{-6} per year, which corresponds to the reliability index $\beta_1 = 4.7$. This value corresponds to the target reliability index accepted in EN 1990 for an ultimate limit state per year.

The reliability index for a period of n years may then be calculated from the following approximate equation:

$$\Phi(\beta_n) = [\Phi(\beta_1)]^n \qquad (C.3)$$

from which the approximate value $\beta_{50} = 3.8$ may be obtained.

It should be emphasized that both values $\beta_1 = 4.7$ and $\beta_{50} = 3.8$ correspond to the same reliability level but to different reference periods considered for the assessment of design values of some actions (1 and 50 years). The reference period may, or may not, coincide with the design working life.

A completely different question is specification of the reliability index for a construction works with a limited design working life. A practical example calculation of the reliability index is given below (Example 9.4).

Clause C6(2)

As stated in *clause C6*(*2*) the actual frequency of failure may be dependent on many factors not considered in partial factor design and, consequently, β may not correspond to the actual frequency of structural failure.

Example 9.4
Consider an agricultural structure with moderate consequences of failure and a limited design working life of 25 years. In this case it may be reasonable to specify $\beta_1 < 4.7$, say

$\beta_1 = 4.2$. Using the *equation* (*C.14*), it can be found that for the design working life of $n = 25$ years

$$\Phi(3.4) = [\Phi(4.2)]^{25}$$

and thus $\beta_1 = 4.2$ corresponds to $\beta_{25} = 3.4$. Note that using the same expression (*equation* (*C.14*)) for $n = 50$ years, it follows that $\beta_{50} = 3.2$. The correct interpretation of this finding is as follows: if the input data (for particular actions) are related to 1 year and the design calculations are done for this period, then $\beta_1 = 4.2$ should be considered, but if the input data are related to 25 years, then $\beta_1 = 3.4$ should be considered in the design verification. This example was calculated using Mathcad sheet 2 (see the appendix to this chapter).

9.7. Approach to calibration of design values

Clause C7(1)

The design value method considered in *clause C7*(*1*), indicated in *Figure C1* as the '*semi-probabilistic method* (*level I*)', is a very important step from probabilistic design methods towards the operational partial factors method. The design value method is linked directly to the principle provided in *clause 3.5*(*2*)*P*, according to which it should be verified that no limit state is exceeded when design values of all the basic variables are used in the models of structural resistance R and action effect E (these models are also referred to as analysis models). Thus, if the design values are defined for all the basic variables, then a structure is considered as reliable when the following expression holds:

Clause 3.5(2)P

$$E_d < R_d \qquad (C.4)$$

Here the design values E_d and R_d are expressed symbolically as

$$E_d = E\{F_{d1}, F_{d2}, \ldots a_{d1}, a_{d2}, \ldots \theta_{d1}, \theta_{d2}, \ldots\} \qquad (C.5a)$$

$$R_d = R\{X_{d1}, X_{d2}, \ldots a_{d1}, a_{d2}, \ldots \theta_{d1}, \theta_{d2}, \ldots\} \qquad (C.5b)$$

where, as before, E is the action effect, R is the resistance, F is an action, X is a material property, a is a geometrical property and θ is a model uncertainty. The subscript 'd' refers to design values.

Equation (*C.4*) together with *equation* (*C.5*) indicates how to ensure in practice that the reliability index β is equal to or greater than the target value. In accordance with *clause C7*(*2*) the design values should be based on the first-order reliability method (FORM) (see Fig. 9.2) (*clause C7*(*2*)). The FORM approach is a basic and very efficient reliability method, and used in a number of software packages. The main steps of the FORM can be summarized as follows:

Clause C7(2)

Clause C7(2)

- the basic variables $\underline{X}$ are transformed into a space of standardized normal variables $\underline{U}$, and the performance function $g(\underline{X}) = 0$ transformed into $g'(\underline{U}) = 0$
- the failure surface $g'(U) = 0$ is approximated at a given point by a tangent hyperplane (using the Taylor expansion)
- the design point, i.e. the point on the surface $g'(U) = 0$ closest to the origin, is found by iteration
- the reliability index β is determined as the distance of the design point from the origin, and the failure probability P_f is given by $P_f = \Phi(-\beta)$.

This method can be refined by approximating the failure surface $g'(U) = 0$ by a quadratic surface. This refined approach is called the second-order reliability method (SORM). A number of other improvements and additional modifications can be found in the literature on structural reliability.

If only two variables E and R are considered, then the design values E_d and R_d can be found using the following approximate formulae (*clause C7*(*3*)):

Clause C7(3)

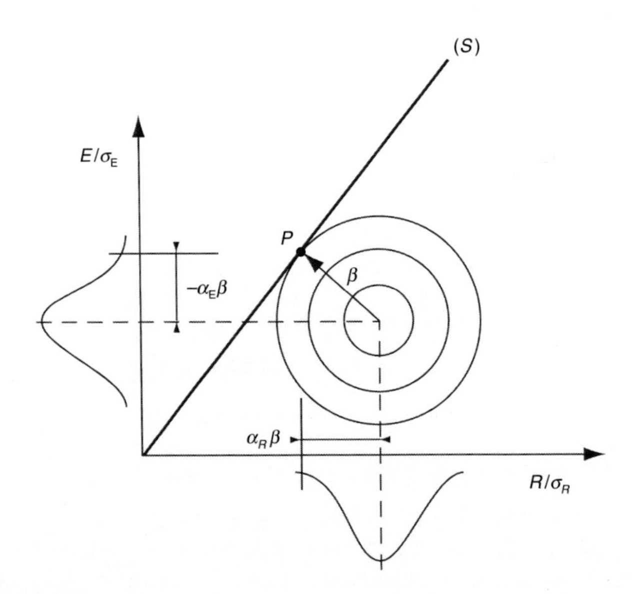

Fig. 9.2. Design point (P) and reliability index β. The design point is the point on the failure surface (g = 0) closest to the average point in the space of normalized variables. (Figure C2 *in* Annex C *of EN 1990)*

$$\text{Prob}(E > E_d) = \Phi(+\alpha_E\beta) \quad (C.6a)$$

$$\text{Prob}(R \leq R_d) = \Phi(-\alpha_R\beta) \quad (C.6b)$$

Clause C6

where β is the target reliability index (see *clause C6*), and α_E and α_R, with $|\alpha| \leq 1$, are the values of the FORM sensitivity factors. The value of α is negative for unfavourable actions and action effects, and positive for resistance.

Note that for the performance function $g = R - E$ the FORM sensitivity factors are given as

$$\alpha_E = \frac{-\sigma_E}{\sqrt{\sigma_E^2 + \sigma_R^2}} \quad (D9.10)$$

$$\alpha_R = \frac{\sigma_R}{\sqrt{\sigma_E^2 + \sigma_R^2}} \quad (D9.11)$$

Obviously it should generally hold that

$$\alpha_E^2 + \alpha_R^2 = 1 \quad (D9.12)$$

Clause C7(3)

In accordance with *clause C7(3,)* α_E and α_R may be taken as –0.7 and 0.8, respectively, provided that

$$0.16 < \sigma_E/\sigma_R < 7.6 \quad (C.7)$$

where σ_E and σ_R are the standard deviations of the action effect and resistance, respectively. Obviously the EN 1990 recommendation is on a safe side as the sum of squares of σ_E and σ_R is greater than 1.

For particular limit states (e.g. fatigue) a more general formulation may be necessary to express a limit state.

Clause C7(4)

Clause C7(5)

Clause C7(4) states '*where condition (C.7) is not satisfied, α = ± 1,0 should be used for the variable with the larger standard deviation, and α = ± 0,4 for the variable with the smaller standard deviation*'. Further, *clause C7(5)* states that '*when the action model contains several basic variables, expression (C.6) should be used for the leading variable only. For the accompanying actions the design values may be defined by*'

$$\text{Prob}(E > E_d) = \Phi(-0.4 \times 0.7 \times \beta) = \Phi(-0.28\beta) \quad (C.9)$$

For $\beta = 3.8$ the values defined by *expression* (*C.18*) correspond approximately to the 0.90 fractile.

Example 9.5

Consider again a steel rod (hanger) made from S235 steel ($f_{yk} = 235$ MPa) exposed to a permanent load $G_k = 1$ MN, as described in Example 9.1 by the performance function $g = R - E$. As before, it is assumed that the mean of the permanent load is equal to the characteristic value $\mu_E = G_k = 1$ MN, and the standard deviation $\sigma_E = 0.1\mu_E = 0.1$ (coefficient of variation 10%). The mean value of resistance is given by the cross-sectional area A and the mean of the yield strength, which is taken as 280 MPa (see Example 9.1), thus $\mu_R = 0.006319 \times 280 = 1.769$ MN (the mean yield strength of 280 MPa follows from long-term experience with S235 steel). Finally, the standard deviation $\sigma_R = 0.08\mu_R = 0.1416$ MN (the coefficient of variation of the yield strength including the variation of the cross section area is assumed to be 8%).

Thus the sensitivity factors given by *equations* (*C.20*) and (*C.21*) are

$$\alpha_E = \frac{-\sigma_E}{\sqrt{\sigma_E^2 + \sigma_R^2}} = \frac{-0.1}{\sqrt{0.1^2 + 0.1416^2}} = -0.577$$

$$\alpha_R = \frac{\sigma_R}{\sqrt{\sigma_E^2 + \sigma_R^2}} = \frac{0.1416}{\sqrt{0.1^2 + 0.1416^2}} = 0.817$$

The design values E_d and R_d follows from *equations* (*C.18*) and (*C.19*)

$$\text{Prob}(E > E_d) = \Phi(+\alpha_E\beta) = 1.417 \times 10^{-2}$$

$$\text{Prob}(R \leq R_d) = \Phi(-\alpha_R\beta) = 9.528 \times 10^{-4}$$

The design values are then

$$E_d = \mu_E - \alpha_E\beta\sigma_E = 1 + 0.577 \times 3.8 \times 0.1 = 1.219$$

$$R_d = \mu_R - \alpha_R\beta\sigma_R = 1.769 - 0.817 \times 3.8 \times 0.1416 = 1.329$$

Thus, it holds that $E_d < R_d$, and the method of design values confirms that the structure is reliable. Mathcad sheet 3 (see the appendix to this chapter) shows this calculation.

Example 9.6

Consider again the steel rod (hanger) from Examples 9.1 and 9.3. If the sensitivity factors α_E and α_R are taken as recommended in *clause C7*(*3*) as –0.7 and 0.8, respectively (*condition* (*C.23*) is satisfied), then

Clause C7(3)

$$E_d = \mu_E - \alpha_E\beta\sigma_E = 1 + 0.7 \times 3.8 \times 0.1 = 1.266$$

$$R_d = \mu_R - \alpha_R\beta\sigma_R = 1.769 - 0.8 \times 3.8 \times 0.1416 = 1.339$$

Thus, the design condition $E_d < R_d$ is also satisfied for the recommended 'safe' factors α_E and α_R even though the difference between the design values R_d and E_d is smaller than in the previous case for the original sensitivity factors α_E and α_R. Mathcad sheet 4 (see the appendix to this chapter) can be used to verify this calculation. When the distribution is unknown and limited experimental data are to be used, then various methods described in Appendix C of this guide may be applied.

Clause C7(*6*) states that the expressions in *Table C3* (see Table 9.1) '*should be used for deriving the design values of variables with the given probability distribution*'.

Clause C7(6)

A simple method of obtaining the relevant partial factor is indicated in *clause C7*(*7*). The partial factor of a variable action Q can be determined from its design value Q_d and characteristic value Q_k as

Clause C7(7)

Table 9.1. *Design values for various distribution functions (based on* Table C3 *of EN 1990)*

Distribution	Design values
Normal	$\mu - \alpha\beta\sigma = \mu(1 - \alpha\beta V)$
Log-normal (two-parameter, with the lower bound at zero)	$\frac{\mu}{\sqrt{1+V^2}}\exp\left(-\alpha\beta\sqrt{\ln(1+V^2)}\right)$
	$\mu\exp(-\alpha\beta V)$ approximation for $V = \sigma/\mu < 0.2$
Three-parameter log-normal	$\mu - \frac{\sigma}{C}\left(1 - \frac{1}{\sqrt{1+C^2}}\exp\left(-\text{sign}(C)\alpha\beta\sqrt{\ln(1+C^2)}\right)\right)$
Gumbel	$u - \frac{1}{a}\ln\{-\ln[\Phi(-\alpha\beta)]\} \cong \mu - \sigma\{0.45 + 0.78\ln(-\ln[\Phi(-\alpha\beta)]\}$
	where $u = \mu - 0.577/a$ and $a = \pi/\sigma\sqrt{6}$

In these expressions, μ, σ and V are, respectively, the mean value, the standard deviation and the coefficient of variation of a given variable. For variable actions, these should be based on the same reference period as the reliability index β

$$\gamma_Q = Q_d/Q_k \tag{D9.13a}$$

This simple formula can be used if both the characteristic and design values of the variable load Q are known or determined using probabilistic methods. The analogous equation for the resistance variable is

$$\gamma_R = R_k/R_d \tag{D9.13b}$$

Example 9.7 illustrates the practical application of the formulae, considering a simple structural member.

Example 9.7

Consider S235 steel for which the yield strength determined using a large sample size (about 800 measurements) indicates that the mean of the population is $\mu = 280$ MPa. The standard deviation $\sigma = 22.4$ MPa, thus the coefficient of variation $V = \sigma/\mu = 0.08$. Assuming a log-normal distribution, the formulae give the design yield strength:

$$\begin{aligned} f_{yd} &= \frac{\mu}{\sqrt{1+V^2}}\exp\left(-\alpha\beta\sqrt{\ln(1+V^2)}\right) \\ &= \frac{280}{\sqrt{1+0.08^2}}\exp\left(-0.7\times 3.8\sqrt{\ln(1+0.08^2)}\right) \\ &= 225.7 \text{ MPa} \end{aligned}$$

It is interesting to note that the characteristic value corresponding to a 5% fractile is

$$\begin{aligned} f_{yk} &= \frac{\mu}{\sqrt{1+V^2}}\exp\left(-1.645\sqrt{\ln(1+V^2)}\right) \\ &= \frac{280}{\sqrt{1+0.08^2}}\exp\left(-1.645\sqrt{\ln(1+0.08^2)}\right) \\ &= 244.8 \text{ MPa} \end{aligned}$$

Thus the determined f_{yk} is greater than 235 MPa. Using formula (D9.13b) the partial factor would be

$$\gamma_Q = f_{yk}/f_{yd} = 244.8/225.7 = 1.085$$

Note that Mathcad sheet 4 (see the appendix to this chapter) may be used to verify this calculation.

9.8. Reliability verification formats in Eurocodes

In accordance with the partial factor methods accepted in EN 1990 to 1999 the design values of the basic variables, X_d and F_d, are usually not introduced directly to the partial factor design equations (*clause C8(1)*). They are introduced in terms of their representative values X_{rep} and F_{rep}, which may be:

Clause C8(1)

- characteristic values, i.e. values with a prescribed or intended probability of being exceeded, e.g. for actions, material properties and geometrical properties (see *clauses 1.5.3.14*, *1.5.4.1* and *1.5.5.1*, respectively)
- nominal values, which may be treated as characteristic values for material properties (see *clause 1.5.4.3*) and as design values for geometrical properties (see *clause 1.5.5.2*). As explained in *clause 6.3*, the representative values X_{rep} and F_{rep} should be divided and/or multiplied, respectively, by the appropriate partial factors to obtain the design values X_d and F_d (*clause C8(2)*). Thus, in general it holds that

Clause 1.5.3.14
Clause 1.5.4.1
Clause 1.5.5.1
Clause 1.5.4.3
Clause 1.5.5.2
Clause 6.3
Clause C8(2)

$$X_d = X_{rep}/\gamma \qquad \text{or} \qquad F_d = \gamma F_{rep} \tag{D9.14}$$

where γ denotes a general partial factor.

Particular forms of the above expressions for design values of actions F, material properties X and geometrical properties a are given in *expressions (6.1)*, *(6.3)* and *(6.4)* of EN 1990, respectively. For example, when an upper value for design resistance is used (see *clause 6.3.3*), *expression (6.3)* takes the form (*clause C8(3)*):

Clause 6.3.3
Clause C8(3)

$$X_d = 7\gamma_{fm} X_{k,\,sup} \tag{C.10}$$

where γ_{fm} is an appropriate factor greater than 1.

Model uncertainties may significantly affect the reliability of a structure. *Clause C8(4)* states '*design values for model uncertainties may be incorporated into the design expressions through the partial factors γ_{Sd} and γ_{Rd} applied on the total model, such that*'

Clause C8(4)

$$E_d = \gamma_{Sd} E\{\gamma_{gj} G_{kj};\ \gamma_P P;\ \gamma_{q1} Q_{k1};\ \gamma_{qi} \psi_{0i} Q_{ki};\ a_d \ldots\} \tag{C.11}$$

$$R_d = R\{\eta X_k/\gamma_m;\ a_d \ldots\}/\gamma_{Rd} \tag{C.12}$$

The coefficient ψ, which takes account of reductions in the design values of variable actions, is applied as ψ_0, ψ_1 or ψ_2 to simultaneously occurring, accompanying variable actions (*clause C8(5)*). The following simplifications may be made to *expressions (C.11)* and *(C.12)*, when required (*clause C8(6)*):

Clause C8(5)
Clause C8(6)

(1) On the loading side (for a single action or where linearity of action effects exists)

$$E_d = E\{\gamma_{F,i} F_{rep,\,i},\ a_d\} \tag{C.13}$$

(2) On the resistance side the general format is given in *expression (6.6)*, and further simplifications may be given in the relevant material Eurocode. Simplifications should only be made if the level of reliability is not reduced. It should be mentioned that non-linear resistance and action models, and multivariable action or resistance models, are commonly encountered in Eurocodes. In such instances the above relations become more complex.

9.9. Partial factors in EN 1990

Clause C9(2) refers to *clause 1.6*, where the different partial factors occurring in EN 1990 are defined. The relationship between individual partial factors in Eurocodes is schematically indicated in Fig. 9.3.

Clause C9(2)
Clause 1.6

In accordance with Fig. 9.3,

$$\gamma_F = \gamma_f \gamma_{Sd} \tag{D9.15}$$

$$\gamma_M = \gamma_m \gamma_{Rd} \tag{D9.16}$$

Note that the subscript 'S' is traditionally used to indicate the model uncertainty of the action effect instead of '*E*'.

9.10. ψ_0 factors

The ψ_0 factor is introduced in *Section 6* to define the combination value of a variable action. Expressions for ψ_0 are given in Table 9.2 (*Table C4* in *clause C10(1)*) for the combination of two variable actions. The expressions in Table 9.2 were derived using the following assumptions and conditions (*clause C10(2)*). The two actions to be combined are independent of each other.

Clause C10(1)

Clause C10(2)

The basic period (T_1 or T_2) for each action is a constant; T_1 is the greater basic period.

It is assumed that the action values within respective basic periods are constant and equal to their maximum, and that the maxima of the action associated with the various basic periods are uncorrelated. For example, when studying a variable climatic action, the basic period is generally taken to be equal to 1 year, and it is assumed that the yearly maxima are uncorrelated. The basic period ranges from 5 to 7 years for imposed loads on building floors, and is about 1 week for road traffic loads. Furthermore, the two considered actions belong to ergodic processes. An ergodic process is a stationary process having an important practical property such that a particular realization over a sufficiently long interval may be used to determine all the characteristics of the process instead of using a sample of different observations. The assumption of ergodicity is especially important for the estimation of the statistical characteristics of stochastic processes when only one realization of a process is available. In practice, ergodicity is in such cases often assumed (e.g. wind velocity characteristics) unless of course there is evidence to the contrary.

A detailed derivation of the formulae in Table 9.2 is provided in ISO 2394[8] and other literature.

The distribution functions in Table 9.2 refer to the maxima within the reference period *T*. These distribution functions are total functions which consider the probability that an action value is zero during certain periods. This means that the distribution function should include the probability of the zero load during its interval *T*. The expressions given in Table 9.2 may be derived assuming a stepwise Borges–Castanheta model for two loads as shown in ISO 2394.[8]

Note that the probability distribution functions listed in Table 9.1 describe the maxima within the reference period *T* (50 years) taking into account the probability that an action

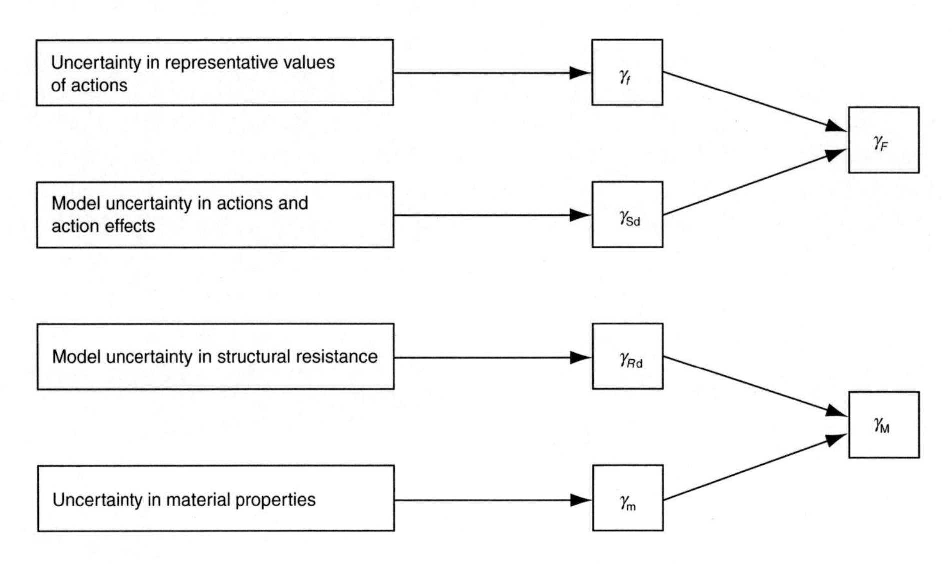

Fig. 9.3. *Relationship between individual partial factors* (Figure C3 *in EN 1990)*

Table 9.2. *Expressions for ψ_0 for the case of two variable actions (Table C4 in EN 1990)*

Distribution	$\psi_0 = F_{accompanying}/F_{leading}$
General	$\dfrac{F_s^{-1}\{\Phi(0,4\beta')^{N_1}\}}{F_s^{-1}\{\Phi(0,7\beta)^{N_1}\}}$ with $\beta' = F_s^{-1}\{\Phi(0,7\beta)/N_1\}$
Approximation for very large N_1	$\dfrac{F_s^{-1}\{\exp[-N_1\Phi(0,4\beta')]\}}{F_s^{-1}\{\Phi(0,7\beta)\}}$ with $\beta' = -\Phi^{-1}\{\Phi(-0,7\beta)/N_1\}$
Normal (approximation)	$\dfrac{1+(0,28\beta - 0,7\ln N_1)V}{1+0,7\beta V}$
Gumbel (approximation)	$\dfrac{1-0,78V[0,58+\ln(-\ln\Phi(0,28\beta))+\ln N_1}{1-0,78V[0,58+\ln(-\ln\Phi(0,7\beta))]}$

$F_s(.)$ is the probability distribution function of the extreme value of the accompanying action in the reference period T;
$\Phi(.)$ is the standard Normal distribution function;
T is the reference period;
T_1 is the greater of the basic periods for actions to be combined;
N_1 is the ratio T/T_1, approximated to the nearest integer;
β is the reliability index;
V is the coefficient of variation of the accompanying action for the reference period.

value is zero during certain periods (*clause C10(3)*). A practical calculation of ψ_0 is given in Example 9.8.

Clause C10(3)

In addition to those assumptions used in Table 9.1, often the so-called Turkstra's rule for combination of two actions is used. In accordance with this rule (see ISO 2394[8]) it is assumed that one load takes its extreme within the reference time T while for the other its point-in-time distribution is considered. Assuming the normal distribution this rule leads to the factor ψ_0 as

$$\psi_0 = \frac{1+\Phi^{-1}[\Phi(0.28\beta)^{N_1}]V}{1+0.7\beta V} \tag{D9.17}$$

where Φ is standard normal distribution function.

Example 9.8

The reliability index $\beta = 3.8$, the reference period $T = 50$ years, $T_1 = 7$ years. Therefore, $N_1 = T/T_1 \cong 7$. Figure 9.4 shows ψ_0 as a function of V for normal and Gumbel distributions (approximation) of an accompanying action in the reference period T. In addition to those two types of distributions, Fig. 9.4 also shows ψ_0 determined using equation (D9.14) for Turkstra's rule assuming a normal distribution.

Figure 9.4 shows that the three assumptions considered for the distribution of the accompanying action lead to slightly different results. For example, assuming $V = 0.2$, the factor ψ_0 is approximately within the interval 0.5 to 0.6. Note that the coefficient of variation V refers to the distribution of extreme values in the reference period T (say 50 years), so $V = 0.2$ may well correspond to imposed loads on building floors or wind actions. Note that the values accepted for most of the imposed loads and wind actions in *Table A1.1* in EN 1990 are, however, slightly conservative (0.7 for imposed load and 0.6 for wind loads).

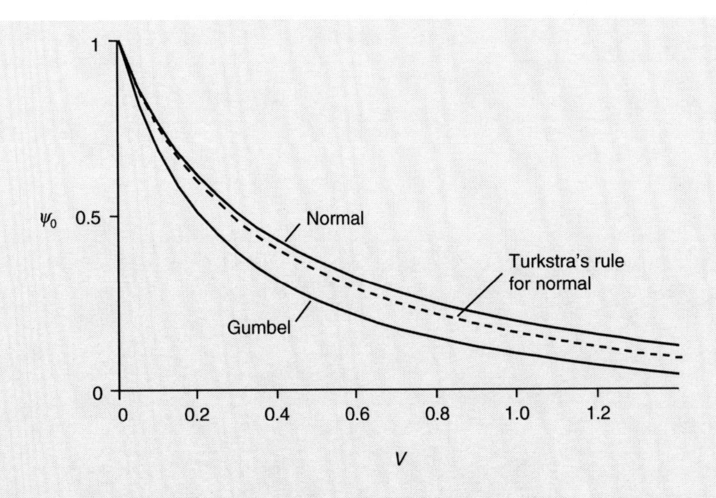

Fig. 9.4. Factor ψ_0 as a function of the coefficient of variation V

This example was calculated using Mathcad sheet 5 (see the appendix to this chapter), which can be used for other types of distribution of accompanying actions than those considered in Table 9.2.

Appendix: Mathcad sheets for example calculations

Sheet 1: a steel hanger exposed to permanent load G – parameter study of γ_G

1. Design of a hanger cross-sectional area $A = G_d/f_d$

Design input data:

$$\mathrm{Gk} := 1 \qquad \gamma\mathrm{G} := 1.0, 1.05..\ 1.6\ \text{(parameter)} \qquad \mathrm{fk} := 235 \qquad \gamma\mathrm{m} := 1.10 \qquad \mathrm{fd} := \frac{\mathrm{fk}}{\gamma\mathrm{m}}$$

Design of the cross-sectional area:

$$\mathrm{A}(\gamma\mathrm{G}) := \frac{(\mathrm{Gk}\cdot\gamma\mathrm{G})}{\mathrm{fd}} \qquad \text{Check: } \boxed{\mathrm{A}(1.35) = 6.32 \times 10^{-3}}$$

2. Parameters of basic variables G and f

Parameters of G and f:

$$\mu\mathrm{G} := \mathrm{Gk} \qquad \mathrm{vG} := 0.1 \qquad \sigma\mathrm{G} := \mathrm{vG}\cdot\mu\mathrm{G} \qquad \omega := \frac{280}{235} \qquad \mu\mathrm{f} := \omega\cdot\mathrm{fk} \qquad \mathrm{vf} := 0.08$$

$$\sigma\mathrm{f} := \mathrm{vf}\cdot\mu\mathrm{f}$$

Model uncertainty:

$$\mu\mathrm{XS} := 1 \qquad \sigma\mathrm{XS} := 0 \qquad \mu\mathrm{XR} := 1 \qquad \sigma\mathrm{XR} := 0.00 \qquad \mathrm{vXR} := \frac{\sigma\mathrm{XR}}{\mu\mathrm{XR}} \qquad \mathrm{vXS} := \frac{\sigma\mathrm{XS}}{\mu\mathrm{XS}}$$

3. Parameters of the resistance R and load effect E

The mean of R and E:

$$\mu\mathrm{R}(\gamma\mathrm{G}) := \mu\mathrm{f}\cdot\mu\mathrm{XR}\cdot\mathrm{A}(\gamma\mathrm{G}) \qquad \mu\mathrm{E} := \mu\mathrm{G}\cdot\mu\mathrm{XS} \qquad \boxed{\mu\mathrm{R}(1.35) = 1.77} \quad \boxed{\mu\mathrm{E} = 1}$$

CoV:

$$\mathrm{vR} := \sqrt{\mathrm{vXR}^2 + \mathrm{vXR}^2\cdot\mathrm{vf}^2 + \mathrm{vf}^2} \qquad \mathrm{vE} := \sqrt{\mathrm{vXS}^2 + \mathrm{vXS}^2\cdot\mathrm{vG}^2 + \mathrm{vG}^2}$$

Check: $\boxed{vR(1.35) = 0.08}$ $\boxed{vE = 0.1}$

Skewness of R for log-normal distribution and E for gamma distribution:

$\alpha R := 3 \cdot vR + vR^3 \qquad \alpha E := 2 \cdot vE$

4. Parameters of the reliability margin $g = R - E$

$\mu g(\gamma G) := \mu R(\gamma G) - \mu E \quad \sigma R(\gamma G) := vR \cdot \mu R(\gamma G) \quad \sigma E := vE \cdot \mu E$ $\boxed{\sigma R(1.35) = 0.14}$

$\sigma g(\gamma G) := \sqrt{(\sigma R(\gamma G))^2 + (\sigma E)^2}$ $\boxed{\mu g(1.35) = 0.77}$ $\boxed{\sigma g(1.35) = 0.17}$

$$\alpha g(\gamma G) := \frac{\alpha R \cdot \alpha R(\gamma G)^3 - \alpha E \cdot \sigma E^3}{\sigma g(\gamma G)^3}$$ $\boxed{\alpha g(1.35) = 0.09}$

5. Reliability assessment without integration

Reliability index assuming a normal distribution for g (a first estimate):

$\beta 0(\gamma G) := \dfrac{\mu g(\gamma G)}{\sigma g(\gamma G)} \qquad Pf0(\gamma G) := pnorm(-\beta 0(\gamma G), 0, 1)$ Check: $\boxed{\beta 0(1.35) = 4.44}$

Reliability index assuming a three-parameter log-normal distribution of g (a refine estimate):

Parameter C of three-parameter log-normal distribution of g:

$$C(\gamma G) := \frac{\left(\sqrt{\alpha g(\gamma G)^2 + 4} + \alpha g(\gamma G)\right)^{\frac{1}{3}} - \left(\sqrt{\alpha g(\gamma G)^2 + 4} + \alpha g(\gamma G)\right)^{\frac{1}{3}}}{2^{\frac{1}{3}}}$$

Parameters of transformed variable:

$$mg(\gamma G) := -\ln(|C|(\gamma G) + \ln(\sigma g(\gamma G)) - (0.5) \cdot \ln(1 + C(\gamma G)^2)$$

$$sg(\gamma G) := \sqrt{\ln(1 + C(\gamma G)^2)} \qquad x0(\gamma G) := \mu g(\gamma G) - \frac{1}{C(\gamma G)} - \sigma g(\gamma G)$$

Check: $\boxed{x0(1.35) = -4.85}$

$Pf1(\gamma G) := plnnorm(0 - x0(\gamma G), mg(\gamma G), sg(\gamma G)) \qquad \beta 1(\gamma G) := -qnorm(Pf1(\gamma G), 0, 1)$

$\boxed{\beta 1(1.35) = 4.76}$

6. Reliability assessment using integration

Assuming a normal distribution for E:

$En(x) := dnorm(x, \mu E, \sigma E)$

Assuming a gamma distribution for E:

$$k := \left(\frac{\mu E}{\sigma E}\right)^2 \qquad \lambda := \left(\frac{\mu E}{\sigma E^2}\right) \qquad Eg(x) := dgamma(\lambda \cdot x, k) \cdot \lambda$$

Assuming a log-normal distribution for R having the lower limit at a (0 default):

$$a(\gamma G) := \mu R(\gamma G) \cdot 0.0 \qquad C(\gamma G) := \frac{\sigma R(\gamma G)}{(\mu R(\gamma G) - a(\gamma G))} \qquad aR(\gamma G) := C(\gamma G)^3 + 3 \cdot C(\gamma G)$$

$$m(\gamma G) := \ln(\sigma R(\gamma G)) - \ln(C(\gamma G)) - (0.5) \cdot \ln(1 + C(\gamma G)^2) \qquad s(\gamma G) := \sqrt{\ln(1 + C(\gamma G)^2)}$$

Probability of a log-normal distribution of R:

$$\mathrm{Rln}(x, \gamma G) := \mathrm{plnorm}[(x - a(\gamma G)), m(\gamma G), s(\gamma G)]$$

Failure probability Prob$\{R < E\}$ and reliability index β:

$$\beta t := 3.8$$

E has a normal distribution and R a log-normal distribution:

$$\mathrm{Pfn}(\gamma G) := \int_0^{\infty} \mathrm{En}(x)\mathrm{Rln}(x, \gamma G)\,dx \qquad \beta n(\gamma G) := -\mathrm{qnorm}(\mathrm{Pfn}(\gamma G), 0, 1)$$

E has a gamma distribution and R a log-normal distribution:

$$\mathrm{Pfg}(\gamma G) := \int_0^{\infty} \mathrm{Eg}(x)\mathrm{Rln}(x, \gamma G)\,dx \qquad \beta g(\gamma G) := -\mathrm{qnorm}(\mathrm{Pfg}(\gamma G), 0, 1)$$

7. Parametric study of γ_G

Check: $\mathrm{Pf0}(1.35) = 4.51 \times 10^{-6}$

$\mathrm{Pf0}(1.35) = 4.51 \times 10^{-6}$

$\mathrm{Pf0}(1.35) = 4.51 \times 10^{-6}$

$\mathrm{Pf0}(1.35) = 4.51 \times 10^{-6}$

$\beta 0(1.35) = 4.44$

$\beta 0(1.35) = 4.44$

$\beta 0(1.35) = 4.44$

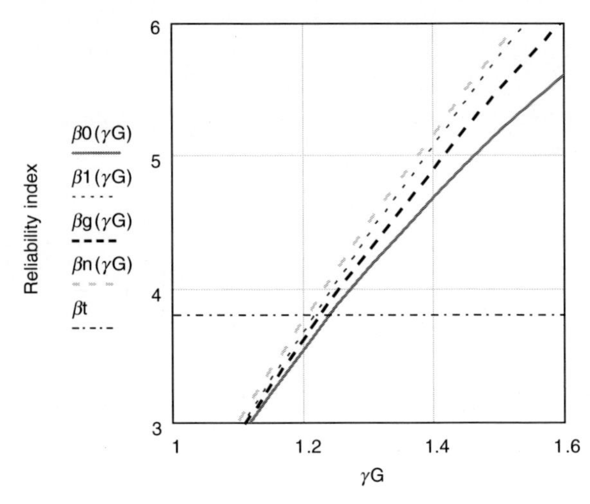

Effect of the partial factor of G

Note

The reliability assessment assuming a normal distribution for E and R seems to be on the safe side (leads to a lower bound for β), while the assessment assuming a three-parameter distribution for the reliability margin g seems to provide a more realistic estimate.

Sheet 2: failure probability P and reliability index β

1. Reliability index β for a given failure probability P: $\beta = -\Phi(P)$

$$P := \begin{pmatrix} 10^{-1} \\ 10^{-2} \\ 10^{-3} \\ 10^{-4} \\ 10^{-5} \\ 10^{-6} \end{pmatrix} \qquad \beta := -\mathrm{qnorm}(P, 0, 1) \qquad \beta = \begin{pmatrix} 1.28 \\ 2.33 \\ 3.09 \\ 3.72 \\ 4.26 \\ 4.75 \end{pmatrix}$$

2. Failure probability P for a given reliability index β: $P = \Phi^{-1}(\beta)$

$$\beta := \begin{pmatrix} 1 \\ 2 \\ 3 \\ 4 \\ 5 \\ 6 \end{pmatrix} \qquad P := \mathrm{pnorm}(-\beta, 0, 1) \qquad P = \begin{pmatrix} 0.16 \\ 0.02 \\ 1.35\times10^{-3} \\ 3.17\times10^{-5} \\ 2.87\times10^{-7} \\ 9.87\times10^{-10} \end{pmatrix}$$

3. Failure probability P_1 and P_n: $P_n = 1-(1-P_1)^n$

$$\mathrm{P1} := \begin{pmatrix} 7.23\times10^{-5} \\ 1.33\times10^{-5} \\ 1.\times10^{-6} \end{pmatrix} \qquad n := 50 \qquad \mathrm{Pn} := 1-(1-\mathrm{P1})^{n} \qquad \mathrm{Pn} = \begin{pmatrix} 3.61\times10^{-3} \\ 6.65\times10^{-4} \\ 6.5\times10^{-5} \end{pmatrix}$$

4. Reliability index β for 1 and 50 years $\Phi(\beta_n) = \Phi(\beta_1)^n$

Directly from β_1:

$$\beta 1 := \begin{pmatrix} 3.8 \\ 4.2 \\ 4.7 \end{pmatrix} \qquad \beta n := \mathrm{qnorm}((\beta 1, 0, 1)^{n}, 0, 1) \qquad \beta n = \begin{pmatrix} 2.69 \\ 3.21 \\ 3.83 \end{pmatrix}$$

Alternatively through the probability P_n:

$$\mathrm{P1} := \mathrm{pnorm}(-\beta 1, 0, 1) \qquad \mathrm{Pn} := 1-(1-\mathrm{P1})^{n} \qquad \beta n := -\mathrm{qnorm}(\mathrm{Pn}, 0, 1) \qquad \beta n = \begin{pmatrix} 2.69 \\ 3.21 \\ 3.83 \end{pmatrix}$$

Sheet 3: a steel hanger exposed to permanent load G – sensitivity coefficients α_E and α_R

1. Design of a hanger cross-sectional area $A = G_d/f_d$

Design input data:

$$\mathrm{Gk} := 1 \qquad \gamma\mathrm{G} := 1.0, 1.05..\ 1.6\ \text{(parameter)} \qquad \mathrm{fk} := 235 \qquad \gamma\mathrm{m} := 1.10 \qquad \mathrm{fd} := \frac{\mathrm{fk}}{\gamma\mathrm{m}}$$

Design of the cross-sectional area:

$$A(\gamma\mathrm{G}) := \frac{(\mathrm{Gk}\cdot\gamma\mathrm{G})}{\mathrm{fd}} \qquad \text{Check: } \boxed{A(1.35) = 6.32\times10^{-3}}$$

2. Parameters of basic variables G and F

Parameters of G and f:

$$\mu\mathrm{G} := \mathrm{Gk} \qquad \mathrm{vG} := 0.1 \qquad \sigma\mathrm{G} := \mathrm{vG}\cdot\mu\mathrm{G} \qquad \omega := \frac{280}{235} \qquad \mu\mathrm{f} := \omega\cdot\mathrm{fk} \qquad \mathrm{vf} := 0.08$$

$$\sigma\mathrm{f} := \mathrm{vf}\cdot\mu\mathrm{f}$$

Model uncertainty:

$$\mu\mathrm{XS} := 1 \qquad \sigma\mathrm{XS} := 0 \qquad \mu\mathrm{XR} := 1 \qquad \sigma\mathrm{XR} := 0.00 \qquad \mathrm{vXR} := \frac{\sigma\mathrm{XR}}{\mu\mathrm{XR}} \qquad \mathrm{vXS} := \frac{\sigma\mathrm{XS}}{\mu\mathrm{XS}}$$

3. Parameters of the resistance *R* and load effect *E*
The mean of *R* and *E*:

$$\mu R(\gamma G) := \mu f \cdot \mu XR \cdot A(\gamma G) \qquad \mu E := \mu G \cdot \mu XS \qquad \boxed{\mu R(1.35) = 1.77} \quad \boxed{\mu E = 1}$$

CoV:

$$vR := \sqrt{vXR^2 + vXR^2 \cdot vf^2 + vf^2} \qquad vE := \sqrt{vXS^2 + vXS^2 \cdot vG^2 + vG^2}$$

Check: $\boxed{vR(1.35) = 0.08}$ $\boxed{vE = 0.1}$

Skewness of *R* for log-normal distribution and *E* for gamma distribution:

$$\alpha R := 3 \cdot vR + vR^3 \qquad \alpha E := 2 \cdot vE$$

4. Parameters of the reliability margin *g* = *R* – *E*

$$\mu g(\gamma G) := \mu R(\gamma G) - \mu E \qquad \sigma R(\gamma G) := vR \cdot \mu R(\gamma G) \qquad \sigma E := vE \cdot \mu E \qquad \boxed{\sigma R(1.35) = 0.14}$$

$$\sigma g(\gamma G) := \sqrt{(\sigma R(\gamma G))^2 + (\sigma E)^2} \qquad \boxed{\mu g(1.35) = 0.77} \quad \boxed{\sigma g(1.35) = 0.17}$$

$$\alpha g(\gamma G) := \frac{\alpha R \cdot \alpha R(\gamma G)^3 - \alpha E \cdot \sigma E^3}{\sigma g(\gamma G)^3} \qquad \boxed{\alpha g(1.35) = 0.09}$$

5. Sensitivity coefficients α_E and α_R

$$\alpha E(\gamma G) := \frac{-\sigma E}{\sigma g(\gamma G)} \qquad \alpha R(\gamma G) := \frac{\sigma R(\gamma G)}{\sigma(\gamma G)}$$

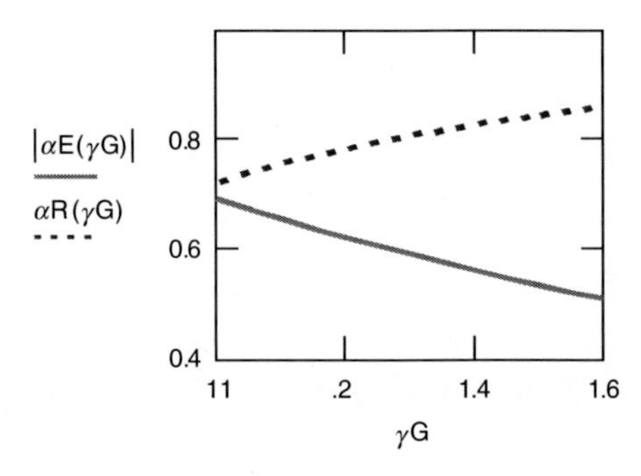

Note
The sensitivity factor α_E is shown with the opposite sign (as a positive quantity).

6. Design values E_d and R_d
EC 1990 recommendation:

$$\beta := 3.8 \qquad \alpha E0 := -0.7 \qquad \alpha R0 := 0.8$$

$$Ed(\gamma G) := \mu E - \alpha E(\gamma G)\beta \cdot \sigma E \qquad Rd(\gamma G) := \mu R(\gamma G) - \alpha R(\gamma G)\beta \cdot \sigma R(\gamma G)$$

$$Ed0(\gamma G) := \mu E - \alpha E0\beta \cdot \sigma E \qquad Rd0(\gamma G) := \mu R(\gamma G) - \alpha R0\beta \cdot \sigma R(\gamma G)$$

$$Rd0ln(\gamma G) := \mu R(\gamma G) \cdot \exp(-\alpha R0\beta \cdot vR)$$

Check: $\boxed{Ed(1.35) = 1.22}$

$\boxed{Ed0(1.35) = 1.27}$

Rd(1.35) = 1.33

Rd0(1.35) = 1.34

Rd0(1.35) = 1.39

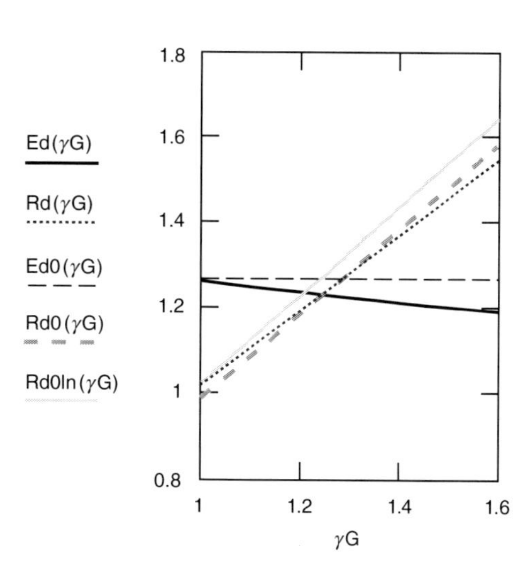

Notes

(1) The figure shows that the partial factor γ_G should be greater than about 1.25 otherwise the design value of the load effect E_d would be greater than the design value of the resistance R_d.

(2) The design value of the resistance R_d determined assuming a log-normal distribution with the lower bound at zero is greater than R_d determined assuming a log-normal distribution.

Sheet 4: lower fractiles for basic types of distributions – definition of the fractile X_p: $P = \text{Prob}(X < X_p)$, relative value $\xi_p = X_p/\mu$

1. Input data for a variable *X*

Basic characteristics of a random variable *X*:

$\mu := 1 \qquad V := 0.2 \qquad \sigma := V \cdot \mu$

An example of the design value for a resistance variable:

$\alpha := 0.8 \qquad \beta := 3.8 \qquad P := \text{pnorm}(-\alpha \cdot \beta, 0, 1)$ Check: $P = 1.183 \times 10^{-3}$

Range for the probability *P* considered below:

p := 0.001, 0.005.. 0.999

Standardized normal fractile given by the inverse distribution function:

u(p) := qnorm(p, 0, 1)

2. Fractiles for the normal distributions $\xi\, n(p) = Xp/\mu$

$\xi n(p) := 1 + u(p) \cdot V$

3. Fractiles for the two-parameter log-normal distribution $\xi\,\ln(p) = Xp/\mu$

Correct formula for any *V*:

$$\xi \ln(p) := \frac{\left(\text{expu}(p) \cdot \sqrt{\ln(1+V^2)}\right)}{\sqrt{1+V^2}}$$

Common approximation for $V < 0.2$:

$\xi \text{lna}(p) := \exp(u(p) \cdot V)$

4. Fractiles for the three-parameter log-normal distribution
Skewness a as a range variable:

$$a := -1, -0.5..\ 1$$

Parameter C of the three-parameter log-normal distribution of g:

$$C(a) := \frac{\left(\sqrt{a^2+4}+a\right)^{\frac{1}{3}} - \left(\sqrt{a^2+4}-a\right)^{\frac{1}{3}}}{2^{\frac{1}{3}}}$$

Parameters of the transformed variable:

$$mg(a) := -\ln(|C(a)|) + \ln(\sigma) - (0.5) \cdot \ln(1 + C(a)^2)$$

$$sg(a) := \sqrt{\ln(1+C(a)^2)} \qquad x0(a) := \mu - \frac{1}{C(a)}\sigma$$

Check: $x0(1) = 0.379$

$$\xi lng(p,\ a) := 1 - \frac{V}{C(a)} \cdot \left(1 - \frac{\exp\left(\text{sign}(a)u(p) \cdot \sqrt{\ln(1+C(a)^2)}\right)}{\sqrt{1+C(a)^2}}\right)$$

5. Fractiles for the gamma distribution
Parameters of the gamma distribution:

$$k := \left(\frac{\mu}{\sigma}\right)^2 \qquad \lambda := \left(\frac{\mu}{\sigma^2}\right)$$

Transformed variable $u = \lambda x$, shape factor $s = k$

No explicit formula is available

$$\xi gam(p) := \frac{qgamma(p,\ k)}{\lambda}$$

6. Fractiles for the Gumbel distribution
Explicit formula:

$$\xi gum(p) := 1 - V \cdot (0.45 + 0.78\ln(-\ln(p)))$$

7. Relative values of fractiles $\xi_p = X_p$ versus probability P

Check: $\xi n(0.001) = 0.382$

$\xi ln(0.001) = 0.532$

$\xi lna(0.001) = 0.539$

$\xi lng(0.001,\ 1) = 0.603$

$\xi lng(0.001,\ -1) = 0.06$

$\xi gam(0.001,\ 0.4) = 0.486$

$\xi gum(0.001) = 0.609$

Notes

(1) It follows from the figure that the skewness of the distribution may have a significant effect on the assessment of the design value (0.0001 fractile).
(2) The approximate formula for the two-parameter log-normal distribution yields sufficiently accurate results for the coefficient of variation $V < 0.2$.
(3) Both the gamma and Gumbel distributions can be closely approximated by the three-parameter log-normal distribution having a skewness $\alpha = 2V$ and $\alpha = 1.14$, respectively.

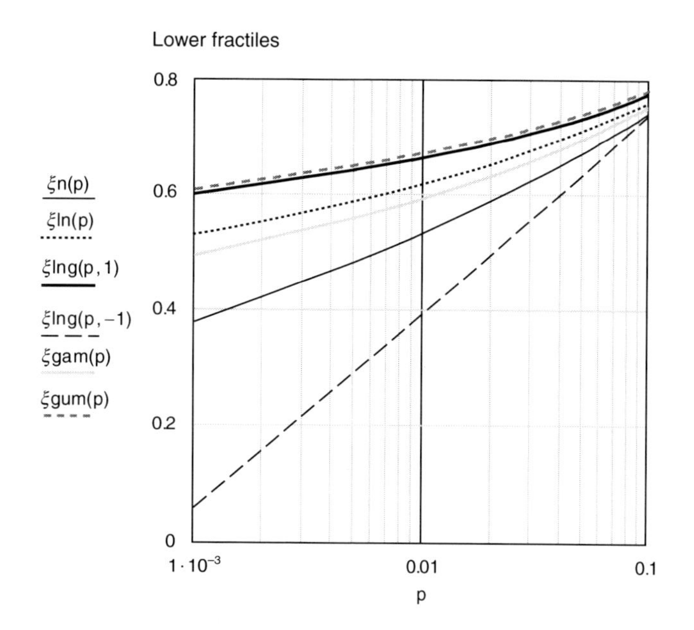

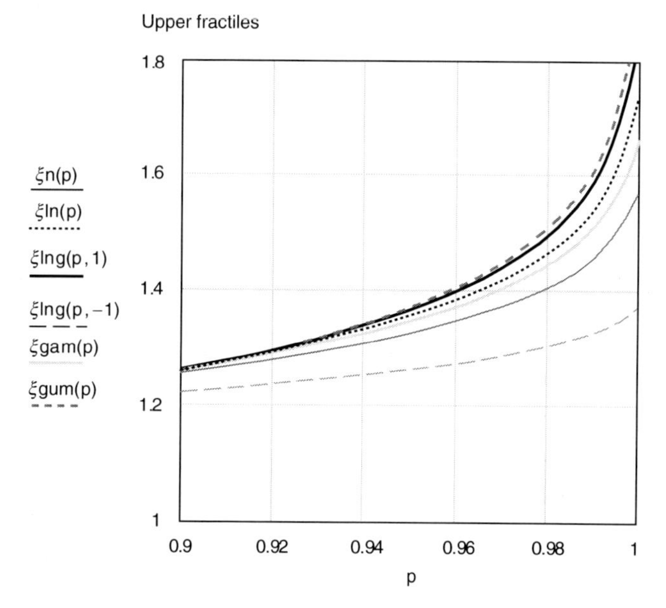

Sheet 5: combination factor ψ_0 for accompanying actions

(1) Input data:

V := 0.0, 0.05.. 1.4 (range variable) N1 := 1.. 10 $\beta := 3.8$

(2) Factor ψ_0 for the normal distribution:

Precise formula following Turkstra's rule $\psi_0 = F^{-1}(\Phi(0.4*0.7\beta)^N{}_1)/F^{-1}(\Phi(0.7\beta))$:

$$\psi0n(V, N1) := \frac{1 + \text{qnorm}(\text{pnorm}(0.28 \cdot \beta, 0, 1)^{N1}, 0, 1)V}{1 + 0.7\beta \cdot V}$$

Check: $\boxed{\psi0n(0.15, 7) = 0.67}$

Approximation in EN 1990:

$$\psi0na(V, N1) := \frac{1 + (0.28 \cdot \beta - 0.7 \cdot \ln(N1)) \cdot V}{1 + 0.7\beta \cdot V}$$

$\boxed{\psi0na(0.15, 7) = 0.683}$

(3) Factor ψ_0 for the Gumbel distribution:

$$\psi 0g(V, N1) := \frac{1 - 0.78 \cdot V \cdot (0.58 + \ln(-\ln(\text{pnorm}(0.28 \cdot \beta, 0, 1))) + \ln(N1))}{1 - 0.78 \cdot V \cdot (0.58 + \ln(-\ln(\text{pnorm}(0.7 \cdot \beta, 0, 1))))}$$

$\psi 0g(0.15, 7) = 0.584$

(4) General $\psi_0 = F^{-1}(\Phi(0.4 \times 0.7\beta_C)^{N}{}_{1})/F^{-1}(\Phi(0.7\beta_C)^{N}{}_{1})$:

$$\beta c(N1) := -\text{qnorm}\left(\frac{\text{pnorm}(-0.7 \cdot \beta, 0, 1)}{N1}, 0, 1\right)$$

$$\psi 0d(V, N1) := \frac{\text{qgamma}[[(\text{pnorm}(0.4 \cdot \beta c(N1), 0, 1))^{N1}], V^{-2}]}{\text{qgamma}[(\text{pnorm}(\beta c(N1), 0, 1))^{N1}, V^{-2}]}$$

$\beta c(7) = 3.259$

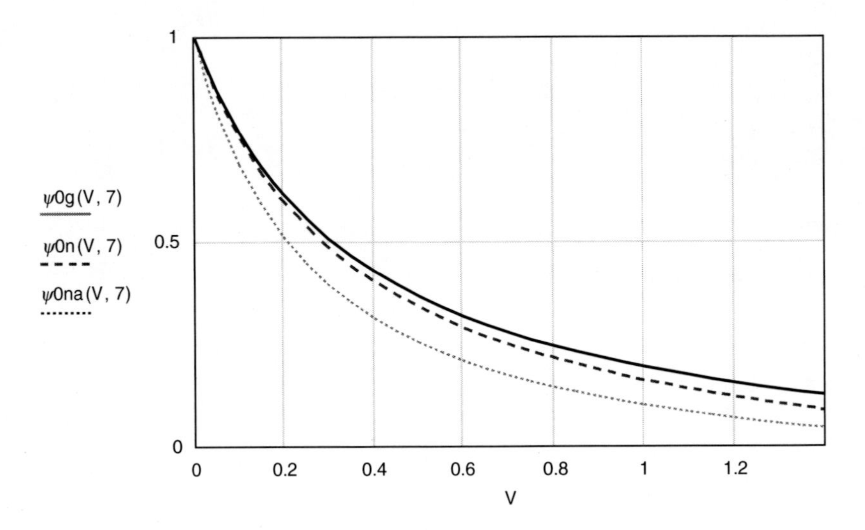

ψ_0 versus V for normal and Gumbel distributions

Check: $V := 0.1, 0.2 .. 0.5$

V=	$\psi 0n(V, 7) =$	$\psi 0na(V, 7) =$	$\psi 0g(V, 7) =$
0.1	0.757	0.766	0.684
0.2	0.598	0.614	0.505
0.3	0.486	0.506	0.391
0.4	0.403	0.427	0.311
0.5	0.339	0.365	0.253

Note
Gumbel distribution provides the lowest $\psi 0$.

Further reading

Augusti, G., Baratta, A. and Casciati, F. (1984) *Probabilistic Methods in Structural Engineering*. Chapman and Hall, London.

Calgaro, J. A. (1996) *Introduction aux Eurocodes – Sécurité des Constructions et Bases de la Théorie de la Fiabilité*. Presses de l'ENPC, Paris.

Cornell, A. C. (1996) A probability based structural code. *Journal of the ACI* **1** (*Proceedings V66*).
Der Kiureghian, A. (1980) Reliability analysis under stochastic loads. *Journal of the Structural Division of the ASCE* **106**, 411–429.
Ditlevsen, O. and Madsen, H. O. (1996) *Structural Reliability Methods. Wiley, Chichister.*
*Euro-International Con*crete Committee (1991) *Reliability of Concrete Structures – Final Report of Permanent Commission I. CEB Bulletin* 202. FIB, Lausanne.
Ferry-Borges, J. and Castanheta, M. (1972) *Structural Safety*. Laboratorio Nacional de Engenheria Civil, Lisbon.
Hasofer, A. M and Lind, N. C. (1974) Exact and invariant second moment code format. *Journal of the Engineering and Mechanics Division of the ASCE* **100**, 111–121.
Madsen, H. O., Krenk, S. and Lind, N. C. (1986) *Methods of Structural Safety*. Prentice-Hall, Englewood Cliffs, NJ.
Schneider, J. (1997) *Introduction to Safety and Reliability of Structures*. IABSE, Zurich.
Tichy, M. (1983) The science of structural actions. *Proceedings the of 4th ICASP* (eds G. Augusti *et al.*), pp. 295–321. Pitagora.
Turkstra, C. J. (1972) *Theory and Structural Design Decision. Solid Mechanics Study, No. 2.* University of Waterloo, Ontario.

CHAPTER 10

Design assisted by testing

This chapter is concerned with design assisted by testing, i.e. the determination of the characteristic or the design value of a single material property or of a resistance model from tests. The material described in this chapter is covered in *Annex D* of EN 1990, *Eurocode: Basis of Structural Design*, which completes *Sections 3.4* (see Chapter 3 of this guide), *4.2* (see Chapter 4) and *5* (see Chapter 5). The material described in this chapter is covered in *Annex D* of EN 1990, in the following clauses:

- Scope and field of application *Clause D1*
- Symbols *Clause D2*
- Types of tests *Clause D3*
- Planning of tests *Clause D4*
- Derivation of design values *Clause D5*
- General principles for statistical evaluations *Clause D6*
- Statistical determination of a single property *Clause D7*
- Statistical determination of resistance models *Clause D8*

10.1. Scope and field of application

Design assisted by testing is a procedure using physical testing (e.g. models, prototypes, *in situ* tests) for establishing design values. This chapter gives guidance for the planning and evaluation of tests to be carried out in connection with structural design, where the number of tests is sufficient for a meaningful statistical interpretation of their results. Nevertheless, the techniques described in this chapter are not '*intended to replace acceptance rules given in harmonised European product specifications, other product specifications or execution standards*' (*clause D1.2*).

Clause D1.2

Basic statistical techniques for estimating fractiles are briefly described in Appendix C of this guide. Some of the procedures described in this chapter may also be useful for the assessment of existing structures.

Annex D of EN 1990 is intended to be cautiously used by specialists and is, for that reason, informative. Nevertheless, detailed procedures are described which give designers some information on the way to use test results. The purpose of this chapter is not to repeat *Annex D*, nor even to develop more sophisticated procedures, but to provide an overview of its content and, where necessary, some additional comments.

10.2. Symbols

Annex D gives a list of symbols. No additional comment is necessary.

10.3. Types of test

Annex D distinguishes several types of test depending on their purpose. These types of test may be classified into two categories, as shown in Table 10.1.

Clause D3(2)

Annex D is mainly applicable to the test types in the first category (*clause D3(2)*). Moreover, it is suggested that conservative estimates of design values are adopted in order to meet the acceptance criteria linked to the test types in the second category (*clause D3(3)*).

Clause D3(3)

It should be recalled that design by testing is justified, in particular, when an economical design could result, but tests should be set up and evaluated in such a way that the structure has the required level of reliability (see Chapter 5); a reduction in the level of reliability achieved by designs using structural Eurocodes is not permitted.

10.4. Planning of tests

Prior to the execution of any tests, a test plan should be agreed with all interested parties, including the testing organization. This plan should include the following:

- the objectives and scope of the tests
- all properties and circumstances that could influence the prediction of test results
- the specification of any test specimens and sampling methods
- load specifications
- the test arrangements
- the measurements to be recorded
- methods for evaluation and reporting the test.

Concerning the properties and circumstances that can influence the prediction of test results, account should be taken of the fact that a structural member, when its resistance is tested, may possess a number of fundamentally different failure modes. For example, a girder may fail by bending at midspan or shear at the supports. It is possible that the average strength region is governed by modes other than the low strength region. As the low strength region (e.g. the mean value minus 2–3 standard deviations) is most important in reliability analysis, the modelling of the member should focus on the corresponding mode.

10.5. Derivation of design values

The derivation of the design values (e.g. for a material property, a model parameter or a resistance) from the results of tests should normally be carried out by appropriate statistical techniques taking into account the sample size. According to *clause D5.1* the design value may be derived in either of the following ways:

Clause D5.1

(a) by assessing a characteristic value, which may have to be adjusted by conversion factors, and by applying partial factors
(b) by direct determination of the design value from test results allowing explicitly or implicitly for conversion aspects.

These two methods are summarized in Fig. 10.1. The notation and symbols are defined in EN 1990. The formulae correspond to a normal distribution.

Both method (a) and method (b) are based on the application of statistical techniques to assess a certain fractile from a limited number of tests results (see Appendix C of this guide).

In general, EN 1990 recommends method (a) with a partial factor taken from the appropriate Eurocode, '*provided there is sufficient similarity between the tests and the usual field of application of the partial factor as used in numerical verifications*' (*clause D5(3)*). Method (b) is intended to be applied in special cases (*clause D5(5)*).

Clause D5(3)
Clause D5(5)

Table 10.1. *Types of test*

First category of tests (results used directly in a design)	Second category of tests (control or acceptance tests)
(a) Tests to establish directly the ultimate resistance or serviceability properties of structures or structural members for given loading conditions	(e) Control tests on identity or quality of delivered products or the consistency of production characteristics
(b) Tests to obtain specific material properties using specified testing procedures such as ground testing or the testing of new materials	(f) Control during execution (e.g. testing of pile resistance, or of cable forces during execution)
(c) Tests to reduce uncertainties in parameters in load or load effect models such as wind tunnel testing or tests to identify actions from waves or currents[a]	(g) Control tests to check the behaviour of an actual structure or of structural members after completion (e.g. vibration frequencies or damping of a footbridge).[b] For example, if a 40 MPa concrete is specified in the design, then the design process should continue on the assumption that concrete meeting that specification will actually be provided as confirmed by cube or cylinder testing just before or during execution
(d) Tests to reduce uncertainties in parameters used in resistance models[a]	

[a] In some cases a tentative calculation model is available, but the accuracy of this model is not known or the uncertainty is too large for some fields of application. Under those circumstances type c tests can be carried out to find the statistical characteristics and design values of the model factors as described in *clause D8* of *Annex D*. This type of testing is often performed in the process of codification of design formulae. It is assumed that the available model, although incomplete, adequately predicts the basic tendencies. In principle, the calculation model can range from simple semi-empirical formulae to advanced finite-element models

[b] In the case of proof loading, which is a particular control test type, special care should be taken that the structure is not unnecessarily damaged during the test. This requires a precise specification of the loading conditions and continuous monitoring of the load and the response, to be specified in the planning. Of course, a distinction is made between an acceptance test and a strength test. The acceptance test is intended to confirm that the overall structural performance complies with design intentions. The load is raised to values to be specified (possibly conditionally), at the maximum between the characteristic value and the design value for the ultimate limit state. Requirements may be set for the deformations, the degree of non-linearity and the residual deformations after removal of the test loading. The strength test is intended to show that a structural element (or the structure) has at least the strength that is assumed in the design. If an assessment for the test element only is required, it is sufficient to raise the load up to its specified value. If the strength test is intended to prove that other but similar elements also have the required strength, a higher load is required. A minimum requirement in this respect would be to correct the design load for the presence of better material properties in the tested element, compared with the design values. This means that the material properties of the tested element have to be measured

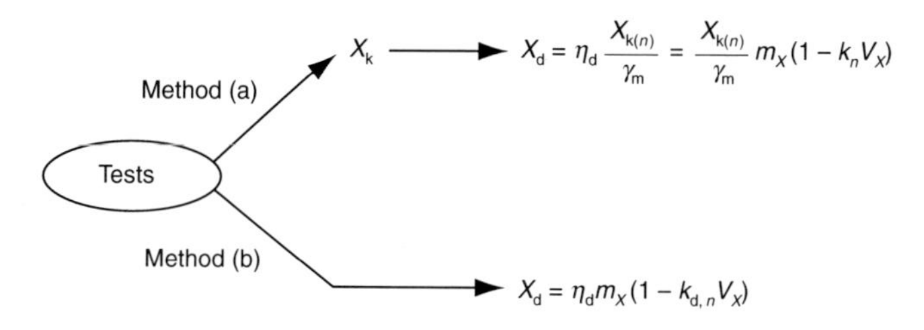

Fig. 10.1. *Representation of the two methods for the derivation of design values*

10.6. General principles for statistical evaluations

Clause D6(1)

EN 1990 draws attention to the fact that all test results should be evaluated critically, i.e. the general behaviour of test specimens and failure modes should be compared with the expected ones (*clause D6(1)*). A suspect experimental result may be discarded when a truly abnormal measurement or result is detected for which no explanation can be sought.

The evaluation of test results should be based on statistical methods, with the use of available (statistical) information on the type of distribution to be used and its associated parameters under the conditions that:

- the statistical data, including more or less extended prior information, are taken from identified populations which are sufficiently homogeneous, and
- a sufficient number of observations or measurements is available.

In fact, any assessment of probabilities involves basically two types of uncertainty, which are to a certain extant related:

(1) statistical uncertainty due to the limited sample size
(2) uncertainty due to vague prior information on the nature of statistical distribution.

Clause D6(2)

These uncertainties may give rise to considerable error. The Eurocode gives some guidance for the interpretation of tests results depending on the number of tests and the available prior information (see note to *clause D6(2)*).

Clause D6(3)

Finally, '*the result of a test evaluation should be considered valid only for the specifications and load characteristics considered in the tests*': any extrapolation to cover other design parameters and loading should be made very cautiously, and if additional information from previous tests or from theoretical bases is available (*clause D6(3)*).

10.7. Statistical determination of a single property

10.7.1. General

Clauses D7.1(1) to D7.1(4)

As already stated, the design value of a single property X, which may represent a resistance of a product or a property contributing to the resistance of a product (e.g. a strength) may be assessed by either method (a) or (b) (*clauses D7.1(1)* to *D7.1(4)*).

Clause D7.1(5)

Two tables in EN 1990 (*Tables D1* and *D2*) give the values of the characteristic fractile factor (for method (a)) and of the design fractile factor (for method (b)), and are based on the following assumptions (*clause D7.1(5)*):

- *all variables follow either a normal or a log-normal distribution;*
- *there is no prior knowledge about the value of the mean;*
- *for the case "*V_X *unknown", there is no prior knowledge about the coefficient of variation;*
- *for the case "*V_X *known", there is full knowledge of the coefficient of variation.*

In practice, EN 1990 recommends the use of 'V_X known' together with a conservative upper estimate of V_X, rather than applying the rules given for 'V_X unknown'. Moreover, V_X, when unknown, should be assumed to be no smaller than 0.10. In fact, the wording 'V_X known' is somewhat ambiguous: what is 'known'? It is assumed that, even if the mean value and standard deviation are unknown, the coefficient of variation may be known: this means that the coefficient of variation may be correctly estimated by good engineering judgement and professional expertise; but it cannot be justified by mathematical considerations alone.

Formulae are given for a normal and a log-normal distribution. Adopting a log-normal distribution for all variables has the advantage that no negative values can occur for the geometrical and resistance variables, which is physically correct.

10.7.2. Assessment via the characteristic value

Clause D7.2(1)

For method (a) the 5% fractile is usually assumed for the characteristic value, and the design value is assessed by using the formula (*clause D7.2(1)*)

$$X_{\mathrm{d}} = \eta_{\mathrm{d}} \frac{X_{\mathrm{k}(n)}}{\gamma_{\mathrm{m}}} = \frac{\eta_{\mathrm{d}}}{\gamma_{\mathrm{m}}} m_X (1 - k_n V_X)$$

k_n is taken from *Table D1* in EN 1990 (the origin of this table is given in Appendix C to this guide).

10.7.3. Direct assessment of the design value for ULS verification

For method (b), much lower probabilities, about 0.1% (corresponding to the product $\alpha_{\mathrm{R}}\beta = 0.8 \times 3.8 = 3.04$ (see Chapter 9)), are appropriate for the design value. Normally, method (b) would involve many more tests and so will be much more expensive than method (a). The design value is assessed by using the formula (*clause D7.3(1)*)

Clause D7.3(1)

$$X_{\mathrm{d}} = \eta_{\mathrm{d}} m_X (1 - k_{\mathrm{d},n} V_X)$$

It should be noted that, is this case, η_{d} includes all uncertainties not covered by the tests. $k_{\mathrm{d},n}$ is taken from *Table D2* (the origin of this table is given in Appendic C to this guide).

10.8. Statistical determination of resistance models

10.8.1. General

After the statistical evaluation of a single property, *Annex D* defines procedures for the statistical determination of resistance models and procedures for deriving design values from tests of type (d) (see *clauses D3(1)* and *D8.1(1)*).

Clause D3(1)
Clause D8.1(1)

Of course, a 'design model' has to be developed for the theoretical resistance r_{t} of the member or structural detail considered. It is assumed that this 'design model' would be adjusted until sufficient correlation is achieved between the theoretical values and the test data (*clause D8.1(2)*): this means, in particular, that, if the design model includes a hidden safety margin, this margin should be clearly identified when interpreting the test results. This question is discussed below. In the same way, deviation in the predictions obtained by using the design model should also be determined from the tests (*clause D8.1(3)*). This deviation will need to be combined with the deviations of the other variables (including deviations in material strength and stiffness, and geometrical properties) in the resistance function in order to obtain an overall indication of deviation.

Clause D8.1(2)
Clause D8.1(3)

As for the determination of a single property, two different methods, (a) and (b), are distinguished (*clause D8.1(5)*), based on seven steps: the six first steps are the same for both methods, and some assumptions regarding the test population are made and explained which are to be considered as recommendations covering some of the more common cases.

Clause D8.1(5)

10.8.2. Standard evaluation procedure (method (a))

Annex D (*clause D8.2.1*) gives a standard procedure for the assessment of a characteristic value based on the following assumptions:

Clause D8.2.1

a) *the resistance function is a function of a number of independent variables* $\underline{X}$*;*
b) *a sufficient number of test results is available;*
c) *all relevant geometrical and material properties are measured;*
d) *there is no correlation (statistical dependence) between the variables in the resistance function;*
e) *all variables follow either a Normal or a log-normal distribution.*

This procedure is detailed in *clauses D8.2.2.1* to *D8.2.2.7*. The procedure is presented in Table 10.2, and illustrated by an example. The selected example is the resistance function for bolts in bearing. Some additional comments follow the table.

Clause D8.2.2.1 to D8.2.2.7

The following symbols are used:

d_0 nominal hole diameter
d_i diameter of bolt i
e_1 end distance
f_{ui} ultimate tensile strength of plate i
f_{u} ultimate tensile strength of the bolt
t_i thickness of plate i

Table 10.2. Standard evaluation procedure: method (a)

Steps	Example
Step 1 Develop a design model (*clause D8.2.2.1*) $r_t = g_{rt}(\underline{X})$ $\underline{X}$ is the vector of basic variables	For bolts in bearing ($e_1 \geq 3d_0$): $r_t = 2.5dtf_u$
Step 2 Compare theoretical and experimental values (*clause D8.2.2.2*): Plot r_e against r_t 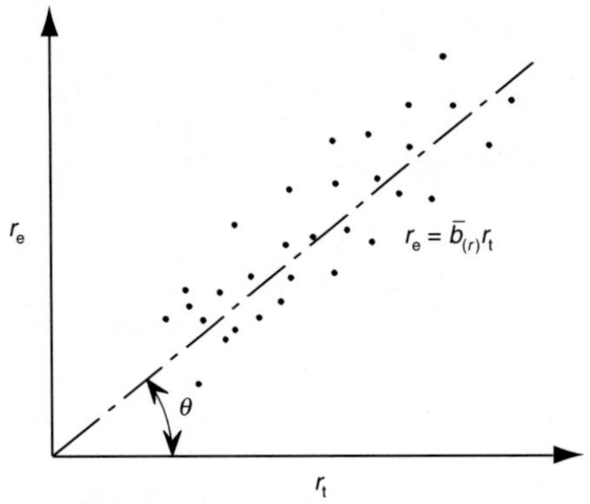 	For bolt *i*: $r_{ti} = 2.5d_i t_i f_{ui}$
The causes of any systematic deviation from the line $\theta = \pi/4$ should be investigated to check whether this indicates errors in the test procedures or in the resistance function	
Step 3 Estimate the mean value correction factor *b* (*clause D8.2.2.3*): Corrected resistance: $r = br_t\delta$ Calculate: $b = \frac{\sum r_e r_t}{\sum r_t^2}$ $r_m = br_t(\underline{X}_m)\delta = bg_{rt}(\underline{X}_m)\delta$	For the example, it is assumed that $b = 1$: $rt_m = bg_{rt}(\underline{X}_m)\delta = 2.5d_m t_m f_{um}$
Step 4 Estimate the coefficient of variation V_δ of the errors (*clause D8.2.2.4*): Calculate: $\delta_i = \frac{r_{ei}}{br_{ti}}$ $\Delta_i = \ln(\delta_i)$ $\bar{\Delta} = \frac{1}{n}\sum_{i=1}^{n}\Delta_i$ $s_\Delta^2 = \frac{1}{n-1}\sum_{i=1}^{n}(\Delta_i - \bar{\Delta})^2$ $V_\delta = \sqrt{\exp(s_\Delta^2) - 1}$	For the example, it is assumed that $V_\delta = 0.08$

Table 10.2. *Contd*

Steps	Example
Step 5 Analyse compatibility of the test population (*clause D8.8.2.5*)	As an illustration, the results of shear tests on bolts are shown in the figure below, split into subsets according to the bolt grade. Clearly in this case the resistance function can be improved if the coefficient 0.7 in the resistance function is replaced by a function of the bolt strength f_{ub} 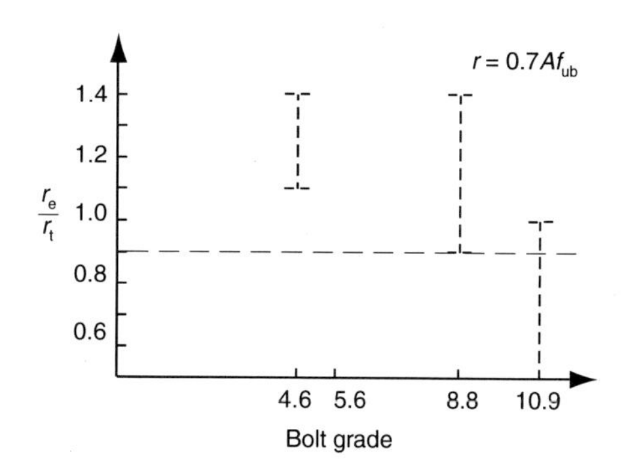 *Shear failure of bolts with the shear in the threaded portion*
Step 6 Determine the coefficients of variation V_{Xi} of the basic variables (*clause D8.8.2.6*)	For the resistance function considered for the bearing resistance of bolts, the following values of the coefficients of variation have been determined from studies on the variability of bolt dimensions and material properties: $V_d = 0.005$ $V_t = 0.05$ $V_{fu} = 0.07$
Step 7 Determine the characteristic value r_k of the resistance: $r = br_t\delta = b(X_1 \times X_2 \times \ldots \times X_j)\delta$ Mean value: $E(r) = b[E(X_1) \times E(X_2) \times \ldots \times E(X_j)]\delta = bg_{rt}(\underline{X}_m)$ Coefficient of variation: $V_r^2 = (V_\delta^2 + 1)\left(\prod_{i=1}^{j}(V_{Xi}^2 + 1)\right) - 1$ For small values of V_δ^2 and V_{Xi}^2: $V_r^2 \cong V_\delta^2 + V_{rt}^2$ with $V_{rt}^2 = \sum_{i=1}^{j} V_{Xi}^2$	For the example: $g_{rt}(X_m) = 2.5d_m t_m f_{um}$ $\sqrt{V_d^2 + V_t^2 + V_{fu}^2} = \sqrt{0.005^2 + 0.05^2 + 0.07^2} = 0.086$ $V_r = \sqrt{V_{rt}^2 + V_\delta^2} = \sqrt{0.086^2 + 0.08^2} = 0.118$

Table 10.2. *Contd*

Steps	Example
For a limited number of tests	
$r_k = bg_{rt}(\underline{X}_m)\exp(-k_\infty \alpha_{rt} Q_{rt} - k_n a_\delta Q_\delta - 0.5Q^2)$	
where	
$Q_{rt} = \sigma_{\ln(rt)} = \sqrt{\ln(V_{rt}^2 + 1)}$	
$Q_\delta = \sigma_{\ln(\delta)} = \sqrt{\ln(V_{rt}^2 + 1)}$	
$Q_r = \sigma_{\ln(r)} = \sqrt{\ln(V_r^2 + 1)}$	
$\alpha_{rt} = \dfrac{Q_{rt}}{Q}$	
$\alpha_\delta = \dfrac{Q_\delta}{Q}$	
k_n is the characteristic fractile factor from *Table D1* for V_X unknown	
k_∞ is the value of k_n for $n \to \infty$ ($k_\infty = 1.64$)	
α_{rt} is the weighting factor for Q_{rt}	
α_δ is the weighting factor for Q_δ	
For a large number of tests:	For a large number of tests:
$r_k = bg_{rt}(\underline{X}_m)\exp(-k_\infty Q - 0.5Q^2)$	$Q \approx V_r$
	$r_k = r_{tm}\exp(-1.64 \times 0.118 – 0.5 \times 0.118^2)$
	$r_k = r_{tm} \times 0.818$

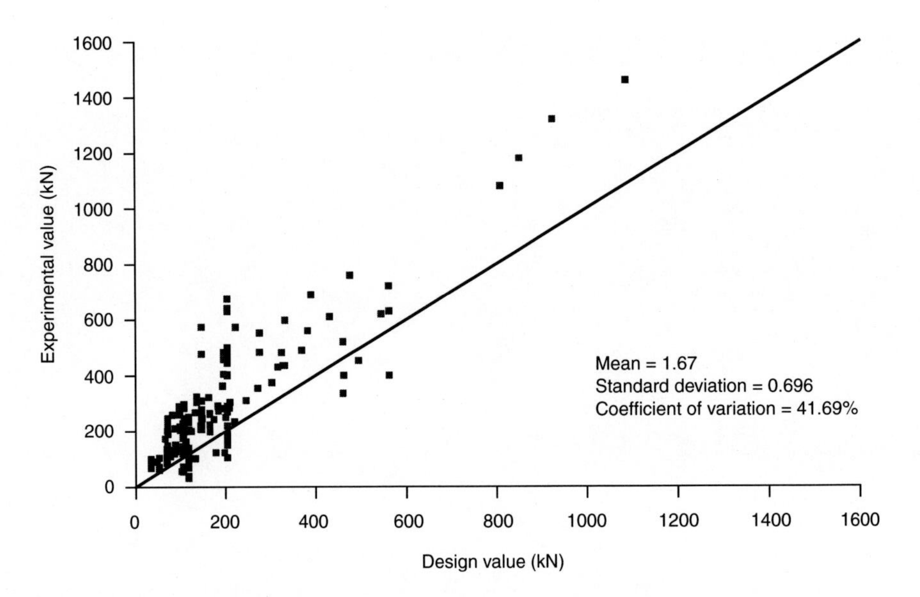

Fig. 10.2. *Comparison between experimental and design shear resistance: reinforced concrete beams with shear reinforcement (167 tests)*

Step 1
No additional comment.

Step 2
The Eurocode is perhaps too restrictive when a systematic deviation from the line $\theta = \pi/4$ appears. In some cases, and more particularly for prefabricated concrete members, the resistance function may include safety margins. For example, Fig. 10.2 shows the experimental values of shear resistance of reinforced concrete beams compared with the design values assessed from Eurocode 2. This figure shows a systematic deviation from the line $\theta = \pi/4$.

Step 3
No additional comment.

Step 4
No additional comment.

Step 5
It is often found that the frequency distribution for resistance from tests cannot be described by a unimodal function, because it represents two or more subsets which result in a bimodal or multimodal function. This can be checked by plotting on Gaussian paper or by using appropriate software. When plotted with the horizontal axis as a linear scale, a unimodal function should give a straight line (if normally distributed) or a monotonically curved line (if log-normal). It is more convenient to plot log-normally distributed functions with a logarithmic horizontal axis because this gives a linear plot.

If no other way is found to separate the subsets, a unimodal function can be extracted from bimodal or multimodal functions using appropriate procedures. The statistical data for the unimodal function can be taken from a tangent to the actual distribution. Thus, $b_{m(r)}$ and $s_{mb(r)}$ are obtained instead of $b_{(r)}$ and $s_{b(r)}$ and hence $s_{m\delta(r)}$ instead of $s_{\delta(r)}$. The evaluation procedure for unimodal functions described hereafter can then be used.

Commonly, it is difficult to construct a representative tangent, in which case a linear regression of the lower end of the data can be carried out and the regression line used in place of the tangent. Generally it is advisable to use at least 20 data points for this regression.

Step 6
No additional comment.

Step 7
No additional comment.

10.8.3. Standard evaluation procedure (method (b))

This procedure is given to derive directly from tests the design value r_d of a resistance. It follows steps 1 to 6 as previously defined and, for step 7, the characteristic fractile factor k_n is replaced by the design fractile factor $k_{d,n}$ equal to the product $\alpha_R\beta$ assessed at $0.8 \times 3.8 = 3.04$. Thus, the last row of Table10.2 is replaced by that in Table 10.3.

10.8.4. Use of additional prior knowledge

This final section may be the most controversial: it develops an aspect of probabilistic interpretation of data which can be done only by experts. However, the assumptions are very important:

- the validity of the resistance function r_t
- an upper bound (conservative estimate) for the coefficient of variation V_r are already known from a significant number of previous tests.

Table 10.3. *Standard evaluation procedure: method (b)*

Steps	Example
Steps 1 to 6 As Table 10.2	
Step 7 Determine the design value r_d of the resistance (*clause D8.3*) For a limited number of tests: $r_d = bg_{rt}(\underline{X}_m)\exp(-k_{d,\infty}\alpha_{rt}Q_{rt} - k_{d,n}a_{\delta}Q_{\delta} - 0.5Q^2)$ where $k_{d,n}$ is the design fractile factor from *Table D2* for V_X unknown $k_{d,\infty}$ is the value of $k_{d,n}$ for $n \rightarrow \infty$ ($k_{d,\infty} = 3.04$) For a large number of tests: $r_d = bg_{rt}(\underline{X}_m)\exp(-k_{d,\infty}Q - 0.5Q^2)$	For the example, and a large number of tests: $\gamma_R = \exp[(3.04 - 1.64)Q]$ $= \exp(1.40 \times 0.118)$ $= 1.18$

Then, the characteristic value r_k may be determined from the result r_e of only one further test using the formula

$$r_k = \eta_k r_e$$

where $\eta_k = 0.9\exp(-2.31V_r - 0.5V_r^2)$, and V_r is the maximum coefficient of variation observed in previous tests.

If two or three further tests are carried out, the characteristic value r_k may be determined from the mean value r_{em} of the test results using the formula

$$r_k = \eta_k r_{em}$$

where

$$\eta_k = \exp(-2.0V_r = 0.5V_r^2)$$

and V_r is the maximum coefficient of variation observed in previous tests, provided that each extreme (maximum or minimum) value r_{ee} satisfies the condition

$$|r_{ee} - r_{em}| \leq 0.10r_{em}$$

Further reading

Ang, A. H. S. and Tang, W. H. (1984) *Probability Concepts in Engineering. Planning and Design*, vols I and II, Wiley, Chichester.

Augusti, G., Baratta, A. and Casciati, F. (1984) *Probabilistic Methods in Structural Engineering*. Chapman and Hall, London.

Benjamin, J. R. and Cornell, C. A. (1970) *Probability, Statistics and Decisions for Civil Engineers*. McGraw-Hill, New York.

Bolotin, V. V. (1969) *Statistical Methods in Structural Mechanics*. Holden-Day, San Francisco.

Borges, J. F. and Castanheta, M. (1985) *Structural Safety*. Laboratorio Nacional de Engenharia Civil, Lisbon.

Ditlevsen, O. (1981) *Uncertainty Modelling*. McGraw-Hill, New York.

Ditlevsen, O. and Madsen, H. O. (1996) *Structural Reliability Methods*. Wiley, Chichester.

Madsen, H. O., Krenk, S. and Lind, N. C. (1986) *Methods of Structural Safety*. Prentice-Hall, Englewood Cliffs, NJ.
Melchers, R. E. (1999) *Structural Reliability: Analysis and Prediction*. Wiley, Chichester.
Thoft-Christensen, P. and Baker, M. J. (1982) *Structural Reliability Theory and its Applications*. Springer-Verlag, Berlin.
Thoft-Christensen, P. and Murotsu, Y. (1986) *Application of Structural Systems Reliability Theory*. Springer-Verlag, Berlin.
Euro-International Concrete Commission (1976) *First Order Concepts for Design Codes*. *CEB Bulletin 112*. FIB, Lausanne.
Euro-International Concrete Commission (1976) *Common Unified Rules for Different Types of Construction and Materials*, vol. 1. *CEB Bulletin 116*. FIB, Lausanne.
Construction Industry Research and Information Association (1977) *Rationalisation of Safety and Serviceability Factors in Structural Codes*. *Report 63*. CIRIA, London.
International Organization for Standardization *General Principles on Reliability for Structures*. ISO, Zurich, ISO 2394.

APPENDIX A

The Construction Products Directive (89/106/EEC)

As compliance to the structural Eurocodes will satisfy the requirement of the Construction Products Directive in respect of mechanical resistance this appendix provides a short introduction to the Construction Products Directive (Directive 89/106/EEC), the essential requirements contained in the Directive and the Interpretative Document to the first essential requirement, 'Mechanical Resistance and Stability'.

Note
The following abbreviations are used in this appendix:

CEC Commission of the European Communities
CEN European Committee for Standardization
CPD Construction Products Directive
EN European Standard
ID Interpretative Document

Compliance with the structural Eurocodes and the Construction Product Directive

Compliance with the structural Eurocodes will satisfy the Essential Requirement of the CPD in respect to 'Mechanical Resistance and Stability', and part of 'Safety in Case of Fire'.

The Construction Products Directive

A major objective of the CEC is the removal of barriers to trade across national borders and to implement the European internal market. This market is characterized by the free movement of goods, services, capital and people. To realize this objective, approximation (i.e. harmonization) of laws, regulations and administrative provisions for EU member states is necessary. The CPD, relating to construction products, which was adopted by the CEC on 21 December 1988, is an important element of this approximation process. The CPD has been transferred into national law by the majority of EU member states.

The main objective of the CPD is to provide a legal basis for the attestation of conformity (see Fig. 1) so that free movement of the relevant product is ensured.

The scope of the CPD is construction products which are defined as products that are produced for incorporation in a permanent manner in construction works, including both building and civil engineering works, in so far as the essential requirements relate to them.

The essential requirements

The essential requirements apply to construction works, not to construction products as such, but they will influence the technical characteristics of these products.

Thus, construction products must be suitable for construction works which, as a whole and in their separate parts, are fit for their intended use, account being taken of economy, and which satisfy the essential requirements where the works are subject to regulations containing such requirements.

The essential requirements relate to:

- mechanical resistance and stability
- safety in case of fire
- hygiene, health and environment
- safety in use
- protection against noise
- energy economy and heat retention.

These requirements must, subject to normal maintenance, be satisfied for an economically reasonable working life.

The essential requirements may give rise to the establishment of classes of a construction product corresponding to different performance levels, to take account of possible differences in geographical or climatic conditions or in ways of life as well as different levels of protection that may prevail at national, regional or local level. EU member states may require performance levels to be observed in their territory only within the classification thus established.

The structural Eurocodes relate to the essential requirement for 'Mechanical Resistance and Stability', which states:

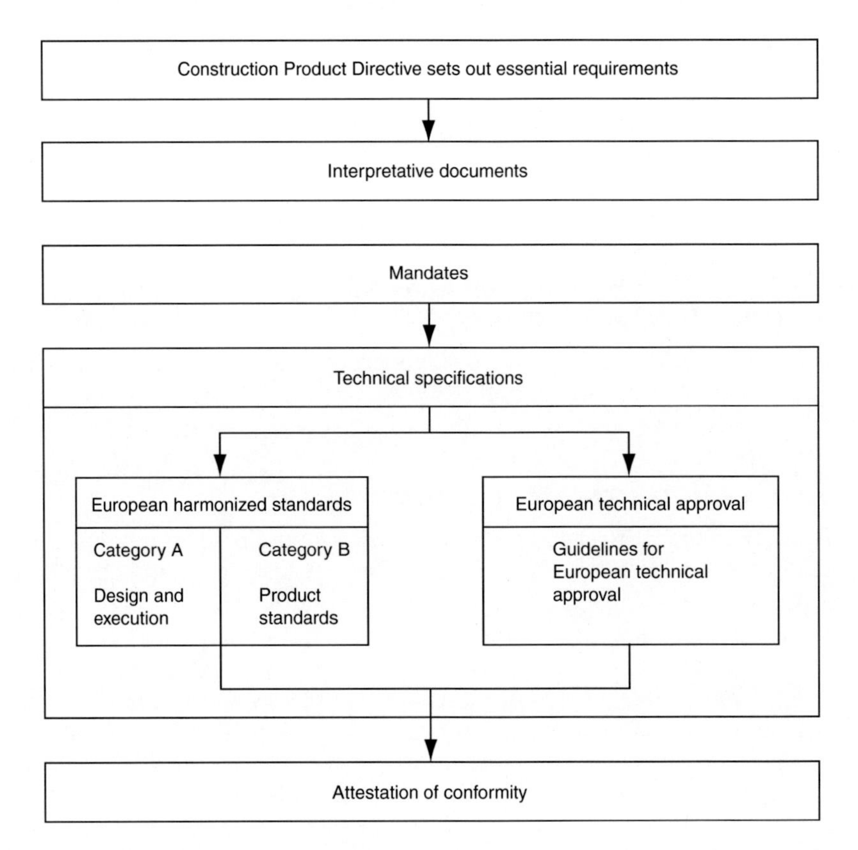

Fig. 1. The European system for the approximation of laws, regulation and administrative provisions relating to construction products

Fig. 2. The EC mark signifying a product complies with the relevant standard or technical approval

a) collapse of the whole or part of the work;
b) major deformations to an inadmissible degree;
c) damage to other parts of the works or to fittings or installed equipment as a result of major deformation of the load bearing construction;
d) damage by an event to an extent disproportionate to the original cause.

The structural Eurocodes also relate to part of the essential requirements for safety in case of fire. The essential requirements are given concrete (i.e. quantitative) form in interpretative documents, which will create the necessary links between those requirements and, for example, the mandates to draw up European standards for particular construction products (Fig. 1). Interpretative Documents for each of the six essential requirements are available. ID 1 refers to 'Mechanical Resistance and Stability'.

Methods of satisfying the Essential Requirements

In practice a product is fit for the intended use when it permits the works in which it is incorporated to satisfy the applicable essential requirements; a product is presumed to be fit for its intended use if it bears the EC marking (Fig. 2), which declares the conformity of the product to technical specifications (Fig. 1). These specifications comprise:

- Harmonized standards (Article 7 of the CPD) established by the CEN on the basis of mandates
- European technical approval (Article 8 of the CPD). Favourable technical assessment of the fitness for use of a product for an intended use, based on the fulfilment of the essential requirements for construction works for which the product is used.

Article 4 of the CPD allows referencing to National Standards but only where harmonized European specifications do not exist.

ID 1: Mechanical Resistance and Stability

With regard to the design of structures, ID 1 provides:

- a definition of the general terms used in all the Interpretative Documents
- a precise definition of the essential requirement 'Mechanical Resistance and Stability'
- the basis for the verification of satisfaction of the requirement 'Mechanical Resistance and Stability'.

With regard to the verification along with other rules, ID 1 states in Clause 3.1(3):

The satisfaction of the essential requirements is assured by a number of interrelated measures concerned in particular with;

- the planning and design of the works, the execution of the works and necessary maintenance;
- the properties, performance and use of the construction products.

Thus, considering the above subclause, ID 1 distinguishes between the design of the buildings and civil engineering works as a whole and the technical properties of the construction products themselves. In Clause 4 of ID 1, design and product standards are defined as follows:

> – Category A: These are standards, which concern the design and execution of buildings and civil engineering works and their parts, or particular aspects thereof, with a view to the fulfilment of the essential requirements as set out in the Council Directive 89/106/EEC.
>
> Category A standards should be taken into consideration within the scope of the Directive as far as differences in laws, regulations and administrative provisions of Member States prevent the development of harmonised product standards.
>
> – Category B: These are technical specifications and guidelines for European technical approval which exclusively concern construction products subject to an attestation of conformity and marking according to Articles 13, 14 and 15 of the Council Directive 89/106/EEC. They concern requirements with regard to performance and/or other properties including durability of those characteristics that may influence the fulfilment of the essential requirements, testing, compliance criteria of a product.
>
> Category B standards that concern a family of products, or several families of products are of different character and are called horizontal (Category B) standards.

ID 1 further states:

> The assumptions made in Category A standards on the one side and those made in Category B specifications on the other side shall be compatible to each other.

Category A standards

The structural Eurocodes are considered as one group of Category A standards.

APPENDIX B

The Eurocode suite

The complete Eurocode suite together with expected EN released dates is given below.

Document	Proposed EN release date (year/month)
EN 1990. Eurocode: Basis of Structural Design	2001/08
Eurocode 1: Actions on Structures	
EN 1991-1.1: Densities, Self-weight and Imposed Loads	2001/08
EN 1991-1.2: Actions on Structures Exposed to Fire	2002/06
EN 1991-1.3: Snow Loads	2002/06
EN 1991-1.4: Wind Actions	2002/02
EN 1991-1.5: Thermal Actions	2003/06
EN 1991-1.6: Actions During Execution	2003/02
EN 1991-1.7: Accidental Actions Due to Impact and Explosions	2004/03
EN 1991–2: Traffic Loads on Bridges	2002/11
EN 1991–3: Actions Induced by Cranes and Machinery	2004/08
EN 1991–4: Actions in Silos and Tanks	2003/02
Eurocode 2: Design of Concrete Structures	
EN 1992-1.1: Common Rules for Buildings and Civil Engineering Structures	2003/02
EN 1992-1.2: Structural Fire Design	2003/12
EN 1992-2: Bridges	2005/03
EN 1992-3: Liquid Retaining and Containment Structures	2005/03
Eurocode 3: Design of Steel Structures	
EN 1993-1.1: General Rules	2003/02
EN 1993-1.2: Structural Fire Design	2003/02
EN 1993-1.3: Cold Formed Thin Gauge Members and Sheeting	2003/02
EN 1993-1.4: Structures in Stainless Steel	2003/02
EN 1993-1.5: Strength and Stability of Planar Plated Structures without Transverse Loading	2004/06
EN 1993-1.6: Strength and Stability of Shell Structures	2004/08
EN 1993-1.7: Strength of Planar Plated Structures Loaded Transversally	2004/08
EN 1993-1.8: Design of Joints	2003/02
EN 1993-1.9: Fatigue Strength	2003/02
EN 1993-1.10: Fracture Toughness Assessment	2003/02
EN 1993-1.11: Use of High Strength Cables	2004/06
EN 1993-2: Bridges	2004/06
EN 1993-3: Buildings	2003/02
EN 1993-4.1: Silos, Tanks and Pipelines – Silos	2005/01
EN 1993-4.2: Silos, Tanks and Pipelines – Tanks	2005/01

Document	Proposed EN release date (year/month)
EN 1993-4.3: Silos, Tanks and Pipelines – Pipelines	2005/01
EN 1993-5: Piling	2004/04
EN 1993-6: Crane Supporting Structures	2004/04
EN 1993-7.1: Towers, Masts and Chimneys – Towers and Masts	2003/11
EN 1993-7.2: Towers, Masts and Chimneys – Chimneys	2003/11
Eurocode 4: Design of Composite Steel and Concrete Structures	
EN 1994-1.1: General – Common Rules and Rules for Buildings	2003/01
EN 1994-1.2: Structural Fire Design	2003/05
EN 1994-2: Bridges	2004/02
Eurocode 5: Design of Timber Structures	
EN 1995-1.1: Common Rules and Rules for Buildings	2002/08
EN 1995-1.2: Structural Fire Design	2003/02
EN 1995-2: Bridges	2004/02
Eurocode 6: Design of Masonry Structures	
EN 1996-1.1: Rules for Reinforced and Unreinforced Masonry	2003/04
EN 1996-1.2: Structural Fire Design	2003/04
EN 1996-1.3: Detailed Rules on Lateral Loading	2003/12
EN 1996-2: Selection and Execution of Masonry	2004/07
EN 1996-3: Simplified Calculation Methods and Simple Rules for Masonry Structures	2004/07
Eurocode 7: Geotechnical Design	
EN 1997-1: General Rules	2003/06
EN 1997-2: Design Assisted by Laboratory Testing	2004/09
EN 1997-3: Design Assisted by Field Testing	2004/09
Eurocode 8: Design of Structures for Earthquake Resistance	
EN 1998-1: General Rules, Seismic Actions and Rules for Buildings	2003/02
EN 1998-2: Bridges	2003/04
EN 1998-3: Strengthening and Repair of Buildings	2003/04
EN 1998-4: Silos, Tanks and Pipelines	2004/01
EN 1998-5: Foundations, Retaining Structures and Geotechnical Aspects	2003/02
EN 1998-6: Towers, Masts and Chimneys	2003/04
Eurocode 9: Design of Aluminium Structures	
EN 1999-1.1: Common Rules	2003/12
EN 1999-1.2: Structural Fire Design	2003/12
EN 1999-2: Structures Susceptible to Fatigue	2003/12

APPENDIX C

Basic statistical terms and techniques

General

This appendix is intended for use by committees drafting standards for structural design and related products, and for testing and execution standards, and for assessing actions and material properties. In addition, it can be used by other users, including designers and constructors, as indicated in the Foreword to EN 1990. It is assumed that the reader of this appendix has only a basic knowledge of statistics and the theory of probability as used in civil engineering problems.

The terms and concepts described in this appendix are those occurring often in EN 1990 (particularly in *Sections 4* and *6* and in *Annexes C* and *D*) and in the international standard ISO 2394, *General Principles on Reliability for Structures*.[8] Definitions presented in this appendix correspond to the probabilistic and general statistical terms given in the international ISO Standards,[18–26] particularly in ISO 3534[22, 23] and ISO 12491,[26] where more comprehensive descriptions and also other terms and definitions may be found.

In addition, for the normal (Gaussian) distribution, statistical methods used in civil engineering[26] for the estimation and tests of basic statistical characteristics are given. Basic statistical techniques for the estimation of fractiles (characteristic and design values) assuming a general three-parameter log-normal distribution characterized by the mean, standard deviation and skewness[27, 28] are also reviewed.

Note that none of the equations in this appendix appear in EN 1990.

Populations and samples

Basic terms and concepts

Actions, mechanical properties and dimensions are generally described by random variables (mainly continuous variables). A random variable X, (e.g. concrete strength) is a variable which may take each of the values of a specified set of values (e.g. any value from a given interval) with a known or estimated probability. As a rule, only a limited number of observations, constituting a random sample x_1, x_2, x_3, ..., x_n of size n taken from a population, is available for a variable X. 'Population' is a general statistical term used for the totality of units under consideration, e.g. for all concrete produced under specified conditions within a certain period of time. The aim of statistical methods is to make decisions concerning the properties of the population using the information derived from one or more random samples.

Sample characteristics

A sample characteristic is a quantity used to describe the basic properties of a sample. The three basic sample characteristics most commonly used in practical applications are

- the mean m representing the basic measure of central tendency
- the variance s^2 describing the basic measure of dispersion
- the coefficient of skewness a giving the basic measure of asymmetry.

The sample mean m (an estimate of the population mean) is defined as the sum

$$m = \frac{\sum x_i}{n} \quad \text{(D1)}$$

with the summation being extended over all the n values of x_i.

The sample variance s^2 (an estimate of the population standard deviation), is defined as

$$s^2 = \frac{\sum (x_i - m)^2}{n-1} \quad \text{(D2)}$$

the summation being again extended over all values x_i. The sample standard deviation s is the positive square root of the variance s^2.

The sample coefficient of skewness (an estimate of the population skewness), characterizing the asymmetry of the distribution, is defined as

$$a = \frac{n\left(\sum (x_i - m)^3\right)/(n-1)/(n-2)}{s^3} \quad \text{(D3)}$$

Thus, the coefficient of skewness is derived from the central moment of order 3 divided by s^3. If the sample has more distant values to the right from the mean than to the left, the distribution is said to be skewed to the right or to have a positive skewness. If the reverse is true, it is said to be skewed to the left or to have a negative skewness.

Another important characteristic describing the relative dispersion of a sample is the coefficient of variation v, defined as the ratio of standard deviation s to the mean m:

$$v = s/m \quad \text{(D4)}$$

The coefficient of variation v can be effectively used only if the mean m differs from zero. When the mean is close to zero, the standard deviation rather than the coefficient of variation should be used as a measure of the dispersion.

Population parameters

'Probability distribution' is a term generally used for any function giving the probability that a variable X belongs to a given set of values. The basic theoretical models used to describe the probability distribution of a random variable may be obtained from a random sample by increasing the sample size or by smoothing either the frequency distribution or the cumulative frequency polygon.

An idealization of a cumulative frequency polygon is the distribution function $F(x)$ giving, for each value x, the probability that the variable X is less than or equal to x:

$$F(x) = P(X \leq x) \quad \text{(D5)}$$

A probability density function, $f(x)$, is an idealization of a relative frequency distribution. It is formally defined as the derivative (when it exists) of the distribution function:

$$f(x) = \mathrm{d}F(x)/\mathrm{d}x \quad \text{(D6)}$$

The population parameters are quantities used in describing the distribution of a random variable, as estimated for one or more samples. As in the case of random samples, three basic population parameters are commonly used in practical applications:

- the mean μ representing the basic measure of central tendency;
- the variance σ^2 as the basic measure of dispersion; and
- the coefficient of skewness α giving the degree of asymmetry.

The population mean μ, for a continuous variable X having the probability density $f(x)$, is defined as

$$\mu = \int x f(x) \mathrm{d}x \tag{D7}$$

the integral being extended over the interval of variation of the variable X. The population variance σ^2, for a continuous variable X having the probability density function $f(x)$, is the mean of the squared deviation of the variable from its mean:

$$\sigma = \int (x-\mu)^2 f(x) \mathrm{d}x \tag{D8}$$

The population standard deviation σ is the positive square root of the population variance σ^2.

The population coefficient of skewness, characterizing the asymmetry of the distribution, is defined as

$$\alpha = \frac{\int (x-\mu)^3 f(x) \mathrm{d}x}{\sigma^3} \tag{D9}$$

Another important parameter is the coefficient of variation V, of the population:

$$V = \sigma/\mu \tag{D10}$$

The same restriction on the practical use of V applies as in the case of samples.

In the Eurocodes, a very important population parameter is the fractile x_p. If X is a continuous variable and p is a probability (a real number between 0 and 1), the p fractile x_p is the value of the variable X for which the probability that the variable X is less than or equal to x_p is equal to p, and, hence, for which the distribution function $F(x_p)$ is equal to p. Thus,

$$P(X \leq x_p) = F(x_p) = p \tag{D11}$$

In civil engineering the probabilities $p = 0.001, 0.01, 0.05$ and 0.10 are used most frequently. The probability p is often written as a percentage (e.g. $p = 0.1, 1, 5$ or 10%). If this is done, then x_p is called a percentile, for example the fifth percentile is used when $p = 5\%$. If $p = 50\%$, then x_p is called the median.

Normal and log-normal distribution

Normal distribution

The very common normal distribution (Gaussian distribution) may often be used to approximate many symmetrical bell-shaped distributions. The normal probability density function of a continuous random variable X having the mean μ and standard deviation σ is defined on the infinite interval $\langle -\infty, +\infty \rangle$ as

$$f(x) = \exp[-(x-\mu)^2/2\sigma^2]/\sigma(2\pi)^{1/2} \tag{D12}$$

Civil and structural engineers should rarely, if ever, need to use expression (D12) since tables of $f(x)$ and its cumulative distribution $F(x)$ can be found in any reasonable set of statistical tables.

If a significant asymmetry is present, however, then use of some other type of distribution, reflecting this asymmetry, should be considered. Often, the three-parameter log-normal distribution is used under such circumstances for material properties as well as for some actions. The log-normal distribution, defined on a semi-infinite interval, is generally described by three parameters: besides the mean μ and variance σ^2 a third characteristic, namely the lower or upper limit value x_0 or, alternatively, the coefficient of skewness α may be used. In the case of material properties, the coefficient of skewness α can be expected to be within the interval $\langle 0, 1 \rangle$. In the case of actions, the coefficient of skewness α can be even greater. If the limit value x_0 is known, then the distribution of a variable X may be easily transformed to a normal distribution of a variable Y:

$$Y = \log|X - x_0| \quad \text{(D13)}$$

which can then be analysed using tables of the normal distribution.

In civil engineering, a log-normal distribution with x_0 as the lower limit (and which consequently has a positive skewness) is often used. Moreover, it is frequently assumed that $x_0 = 0$, and then only two parameters (μ and σ) are involved. In this case the normal variable Y is given as

$$Y = \log X \quad \text{(D14)}$$

and the original variable X has a positive skewness. The coefficient of skewness is dependent upon the coefficient of variation, $V = \sigma/\mu$, of the variable X, and is written as

$$\alpha = V^3 + 3V \quad \text{(D15)}$$

A log-normal distribution is close to a normal distribution if the coefficient of skewness α is zero and the absolute value of the limit value x_0 approaches infinity (is very large).

Standardized variable

To simplify calculation procedures, standardized variables, with means of zero and variances of 1, can frequently be used. If the variable X has the mean μ and standard deviation σ, the corresponding standardized variable U is defined as

$$U = (X - \mu)/\sigma \quad \text{(D16)}$$

The distribution of the standardized variable U is called a standardized distribution; it is these which are usually tabulated. For example, the standardized normal distribution has a probability density function $\varphi(u)$ of the form

$$\varphi(u) = \exp(-u^2/2)/(2\pi)^{1/2} \quad \text{(D17)}$$

Detailed tables are available for the standardized probability distribution function $\Phi(u)$ and the standardized probability density function $\varphi(u)$ (e.g. ISO 12491[26]). Using these tables the p fractile u_p of the standardized variable u is given by

$$p = \Phi(u_p) \quad \text{(D18)}$$

It follows from expression (D12) that the p fractile x_p of the original variable x may be determined from the fractile u_p of the standardized variable u as

$$x_p = \mu + u_p\sigma \quad \text{(D19)}$$

For a three-parameter log-normal distribution, selected values of fractiles u_p for commonly used probabilities p and for three coefficients of skewness $\alpha = -1$, 0 and +1, are given in Table 1. Note that u_p for $\alpha = 0$ corresponds to the normal distribution and to the negative values of the reliability index β given in *Table C1* of EN 1990.

Normality tests

Any assumption of a normal distribution for a variable X needs to be checked. This can be done by using various normality tests: the random sample is compared with the normal distribution having the same mean and standard deviation, and the differences between the two are tested to see whether or not they are significant. If the deviations are insignificant, then the assumption of a normal distribution is not rejected; otherwise it is rejected. There will always be a difference between the two, but whether or not those differences are significant will depend upon the use of the model. It is usual to express the overall fit as a

Table 1. *Selected values of the standardized variable u_p for the three-parameter log-normal distribution*

$\Phi(u_p)$	u_p for $\alpha = -1$	u_p for $\alpha = 0$	u_p for $\alpha = +1$
10^{-6}	−10.05	−4.75	−2.44
10^{-5}	−8.18	−4.26	−2.33
10^{-4}	−6.40	−3.72	−2.19
10^{-3}	−4.70	−3.09	−1.99
0.01	−3.03	−2.33	−1.68
0.05	−1.85	−1.64	−1.34
0.10	−1.32	−1.28	−1.13

significance level, which can be thought of as being the probability that the actual population does not follow the assumed normal distribution.

Various normality tests, well established in ISO/DIS 5479,[25] may be used. The recommended significance level to be used in building is 0.05 or 0.01.

Statistical methods

Basic statistical methods used in civil engineering

As indicated above, the aim of statistical methods is to make decisions concerning properties of populations using the information derived from one or more random samples. Basic statistical methods used in civil engineering consist of estimation techniques, methods of testing of statistical hypotheses and of methods of sampling inspection. In the following, only the main estimation techniques and tests are described. More extensive descriptions of statistical methods and statistical techniques for sampling inspection as used in civil engineering are contained in ISO/DIS 12491.[26]

Principles of estimation and tests

Two types of technique for estimating population parameters are generally used in practical applications:

(1) point estimation
(2) interval estimation.

A point estimate of a population parameter is a single number, which is the value of an estimator derived from a given sample. The best point estimate of a population parameter is unbiased (the mean of the estimator is equal to the corresponding population parameter) and efficient (variance of the unbiased estimator is a minimum).

An interval estimate of a population parameter is given by two numbers, and contains the parameter with a certain probability γ, called the confidence level. The values $\gamma = 0.90$, 0.95 and 0.99, and in some cases also $\gamma = 0.75$, are recommended for use in the quality control of a building, depending on the type of variable and possible consequences of exceeding the estimated values. Interval estimates indicate the precision of an estimate, and are therefore preferable to point estimates.

Those methods for testing a hypothesis concerning population parameters which are commonly used in civil engineering, may be divided into two groups:

(1) comparison of sample characteristics with corresponding population parameters
(2) comparison of the characteristics of two samples.

A test of a statistical hypothesis is a procedure which is intended to indicate whether or not a hypothesis about the distribution of one or more populations should be rejected. If the results derived from random samples do not differ markedly from those expected under the assumption that the hypothesis is true, then the observed difference is said to be insignificant, and the hypothesis is not rejected; otherwise the hypothesis is rejected. The recommended significance level $\alpha = 0.01$ or 0.05 guarantee that the risk of rejection of a true hypothesis is of the same order as the risk of non-rejection of a wrong hypothesis.

Methods for estimating and testing of means and variances are generally covered by ISO 12491[26] and also by other ISO documents.[18–25] A normal or log-normal distribution is assumed in most of these documents. In the following, the basic methods for estimating of means and variances are summarized. Also, important statistical techniques for estimating fractiles are briefly examined.

Estimation of the mean

The best point estimate of the population mean μ is the sample mean m. Any interval estimate of the mean μ depends on whether or not the population standard deviation σ is known. If the population standard deviation σ is known, then the two-sided interval estimate at the confidence level $\gamma = 2p - 1$ is

$$m - u_p\sigma/n^{1/2} \leq \mu \leq m + u_p\sigma/n^{1/2} \qquad \text{(D20)}$$

where u_p is the fractile of the normal distribution corresponding to the probability p (close to 1) given in Table 1 of ISO 12491[26] (see also ISO 2854[19]).

If the population standard deviation σ is unknown, then the two-sided interval estimate at the confidence level $\gamma = 2p - 1$ is

$$m - t_p s/n^{1/2} \leq \mu \leq m = t_p s/n^{1/2} \qquad \text{(D21)}$$

where s is the sample standard deviation and t_p is the fractile of the t distribution for $\nu = n - 1$ degrees of freedom and the probability p (close to 1), as given in Table 3 of ISO 12491[26] (see also ISO 2854[19]). In each of the above cases the one-sided interval estimate at the confidence level $\gamma = p$ may be used if only the lower or only the upper limit of the above estimates is being considered. The values of p and the corresponding fractiles u_p and t_p should be specified in accordance with the chosen confidence level $\gamma = p$.

Estimation of the variance

The best point estimate of the population variance σ^2 is the sample variance s^2 (see the comment on expression (D2)). The two-sided interval estimate for the variance σ^2 at the confidence level $\gamma = p_2 - p_1$, where p_1 and p_2 are chosen probabilities, is given as

$$(n - 1)s^2/\chi_{p2}^{\ 2} \leq \sigma^2 \leq (n - 1)s^2/\chi_{p1}^{\ 2} \qquad \text{(D22)}$$

where $\chi_{p1}^{\ 2}$ and $\chi_{p2}^{\ 2}$ are fractiles of the χ^2 distribution for $\nu = (n - 1)$ degrees of freedom, corresponding to the probabilities p_1 (close to 0) and p_2 (close to 1), given in Table 2 of ISO 12941[26] (see also ISO 2854[19]). Often, the lower limit of the above interval estimate for the variance σ^2 is considered to be 0, and then the confidence level γ of the estimate is $1 - p_1$. The estimate for the standard deviation σ is the square root of the variance σ^2.

Comparison of means

To test the significance of the difference between the sample mean m and a supposed population mean μ if the population standard deviation σ is known, the test value

$$u_0 = |m - \mu| n^{1/2}/\sigma \qquad \text{(D23)}$$

is compared with the critical value u_p (see Table 1 in ISO 12491[26]), which is the p fractile of the normal distribution corresponding to the significance level $\alpha = 1 - p$ (where α is a value close to 0). If $u_0 \leq u_p$, then the hypothesis that the sample has been taken from the population with the mean μ is not rejected; otherwise it is rejected.

If the population standard deviation σ is unknown, then the test value

$$t_0 = |m - \mu| n^{1/2}/s \qquad \text{(D24)}$$

is compared with the critical value t_p (given in Table 3 in ISO 12491[26]), which is the p fractile of the t distribution for the $\nu = n - 1$ degrees of freedom corresponding to the significance level $\alpha = 1 - p$ (where α is a small value close to 0). If $t_0 \leq t_p$, then the hypothesis that the sample has been taken from the population with the mean μ is not rejected; otherwise it is rejected.

To test the difference between the means m_1 and m_2 of two samples of sizes n_1 and n_2, respectively, and which has been taken from two populations having the same population standard deviation σ, the test value

$$u_0 = |m_1 - m_2|(n_1 n_2)^{1/2}/\sigma(n_1 + n_2)^{1/2} \qquad \text{(D25)}$$

is compared with the critical value u_p (see Table 1 in ISO 12491[26]), which is the p fractile of the normal distribution corresponding to the significance level $\alpha = 1 - p$ (α is a value close to 0). If $u_0 \leq u_p$, then the hypothesis that both samples have been taken from populations with the same (even though unknown) mean μ is not rejected; otherwise it is rejected.

If the standard deviation σ of both populations is the same but unknown, then it is necessary to use the sample standard deviations s_1 and s_2. The test value

$$t_0 = |m_1 - m_2|[(n_1 + n_2 - 2)(n_1 n_2)]^{1/2}/\{[(n_1 - 1)s_1^2 + (n_2 - 1)s_2^2](n_1 + n_2)\}^{1/2} \qquad \text{(D26)}$$

is compared with the critical value t_p (see Table 3 in ISO 12491[26]), which is the fractile of the t distribution for the $\nu = n_1 + n_2 - 2$ degrees of freedom corresponding to the significance level $\alpha = 1 - p$ (a small value close to 0). If $u_0 \leq u_p$, then the hypothesis that the samples have been taken from the populations with the same (though unknown) mean μ is not rejected; otherwise it is rejected.

For two samples of the same size $n_1 = n_2 = n$, for which observed values may be meaningfully coupled (paired observations), the difference between the sample means may be tested using the differences of coupled values $w_i = x_{1i} - x_{2i}$. The mean m_w and standard deviation s_w are firstly found and then the test value

$$t_0 = |m_w| n^{1/2}/s_w \qquad \text{(D27)}$$

is compared with the critical value t (given in Table 3 of ISO 12491[26]), which is the fractile of the t distribution for the $\nu = n - 1$ degrees of freedom corresponding to the significance level $\alpha = 1 - p$ (α is a small value close to 0). If $t_0 \leq t_p$, then the hypothesis that both samples are taken from populations with the same (unknown) mean μ is not rejected; otherwise it is rejected.

Comparison of variances

To test the difference between the sample variance s^2 and a population variance σ^2 the test value

$$\chi_0^2 = (n - 1)\, s^2/\sigma^2 \qquad \text{(D28)}$$

is firstly found. If $s^2 \leq \sigma^2$, then the test value χ_0^2 is compared with the critical value χ_{p1}^2 (see Table 2 in ISO 12491[26]) corresponding to $\nu = n - 1$ degrees of freedom and to the significance level $\alpha = p$. If $\chi_0^2 \geq \chi_{p1}^2$, then the hypothesis that the sample is taken from the population with the variance σ^2 is not rejected; otherwise it is rejected.

If $s^2 \geq \sigma^2$, then the test value χ_0^2 is compared with the critical value χ_{p2}^2 (see Table 2 in ISO 12491[26]) corresponding to $\nu = n - 1$ degrees of freedom and to the significance level $\alpha = 1 - p_2$. When $\chi_0^2 \leq \chi_{p2}^2$, then the hypothesis that the sample is taken from the population with the variance σ^2 is not rejecte;, otherwise it is rejected.

For two samples of size n_1 and n_2 the difference of the sample variances s_1^2 and s_2^2 (the lower subscripts are chosen such that $s_1^2 \leq s_2^2$) may be tested by comparing the test value

$$F_0 = s_1^2/s_2^2 \qquad \text{(D29)}$$

with the critical value F_p, which is the fractile of the F distribution given in Table 4 of ISO 12491[26] (see also ISO 2854[19]) for $\nu_1 = n_1 - 1$ and $\nu_2 = n_2 - 1$ degrees of freedom and for the significance level $\alpha = 1 - p$ (a small value close to 0). If $F_0 \leq F_p$, then the hypothesis that both samples are taken from populations with the same (though unknown) variance σ^2 is not rejected; otherwise it is rejected.

Estimation of fractiles

Introduction

From the probabilistic point of view, the characteristic value and the design value of a material strength can be defined as specific fractiles of the appropriate probability distribution. The fractile x_p is the value of a variable X satisfying the relation

$$P\{X \le x_p\} = p \tag{D30}$$

where p denotes specified probability (see also expression (D11)). For the characteristic strength, the probability $p = 0.05$ is often assumed. However, for the design strength, lower probabilities, say $p \cong 0.001$, are used. On the other hand, the design value of non-dominating variables may correspond to greater probabilities, say $p \cong 0.10$.

Applied statistical techniques should be chosen cautiously, particularly when the design strength corresponding to a small probability is considered. For example, when the strength of concrete is estimated using test data, usually a very limited number of observations is available only. Moreover, relatively high variability (coefficient of variation around 0.15) and usually a positive skewness can be expected. All of these factors can produce a relatively high degree of statistical uncertainty.

Various statistical techniques for the assessment of characteristic and design strengths, corresponding to different assumptions concerning the type of distribution and the nature of available data, can be found in the literature. Commonly used methods assuming a normal distribution are well described in ISO 2394[8] and in a number of other publications.

Generalized statistical techniques assuming the three-parameter distribution, where the coefficient of skewness is considered as an independent parameter, are available only for the log-normal distribution.[27, 28] Statistical techniques developed in the literature[27, 28] is included in the following brief review of the most important statistical methods.

Method of order

The most general method, which does not make any assumption about the type of distribution, is based on the statistics of order. A sample $x_1, x_2, \ldots, x_n$ is transformed into the ordered sample $x_1' \le x_2' \le x_3' \ldots \le x_n'$, and the estimate $x_{p,\,\text{order}}$ of the unknown fractile x_p is

$$x_{p,\,\text{order}} = x'_{k+1} \tag{D31}$$

where the index k follows from the inequality

$$k \le np < k + 1 \tag{D32}$$

Obviously, this method needs a large number of observations if it is to be reliable.

Coverage method

The following classical technique (the so-called coverage method) is very frequently used. The key idea of this method is that the confidence level γ (often assumed to be 0.75, 0.90 or 0.95) for the lower p fractile estimate $x_{p,\,\text{cover}}$ is determined in such a way that

$$P\{x_{p,\,\text{cover}} < x_p\} = \gamma \tag{D33}$$

If the population standard deviation σ is known, the lower p fractile estimate $x_{p,\,\text{cover}}$ is given in terms of the sample mean m as

$$x_{p,\,\text{cover}} = m - \kappa_p \sigma \tag{D34}$$

If σ is unknown, then the sample standard deviation s also needs to be used:

$$x_{p,\,\text{cover}} = m - k_p s \tag{D35}$$

The coefficients κ_p and k_p depend on the type of distribution, on the probability p corresponding to the desired fractile x_p, on the sample size n, and on the confidence level γ. Explicit knowledge of γ, so the probability that the estimate $x_{p,\,\text{cover}}$ will be on the safe side of the actual value x_p, is the most important advantage of this method. To take account of statistical uncertainty the value for γ of 0.75 is recommended in ISO 2394.[8] However, when an unusual reliability consideration is required, a higher confidence level of 0.95 would seem to be appropriate.

Note that in ISO 2394[8] and ISO 12491[26] only the normal distribution is considered without taking into account any possible asymmetry of the population distribution.

Prediction method

Another estimation method, developed assuming a normal distribution, is the prediction method. Here, the lower p fractile x_p is assessed by the prediction limit $x_{p,\,\text{pred}}$, determined in such a way that an additional value x_{n+1} randomly taken from the population would be expected to occur below $x_{p,\,\text{pred}}$ with the probability p, thus

$$\mathrm{P}\{x_{n+1} < x_{p,\,\text{pred}}\} = p \qquad \text{(D36)}$$

It can be shown that the prediction limit $x_{p,\,\text{pred}}$, defined by expression (D36), does approach the unknown fractile x_p with increasing n, and from this point of view $x_{p,\,\text{pred}}$ can be considered as an approximation to x_p. If the standard deviation of the population σ is known, then $x_{p,\,\text{pred}}$ can be calculated from

$$x_{p,\,\text{cover}} = m - u_p\sigma(1/n + 1)^{1/2} \qquad \text{(D37)}$$

where u_p is the p fractile of the standardized normal distribution. If σ is unknown, then

$$x_{p,\,\text{cover}} = m - t_p s(1/n + 1)^{1/2} \qquad \text{(D38)}$$

where t_p is the p fractile of the known Student t distribution with $n - 1$ degrees of freedom.

Bayesian method

When previous observations of a continuous production are available, an alternative technique is provided by the Bayesian approach.[8, 26] Let m be the sample mean and s the sample standard deviation, as determined from a sample of the size n. In addition, assume that from previous observations we also know the sample mean m' and sample standard deviation s' for a sample for which the individual results and the size n' are, however, unknown. Both samples are assumed to be taken from the same population having theoretical mean μ and standard deviation σ. Hence, both samples can be considered jointly.

Parameters for the combination of both samples are[26]

$$\begin{aligned} n'' &= n + n' \\ \nu'' &= \nu + \nu' - 1 \qquad (n' \geq 1) \\ \nu'' &= \nu + \nu' \qquad (n' = 0) \\ m'' &= (mn + m'n')/n'' \\ s''^2 &= (\nu s^2 + \nu' s'^2 + nm^2 + n'm'^2 - n''m''^2)/\nu'' \end{aligned} \qquad \text{(D39)}$$

The unknown values n' and ν' may be estimated using formulas for the coefficients of variation $V(m')$ and $V(s')$[26]

$$n' = [\sigma/(\mu V(m')]^2, \; \nu' = 0.5/[V(s')]^2 \qquad \text{(D40)}$$

n' and ν' may each be chosen independently (here it does not hold that $\nu' = n' - 1$) with regard to previous experience concerning the degree of uncertainty in estimating the mean μ and standard deviation σ.

The Bayesian limit $x_{p,\,\text{Bayes}}$ considered as an estimate of x_p is given by an expression similar to expression (D38) used by the prediction method when σ is unknown:

$$x_{p,\,\mathrm{Bayes}} = m'' - t''_p s''(1/n'' + 1)^{1/2} \qquad \text{(D41)}$$

where t''_p is the p fractile of the Student t distribution for ν'' degree of freedom. Furthermore, if the standard deviation σ is known and sample data are used to determine mean values only, then $\nu = \infty$, s'' should be replaced by σ, and instead of expression (D41) the following formula, similar to expression (D37) used by the prediction method when σ is known, is used:

$$x_{p,\,\mathrm{Bayes}} = m'' - u_p\sigma(1/n'' + 1)^{1/2} \qquad \text{(D42)}$$

When applying the Bayesian technique for determining, for example, strength, advantage may be taken of the fact that the long-term variability of strength is usually stable. Thus, the uncertainty in determining σ is relatively small, the value $V(s')$ is also small, and ν' given by expression (D40) and ν'' given by expression (D39) are high. This may lead to a favourable decrease of the resulting value t''_p and to a favourable increase of the estimate of the lower fractile x_p (see expression (D41)). On the other hand, uncertainty in determining μ and $V(m')$ is usually high, and so any previous information might not significantly affect the value of n'' and m''.

If no prior information is available, then $n' = \nu' = 0$ and the characteristics m'', n'', s'', ν'' equal the sample characteristics m, n, s, ν, respectively. Expressions (D41) and (D42) now reduce to the previous expressions (D37) and (D38) respectively. In this special case, the Bayesian approach leads to the same result as for the prediction method, and expressions (D37) and (D38) are used. It should be noted that this special case of Bayesian techniques with no prior information is considered in *Annex D* of EN 1990 and in ISO 2394[8] and ISO 12491.[26]

Comparison of the coverage and prediction methods

When estimating the characteristic and design values, the coverage and prediction methods are most frequently used. Assuming a normal distribution for the population, these two methods are compared here.

Table 2 shows the coefficients κ_p and $u_p(1/n + 1)^{1/2}$ used in expressions (D34) and (D37) for selected values of n and γ. It follows from Table 2 that differences between both coefficients are dependent on the sample size n as well as on the confidence level γ. For $\gamma = 0.95$ and for small n the coefficient κ_p of the coverage method is almost 40% higher than the coefficient $u_p(1/n + 1)^{1/2}$ of the prediction method. If $\gamma = 0.75$ is accepted (as recommended in ISO 2394[8] and ISO 12491[26]) then the differences are less than 10%. Generally, however, for a confidence level $\gamma \geq 0.75$ the prediction method would obviously lead to higher (less safe) characteristic values than the classical coverage method. Note that the κ_p for $\gamma = 0.75$ is very close to the coefficient $u_p(1/n + 1)^{1/2}$ given as k_n for V_X known in *Table D1* in EN 1990.

If the standard deviation σ is unknown, then expressions (D35) and (D38) are to be compared.

Table 3 shows the appropriate coefficients k_p and $t_p(1/n + 1)^{1/2}$, for the same number of observations n and confidence levels γ as in Table 2. Obviously, differences between the coefficients corresponding to different confidence levels γ are much more significant than in

Table 2. *Coefficients* κ_p *and* $u_p(1/n + 1)^{1/2}$ *for* $p = 0.05$ *and known* σ

	Number of observations n								
Coefficient	3	4	5	6	8	10	20	30	∞
κ_p for $\gamma = 0.75$	2.03	1.98	1.95	1.92	1.88	1.86	1.79	1.77	1.64
κ_p for $\gamma = 0.90$	2.39	2.29	2.22	2.17	2.10	2.05	1.93	1.88	1.64
κ_p for $\gamma = 0.95$	2.60	2.47	2.38	2.32	2.23	2.17	2.01	1.95	1.64
$U_p(1/n + 1)^{1/2}$	1.89	1.83	1.80	1.77	1.74	1.72	1.68	1.67	1.64

Table 3. *Coefficients* k_p *and* $t_p(1/n + 1)^{1/2}$ *for* $p = 0.05$ *and unknown* σ

	Number of observations n								
Coefficient	3	4	5	6	8	10	20	30	∞
k_p for $\gamma = 0.75$	3.15	2.68	2.46	2.34	2.19	2.10	1.93	1.87	1.64
k_p for $\gamma = 0.90$	5.31	3.96	3.40	3.09	2.75	2.57	2.21	2.08	1.64
k_p for $\gamma = 0.95$	7.66	5.14	4.20	3.71	3.19	2.91	2.40	2.22	1.64
$t_p(1/n + 1)^{1/2}$	3.37	2.63	2.33	2.18	2.00	1.92	1.76	1.73	1.64

Note that the k_p for $\gamma = 0.75$ is very close to the coefficient $t_p(1/n + 1)^{1/2}$ given as k_n for V_X unknown in *Table D1* in EN 1990

Table 4. *Coefficients* k_p *and for* $p = 0.05$, $\gamma = 0.75$ *and unknown* σ

Coefficient of skewness	Number of observations n								
	3	4	5	6	8	10	20	30	∞
$\alpha = -1.00$	4.31	3.58	3.22	3.00	2.76	2.63	2.33	2.23	1.85
$\alpha = 0.00$	3.15	2.68	2.46	2.34	2.19	2.10	1.93	1.87	1.64
$\alpha = 1.00$	2.46	2.12	1.95	1.86	1.75	1.68	1.56	1.51	1.34

the previous case of known σ. For $\gamma = 0.95$ and small n the coefficient k_p used by the coverage method is almost 100% greater than the coefficient $t_p(1/n + 1)^{1/2}$ used by the prediction method. For $\gamma = 0.75$ the two coefficients are nearly the same. The coefficient k_p is, however, always slightly greater than $t_p(1/n + 1)^{1/2}$ except for $n = 3$. As in the previous case of known σ, the prediction method would generally lead to greater (less safe) characteristic strengths than the classical coverage method. This difference increases with increasing confidence level.

Similar comparison of coverage and prediction is available for the 0.001 fractile, often referred to as the design value of a random variable X. *Table D2* in EN 1990 gives values for the appropriate coefficient $k_{d,n}$ assuming V_X known and unknown and for the prediction method. As in the case of the 0.05 fractile the coefficients $k_{d,n}$ valid for 0.001 fractile correspond approximately to the confidence level $\gamma = 0.75$ of the coverage method.

Use of the three-parameter log-normal distribution

Actual asymmetry of the population distribution may also have a significant effect on fractile estimation, particularly when small samples are taken from a population with high variability and small probabilities are considered. Assuming a general three-parameter log-normal distribution with an independent coefficient of skewness α, operational statistical techniques can often be effectively used when assessing material properties.

The effect of population asymmetry on the 0.05 fractile estimate (the characteristic value) is shown below for two confidence levels and for three coefficients of skewness $\alpha = -1$, 0 and +1. Only the coverage method for the situation where σ is unknown, described above by expression (D35), is considered. Table 4 shows the coefficient k_p for a selection of numbers of observations n and for a confidence level $\gamma = 0.75$. Table 5 shows the coefficient k_p for the same numbers of observations n as in Table 4 but for the greater confidence level $\gamma = 0.95$.

Using data from Table 5 the coefficient k_p is shown in Fig. 1 as a function of n for the three coefficients of skewness α. Comparing data given in both Tables 4 and 5, it follows that the effect of asymmetry on the estimate $x_{p,\text{cover}}$ considerably increases with increasing confidence level γ. Generally, the effect decreases with increasing n, but it never vanishes even for $n \to \infty$. Detailed analysis[27] shows that when assessing the characteristic strength of a material

Table 5. *Coefficients* k_p *and for* $p = 0.5$, $\gamma = 0.95$ *and unknown* σ

Coefficient of skewness	Number of observations n								
	3	4	5	6	8	10	20	30	∞
$\alpha = -1.00$	10.9	7.00	5.83	5.03	4.32	3.73	3.05	2.79	1.85
$\alpha = 0.00$	7.66	5.14	4.20	3.71	3.19	2.91	2.40	2.22	1.64
$\alpha = 1.00$	5.88	3.91	3.18	2.82	2.44	2.25	1.88	1.77	1.34

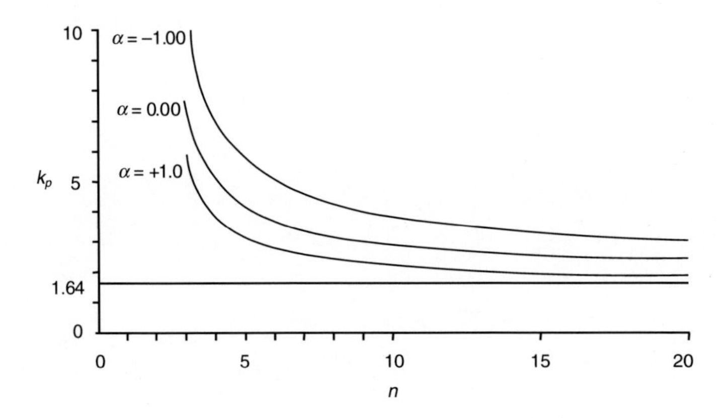

Fig. 1. *Coefficients* k_p *for* $p = 0.05$, $\gamma = 0.95$ *and unknown* σ

property corresponding to the 0.05 fractile, the actual asymmetry of the probability distribution should be considered whenever the coefficient of skewness is greater (in absolute value) than 0.5.

The differences between estimates obtained by using a general log-normal distribution with a given coefficient of skewness $\alpha \neq 0$ and the corresponding estimates based on a normal distribution with $\alpha = 0$, increase with decreasing probability p. Thus, the design value of concrete strength of a material property corresponding to a very small probability p (say 0.001), should be determined directly from test data only in those cases for which there is:

(1) a sufficient number of observations
(2) convincing evidence concerning the appropriate probabilistic model (including information on asymmetry).

When such evidence is not available, the design value should preferably be determined by assessing a characteristic value, to be divided by a partial factor and possibly by an explicit conversion factor.

Example

A sample of concrete strength measurements of the size $n = 6$, with $m = 23.9$ MPa and $s = 4.2$ MPa, is to be used to assess the characteristic value of the strength $f_{ck} = xp$, where $p = 0.05$.

Using the coverage method, it follows from expression (D6) and Table 3 that for the confidence level $\gamma = 0.75$

$$f_{ck,\,cover} = 23.9 - 2.34 \times 4.2 = 14.1 \text{ MPa} \tag{D43}$$

and, for the confidence level $\gamma = 0.95$,

$$f_{ck,\,cover} = 23.9 - 3.71 \times 4.2 = 8.3 \text{ MPa} \tag{D44}$$

If the prediction method is used, it follows from expression (D38) and Table 3 that

$$f_{\mathrm{ck,\,pred}} = 23.9 - 2.18 \times 4.2 = 14.7 \text{ MPa} \qquad \text{(D45)}$$

Thus, using the prediction method (which is identical to the Bayesian technique when no prior information is available),[8] the characteristic strength is almost 80% higher than the strength determined by the coverage method with a confidence level of 0.95.

When information from previous production is available, the Bayesian approach can be used. Assuming the following prior information

$$s' = 4.4 \text{ MPa}, \; V(s') = 0.28 \qquad \text{(D46)}$$

it then follows from expression (D40) that

$$n' = [4.4/(25.1 \times 0.50)]^2 < 1, \qquad \nu' = 0.5/0.28^2 \approx 6 \qquad \text{(D47)}$$

So the following characteristics are used: $n' = 0$ and $\nu' = 6$. Taking into account that $\nu = n - 1 = 5$, expressions (D39) yield

$$n'' = 6, \qquad \nu'' = 11, \qquad m'' = 23.9 \text{ MPa}, \qquad s'' = 4.3 \text{ MPa} \qquad \text{(D48)}$$

and finally it follows from expression (D41)

$$f_{\mathrm{ck,\,Bayes}} = 23.9 - 1.8 \times 4.3 \times (1 + 1/6)^{1/2} = 15.5 \text{ Mpa} \qquad \text{(D49)}$$

where the value t_p'' is taken from tables of the Student t distribution. The resulting characteristic strength is therefore greater (by 0.8 MPa) than the value obtained by the prediction method. Also, other available information on the application of the Bayesian approach clearly indicates (see Annex D of ISO 2394[8]), that when previous experience is available this technique can be effectively used. This is particularly so in the case of a relatively high variability of concrete quality for the assessment of existing structures.

For some materials such as normal-strength concrete, a positive asymmetry of the probability distribution (with a coefficient of skewness up to 1) is often observed. The following example of the effect of such skewness assumes that the sample of $n = 6$ concrete strength measurements, analysed above, is taken from a population with a log-normal distribution having the coefficient of skewness equal to 1. Using the classical coverage method for the confidence level $\gamma = 0.75$, expression (D35) and Table 4 yield

$$f_{\mathrm{ck,\,cover}} = 23.9 - 1.86 \times 4.2 = 16.1 \text{ MPa} \qquad \text{(D50)}$$

For the confidence limit $\gamma = 0.95$, expression (D35) and Table 5 yield

$$f_{\mathrm{ck,\,cover}} = 23.9 - 2.82 \times 4.2 = 12.1 \text{ MPa} \qquad \text{(D51)}$$

These values are greater by 14 and 46%, respectively, compared with the previous cases where asymmetry was disregarded; so, by taking positive asymmetry in account, more favourable estimates are obtained. Similar effects of asymmetry on characteristic and design strengths are to be expected if the prediction and Bayesian methods are used. It should be noted that possible negative asymmetry, which may occur in case of high-strength materials, would correspondingly cause an unfavourable effect on the resulting values.

APPENDIX D

National standard organizations

It is stated in the Foreword to EN 1990, *Eurocode: Basis of Structural Design*, that EN 1990 will be used for design purposes, in conjunction with the particular National Annex valid in the country where the designed structures are to be located.

Users of EN 1990 may obtain information with regard to the availability of a particular National Annex from the relevant national standard authority listed below.

CEN national members

Austria	Osterreichisches Normungsinstitut (ON) Postfach 130 Heinestrasse 38 A-1021 Wien Tel: +43 1 213 00 Fax: +43 1 213 00 650 Web: www.on-norm.at
Belgium	Institut Belge de Normalisation/ Belgisch Instituut voor Normalisatie (BN/BIN) Avenue de la Brabanconne 29 Brabanconnelaan 29 B-1040 Bruxelles Tel: +32 2 738 00 90 Fax: +32 2 733 42 64 E-mail: vourhof@ibn.be
Czech Republic	Czech Standards Institute (CSNI) Biskupsky Dvur 5 CS-113 47 Praha 1 Tel: +420 2 21 80 21 11 Fax: +420 2 21 80 23 11 Web: www.csni.cz
Denmark	Dansk Standard (DS) Kollegievej 6 DK-2920 Charlottenlund Tel: +45 39 96 61 01 Fax: +45 39 96 61 02 Web: www.ds.dk

Finland	Suomen Standardisoimisliitto r.y. (SFS) PO Box 116 FIN-00241 Helsinki Tel: +358 9 149 93 31 Fax: +358 9 146 49 25 Web: www.sfs.fi
France	Association Française de Normalisation (AFNOR) 11 Avenue Francis de Pressensé 93571 Saint-Denis la Plaine CEDEX Tel: +33 1 41 62 8000 Fax: +33 1 49 17 9000 Web: http://www.afnor.fr
Germany	Deutsches Institut für Normung e.V. (DIN) Burggrafenstrasse 6 D-10772 Berlin Tel: +49 30 26 01 0 Fax: +49 30 26 01 12 31 Web: www.din.de
Greece	Hellenic Organisation for Standardisation (ELOT) 313 Acharnon Street GR-11145 Athens Tel: +30 1 21 20 100 Fax: +30 1 21 20 131 Web: www.elot.gr
Iceland	Icelandic Council for Standardization (STRI) Laugavejur 178 IS-105 Reykjavik Tel: +354 520 71 50 Fax: +354 520 71 71 Web: www.stri.is
Ireland	National Standards Authority of Ireland (NSAI) Glasnevin IRL-Dublin 9 Tel: +353 1 807 38 00 Fax: +353 1 807 38 38 Web: www.nsai.ie
Italy	Ente Nazionale Italiano di Unificazione (UNI) Via Battistotti Sassi, 11 b I–20133 Milano MI Tel: +39 02 70 02 41 Fax: +39 02 70 10 61 49 Web: www.uni.com

Luxembourg	Inspection du Travail et des Mines (ITM) PO Box 27 26, rue Zithe L-2010 Luxembourg Tel: +352 478 61 50 Fax: +352 49 14 47 Web: www.etat.lul.ITM
The Netherlands	Nederlands Normalisatie Instituut (NNI) Postbus 5059 Kalfjeslaan 2 NL-2600 GB Delft Tel: +31 15 269 03 90 Fax: +31 15 269 01 90 Web: www.nen.ni
Norway	Norges Standardiseringsforbund (NSF) PO Box 353 Skoyen N-0212 Oslo Tel: +47 22 04 92 00 Fax: +47 22 04 92 11 Web: www.standard.no
Portugal	Instituto Portugues da Qualidade (IPQ) Rua C, Av.do Tres Vales P-2825 Monte da Caparica Tel: +351 1 294 81 00 Fax: +351 1 294 81 01 Web: www.ipq.pt
Spain	Asociacion Espanola de Normalizacion y Certificacion (AENOR) Genova 6 E-28004 Madrid Tel: +34 91 432 60 00 Fax: +34 91 310 49 76 Web: www.aenor.es
Sweden	Standardiseringen I Sverige (SIS) Box 6455 S-113 82 Stockholm Tel: +46 8 610 30 00 Fax: +46 8 30 77 57 Web: www.sis.se
Switzerland	Schweizerische Normen Vereinigung (SNV) Büglistrasse 29 CH-8400 Winterthur Tel: +41 52 224 54 54 Fax: +41 52 224 54 75 Web: www.snv.ch

UK	British Standards Institution (BSI) 389 Chiswick High Road London W4 4AL Tel: +44 208 996 90 00 Fax: +44 208 996 74 00 Web: www.bsi-global.com

CEN affiliates for CEN/TC 250

Bulgaria	Committee for Standarization and Metrology (BRS) 21 rue du 6 Septembre BG-1000 Sofia Tel: +359 2 989 84 88 Fax: +359 2 986 17 04
Croatia	State Office for Standardization and Metrology (DZNM) Ulica grada Vukovara 78 HR-41000 Zagreb Tel: +385 1 610 63 20 Fax: +385 1 610 93 20 Web: www.dznm.hr
Estonia	Eesti Standarddiskesbus 10 Aru Street 10317 Tallinn Tel: +372 651 92 00 Fax: +372 651 92 20 Web: www.evs.ee
Poland	Polish Committee for Standardization (PKN) Ul. Elektroralna 2 PL-00–139 Warszawa Tel: +48 22 620 54 34 Fax: +48 22 620 07 41 Web: www.pkn.pl
Slovakia	Slovak Institute for Standardisation (SUTN) PO Box 246 Krloveska 63 84000 Bratislava 4 Tel: +421 760 29 44 74 Fax: +421 765 41 18 88 Web: www.sutn.go.sk
Slovenia	Standards and Metrology Institute (SMIS) Kotnikova 6 SI-61000 Ljubljana Republic of Slovenia Tel: +386 1 478 30 30 Fax: +386 1 478 31 96 Web: www.usm.mzt.si

References

1. The European Commission (2001) *Guidance Paper L (Concerning the Construction Products Directive – 89/106/EEC). Application and Use of Eurocodes.* EC, Brussels.
2. International Organization for Standardization (2001) *Basis of Design of Structures – Assessment of Existing Structures.* ISO, Geneva, ISO 13822.
3. Institution of Structural Engineers (1980) *Appraisal of Existing Structures.* Institution of Structural Engineers, London.
4. Building Research Establishment (1991) *Structural Appraisal of Existing Buildings for Change of Use. BRE Digest 366.* BRE, Garston.
5. Société Suisse des Ingénieurs et des Architectes (1994) *Evaluation de la Sécurité Structurale des Ouvrages Existants. SIA Directive 462.* SIA, Zürich.
6. Czech Office for Standards, Metrology and Testing (1987) *Navrhování a Posuzování Stagebních Konstrukcí pri Prestavbách [Design and assessment of Building Structures Subjected to Reconstruction].* ÚNM, Prahe, CSN 730038-1988.
7. International Organization for Standardization (1987) *General Principles on Reliability of Structures – Lists of Equivalent Terms.* Trilingual edition. ISO, Geneva, ISO 8930.
8. International Organization for Standardization (1998) *General Principles on the Reliability of Structures.* ISO, Geneva, ISO 2394.
9. International Organization for Standardization (1997) *Basis of Design for Structures – Notation – General Symbols.* ISO, Geneva, ISO 3898.
10. UK Department of the Environment and The Welsh Office (1985) *Approved Document A (Structure) to the UK Building Regulations, 1985.* HMSO, London.
11. British Standards Institution (1978) *Code of Practice for Use of Masonry. Part 1: Structural Use of Unreinforced Masonry.* BSI, London, BS 5628: Part 1.
12. British Standards Institution (1990) *Structural Use of Steelwork in Building Part 1: Code of Practice for Design in Simple and Continuous Construction: Hot Rolled Sections.* BSI, London, BS 5950: Part 1.
13. British Standards Institution (1985) *Structural Use of Concrete. Part 1: Code of Practice for Design and Construction.* BSI, London, BS 8110: Part 1.
14. British Standards Institution (1985) *Structural Use of Concrete. Part 2: Code of Practice for Special Circumstances.* BSI, London, BS 8110: Part 2.
15. International Council for Research and Innovation in Building and Construction (2001) *Risk Assessment and Risk Communication in Civil Engineering. CIB Report 259.* CIB, Rotterdam.
16. Euro-International Concrete Committee (1978) *International System of Unified Standard Codes of Practice for Structures. CEB Bulletins 124 and 125.* FIB, Lausanne.
17. Euro-International Concrete Committee (1991) *Reliability of Concrete Structures – Final Report of Permanent Commission 1. CEB Bulletin 202.* FIB, Lausanne.
18. International Organization for Standardization. *Statistical Interpretation of Test Results. Estimation of the Mean. Confidence Interval.* ISO, Geneva, ISO 2602.

19. International Organization for Standardization. *Statistical Interpretation of Data. Techniques of Estimation and Tests Relating to Means and Variances*. ISO, Geneva, ISO 2854.
20. International Organization for Standardization. *Statistical Interpretation of Data. Determination of a Statistical Tolerance Interval*. ISO, Geneva, ISO 3207
21. International Organization for Standardization. *Statistical Interpretation of Data. Comparison of Two Means in the Case of Paired Observations*. ISO, Geneva, ISO 3301.
22. International Organization for Standardization. *Statistics. Vocabulary and Symbols. Part 1: Probability and General Statistical Terms*. ISO, Geneva, ISO/DIS 3534/1.
23. International Organization for Standardization. *Statistics. Vocabulary and Symbols. Part 2: Statistical Quality Control*. ISO, Geneva, ISO/DIS 3534/2.
24. International Organization for Standardization. *Sampling Procedures and Charts for Inspection by Variables for Percent Nonconforming*. ISO, Geneva, ISO 3951.
25. International Organization for Standardization. *Normality Tests*. ISO, Geneva, ISO/ DIS 5479.
26. International Organization for Standardization. *Statistical Methods for Quality Control of Building Materials and Components*. ISO, Geneva, ISO 12491.
27. Holický, M. and Vorlícek, M. (1995) General lognormal distribution in statistical quality control. In: *ICASP 7*, pp. 719–724. Paris.
28. Holický, M. and Vorlícek, M. (1995) *Modern Design of Concrete Structures*. Aalborg, Denmark.
29. Benjamin, J. R. and Cornell, A. C. (1971) *Probability Statistics and Decision for Civil Engineers*. McGraw-Hill, New York.

Index